Charles Seale-Hayne Library

University of Plymouth

(01752) 588 588

LibraryandITenquiries@plymouth.ac.uk

APPLIED MINERALOGY

APPLIED MINERALOGY

for engineers, technologists and students

HELMUT KIRSCH,
Dr. rer. nat.

*Director of the Materials Testing Station
of L. and C. Steinmüller GmbH
and Lecturer in Applied Mineralogy, University of Münster*

Translated by

K. A. Jones, B.Sc., Ph.D., F.G.S.

Lecturer in Geology, The Queen's University of Belfast

CHAPMAN AND HALL LTD
and
SCIENCE PAPERBACKS

11 New Fetter Lane · EC4

Distributed in the U.S.A.
by Barnes & Noble, Inc.

This book is available in both hardbound and paperback editions

CONTENTS

Foreword   *page* ix
Translator's Note   xi

1 General   1
Definitions · subdivision of mineralogy · historical

2 General Mineralogy   5
Crystal structure and crystal morphology · crystal growth,
crystal chemistry . crystal physics

3 Geochemistry   37
Composition of the earth · geochemical balance of the
⌐ elements of the earth's crust

4 Petrology   43
Subdivision and classification of rocks according to age · rock-
forming minerals · magmatic mineral and rock formation ·
survey of magmas and igneous rocks · formation and survey
of sedimentary and metamorphic rocks

5 Mineral Deposits   70
Magmatic · sedimentary and metamorphic mineral deposits

6 Systematic Mineralogy   83
6.1 Classification of minerals   83
6.2 Summary of important ore-minerals and their uses   83
6.3 Summary of important non-ore-minerals, rocks and soils   98

7 Applied Mineralogy   119
7.1 Ceramics, including refractory building materials   119
7.2 Glasses and enamels   134
7.3 Raw and constructional materials for nuclear reactors   140
7.4 Bonding materials   143

7.5   Metallurgical industry (slags, moulding sands)   150
7.6   Engineering geology, rock and soil mechanics, mining   158
7.7   Weathering of natural and artificial stone structures   175
7.8   Treatment of reservoir water, microfilters   177
7.9   Soils and mineral fertilizers   178
7.10 Asbestos   180
7.11 Mineral pigments   181
7.12 Meteorites   183
7.13 Grinding and polishing agents   184
7.14 Power generation by high-pressure steam   186
7.15 Single crystals   192
7.16 Metal surfaces   200
7.17 Biomineralogy including silicosis   204
7.18 Silicones   207
7.19 Applications of X-ray investigation of crystal structures   209
7.20 Application of polarization microscopy to materials-testing 212
      Bibliography   215
      Index   217

FOREWORD

Although one of the oldest sciences of all mineralogy is no longer a subject whose content and methods command general interest and whose basic principles are essential to everyone concerned with understanding the physical world. Engineers and technologists rarely need to concern themselves with mineralogy during their formal training. This is true, in spite of the fact that mineralogy is the study of the entire naturally-formed inorganic matter of the earth and cosmos, and extends into a large number of other fields.

That this short survey of the application of mineralogy to technology has been published is, however, an acknowledgement that in the past decade mineralogy, for the most part unnoticed, has found increasing application and has accelerated progress in many fields. In the future mineralogy, which originated as a child of man's first practical endeavours, will be applied more and more to technological science. Many engineers and technologists who, until now, have had no contact with the subject, will have to come to terms with it.

The treatment of the subject in the form of a short, simple survey, presented several difficulties to the author. Two factors, above all, were therefore decisive: firstly, mineralogy has very wide applications, extending from biology, medicine, geology, chemistry, metallurgy, physics, astronomy and mathematics to engineering science. Secondly, it could not be assumed that the majority of the readers would possess any of the mineralogical knowledge essential for a full understanding of the book, as would normally be the case in chemistry and physics. In consequence, it was unavoidable that some of the basic principles of crystallography, geochemistry, petrology and the science of mineral deposits, should be given. It also seemed essential because these principles give a useful basis for understanding many technical processes and engineering projects.

Since no summary of the entire field of applied mineralogy has appeared until now, the foregoing short outline could not be modelled on any well-tried form. Most of the information presented had to be gathered together and arranged from the widely-scattered and often contradictory articles in the literature, because, understandably, the author could cover only a limited part of the very extensive range of the subject from his own personal work. For the sake of brevity, the presentation is in note form in many places.

The book has been written primarily for engineers, students in technical colleges and universities, and technologists. It also provides a first introduction to problems connected with mineralogy and raw materials for industrial sanitation engineers, and specialists concerned with dust prevention. Simplification of the material presented was therefore unavoidable, so that the specialist mineralogist who reads the book will be interested only in the surprising number of applications of his science which are discussed.

The bibliography at the end of the book deserves special mention. It will enable those interested to acquire a deeper insight into the whole subject or into detailed parts of it.

Thanks are due to Professor Dr Correns (Göttingen), Prof. Dr Jung (Freiberg), Prof. Dr Miller (Stuttgart), Prof. Dr Keil (Münster), Prof. Dr Kleber (Berlin), Prof. Dr Schumann (Braunschweig) and Prof. Dr de Quervain (Zurich) for permission to reproduce text figures or tables from their publications. Prof. Dr Harder (Münster) is thanked for making valuable suggestions. Prof. W. Eitel (Toledo, U.S.A.) and Mr F. J. R. Taylor (C.E.G.B., London) are also thanked for taking trouble over the arrangements for an English edition.

The author and publishers are always grateful for any corrections or suggestions.

Gummersbach/Rhld.   H. KIRSCH

TRANSLATOR'S NOTE

To increase the value of the book to readers in Great Britain, a number of minor corrections and changes have been made to the text of the German edition. In addition, the Bibliography has been revised and titles likely to be more accessible in this country have been included.

I am very grateful to Mr J. H. Duncan of Ceramic Research, The English Electric Company Limited's Nelson Research Laboratories, who wrote the paragraph on ball clay and the definition of ceramics, enlarged the paragraph on glazes, and re-wrote the section on moulding sands. My thanks are also due to Mr W. E. C. Creyke of the same Department, who suggested the changes which were later implemented.

The Queen's University of Belfast   K. A. JONES

1
GENERAL

1.1. Basic definitions

Mineralogy is the study of the formation, properties, occurrence, alteration, and utilization of minerals and rocks. Mineralogical knowledge, however, helps us to understand not only problems concerning inorganic, naturally-occurring material, but also a great variety of questions concerning artificial inorganic or organic products. Knowledge of mineralogy also helps us to understand, design and carry out advanced technical projects. The scope of the study, therefore, is not confined only to the mineral kingdom, but in certain respects covers the whole range of solids, which are nearly always crystalline.

Minerals are naturally-formed, homogeneous, almost exclusively solid constituents of the earth and extra-terrestrial bodies. They possess a definite chemical composition and are usually crystalline with a specific crystal structure. Up to the present time, about 3,000 mineral species have been recognized, most of which are inorganic; a few, however, are organic. Examples of inorganic minerals are: quartz, felspar, mica, cassiterite (tinstone), magnetite, gold, mercury, etc.; and of organic minerals: mellite (honeystone), whewellite.

It is usually convenient, also, to regard as minerals those products of artificial processes which are formed by the alteration of rocks or minerals, and which may also occur naturally; for example: 'slag minerals' (felspar, gehlenite, mullite, magnetite), which are formed from the mineral content in fuels, or from the gangue of metal ores, and 'cement materials', which are formed by firing of the raw material used for cement manufacture. In the sense of the above definition, that minerals must be naturally formed, it is convenient to denote these crystalline products as '*crystalline phases*' and not as minerals.

Rocks are larger masses occurring in the earth and consist of a mixture of minerals which, in certain cases, are arranged in the rock in specific ways. They may also, though less commonly, be composed of only one type of mineral. 'Granite' (felspar + quartz + mica with a granular texture, and usually no regular arrangement or orientation of the different minerals) is an example of those rocks which are composed of a variety of minerals. Marble (calcite crystals with sutured boundaries), for example, is a monomineralic rock. Most rocks are inorganic (granite, basalt, gneiss, sandstone) and only a few are organic in origin (coals). Only about one hundred minerals have any importance as constituents of rocks, and, of these, only twenty are of great quantitative significance. A rock consists normally of a mixture of only 1–4 main constituents (rock-forming minerals).

Minerals which provide sources of metals in economic quantities are termed *ore-minerals* (for example, magnetite for iron and steel production).

Stone and soils (non-ore) provide sources of raw material for non-metallic commodities (gypsum, common salt, clay, building stones, asbestos, mica).

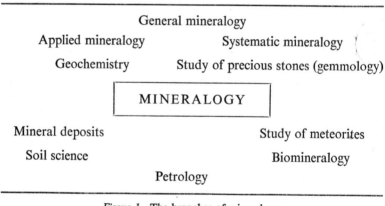

Figure 1   The branches of mineralogy.

1.2. Branches of mineralogy (Fig. 1)

(a) General mineralogy (study of crystals) embraces the study of crystal structure, crystal morphology, crystal chemistry, crystal growth and dissolution, and crystal physics.

(b) Systematic mineralogy is the study of the origin, occurrence and properties of specific minerals, and of their relationships to one another.

(c) The study of gemstones is concerned with the origin, occurrence and properties of precious minerals, knowledge of imitations, synthetic gemstones, as well as specific methods of investigation.

(d) The study of meteorites embraces the mineralogy of solid extra-terrestrial bodies, which collide with the earth.

(e) Biomineralogy is the science of mineral substances which occur in human and animal bodies and plants (for example, gallstones, pneumoconiosis).

(f) Petrology is the study of the formation, properties, and alteration of rocks.

(g) Soil science deals with the mode of formation, composition and properties of the various soil types of the earth's surface.

(h) The study of mineral deposits deals with the genesis, structure and composition of economically-workable mineral concentrations in the earth's crust.

(i) Geochemistry is concerned with the abundance of the chemical elements (including isotopes) in the earth, together with their distribution and the laws which govern this distribution.

(k) Applied mineralogy forms a bridge between mineralogy and its application to other branches of science and technology, for example to geology, metallurgy, chemistry, physics, biology, astronomy, medicine, archaeology, geography, metallurgical industry, mining, the oil industry, the chemical industry, ceramics, nuclear technology, the glass industry, the electrical industry, rock and soil mechanics, the abrasives industry, water supply, fertilizer manufacturing and so on.

1.3. Historical

Pre-history and antiquity

CENTRAL EUROPE

Stone age (200,000–2,000 B.C.): flint and nephrite (jade) as weapons and tools; pyrites to light fires; clay for vessels.

Copper and bronze age (2,000–750 B.C.): bronze from copper and tin ores; amber; gold; beautiful stones as charms or ornaments.

Iron age (from 750 B.C.): iron from iron ores; glass.

THE MEDITERRANEAN AND THE ORIENT

Egypt: gold; silver; emeralds; lapis lazuli; various kinds of stone as building material. 'Papyrus Ebers' (1,600 B.C.): use of minerals in medicine.

Greece (around 500 B.C.): silver mines of Laurion. Theophrastus (about 300 B.C.): 'about stones'; Aristotle's book on stones (not by Aristotle but written about A.D. 800). Pliny (A.D. 23–75): account of minerals.

Middle ages

Writings on minerals by Avicenna (980–1037) and Albertus von Bollstaedt called Magnus (1193–1280).

Modern times

Crystallography	Petrology, study of mineral deposits, geochemistry
Johannes Kepler (1571–1630): snow crystals.	Agricola (1494–1555): 'De re metallica', founder of modern mineralogy.
Nicolaus Steno (1638–1687): law of constancy of interfacial angles in crystals.	M. W. Lomonossov (1711–1765): geological occurrence of minerals.
Erasmus Bartolinus (1669): double refraction in calcite (Steno and Bartolinus were the founders of crystallography).	Abraham Gottlob Werner (1750–1817): mineral systematics.
René Just Hauy (1743–1822): law of rational indices.	Breithaupt (1791–1873): mineral paragenesis.
Ch. Samuel Weiss (1780–1856): relation between crystal faces and crystallographic axes.	Sorby and Oschatz (around 1850): preparation of the first thin section of a rock.
L. A. Saeber (1824): first introduction of the space-lattice concept.	C. F. Naumann (1797–1873): founder of modern petrography.
Auguste Bravais and M. L. Frankenheim (about 1850): establishment of 14 fundamental space-lattices.	C. F. Schönbein (1838): geochemistry.
E. von Fedorov and A. Schönfliess (about 1890): formulation of the 230 space-groups.	H. Rosenbusch (1836–1914): microscopic investigation of rocks.
P. von Groth (1843–1927): chemical crystallography.	P. Niggli (1888–1953): magmatic differentiation.
M. von Laue (1912): discovery of X-ray diffraction as a means of establishing the atomic structure of crystals.	H. Schneiderhöhn (1887–1962): ore-deposits.
W. H. Bragg (1862–1942); crystal structures.	
V. M. Goldschmidt (1888–1947): crystal chemistry and geochemistry.	

2
GENERAL MINERALOGY

2.1. *Structural crystallography and crystal morphology*

STRUCTURAL CRYSTALLOGRAPHY is the science of the atomic structure of crystals.

CRYSTAL MORPHOLOGY is the study of the external form of crystals.

CORRESPONDENCE is the relationship between crystal structure and morphology.

Crystals are homogeneous, anisotropic bodies (a homogeneous body is materially and physically uniform; an anisotropic body has different physical and chemical properties in different directions. In contrast, an isotropic body has the same physical and chemical properties in different directions, for example: glass).

Nearly all solid substances, not only minerals, are crystalline. Homogeneous bodies may be either isotropic or anisotropic (Figs. 2 and 3):

Isotropic (*Disordered in every direction*)	*Anisotropic* (*Ordered in three spacially-different directions*)
Amorphous bodies (e.g. glass) Gases Most liquids	Crystals 'Liquid crystals' (only ordered in two directions, or in some cases, just one direction)

The units of crystal structure are atoms, ions or molecules, which exhibit a rigorous three-dimensional arrangement in space. The spacings of these structural units are of the order of magnitude of 10^{-8} cm $= 1$ Ångström unit (Å).

A crystal is a three-dimensional periodic arrangement of atoms, ions, or molecules. The arrangement of particles in a crystal is represented

B

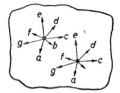 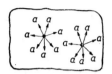

Figure 2 Homogeneous – anisotropic. Physical and chemical properties are dependent on the direction. Non-parallel lines are not equivalent.

Figure 3 Homogeneous – isotropic. All directions are physically and chemically identical.

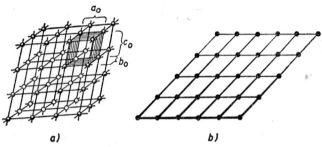

a)   *b)*

Figure 4 (*a*) Space-lattice (simple lattice) with the unit cell shown. (*b*) Lattice-plane.

by a *crystal lattice*, or *space-lattice* [Fig. 4a]. Planes lying in different directions through the lattice-points are called *lattice-planes*. Crystal faces represent lattice-planes [Fig. 4b]. The ordered structure of crystal lattices is, however, not always reflected by the crystal's possession of a distinct crystal form. Typical outwardly recognizable crystals are relatively uncommon. The space-lattice is built up by repetition of the smallest three-dimensional units, the *unit cells*. The spacing from one lattice-point to another is the *unit translation*. The shortest spacings in the three directions in space are labelled a_0, b_0, c_0 (characteristic spacings, lattice-constants). Fourteen different types of unit cell ('Bravais-lattices') are possible (Fig. 5).

SYMMETRY

The same pattern, in both external crystal form and space-lattice, can be repeated by certain geometric operations (e.g. rotation and reflection). Symmetry relationships are characteristic of crystalline bodies (Figs. 6 and 7). Each point of the space-lattice (lattice-point) has an identical environment which is dependent on the lattice-type.

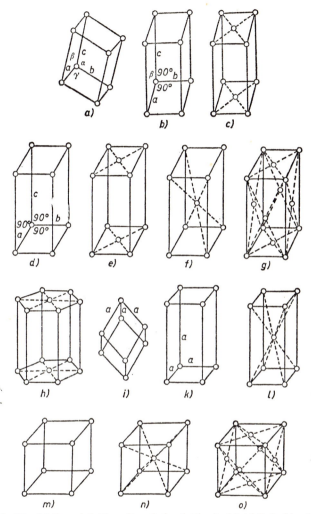

Figure 5 The 14 Bravais-lattices (translation-lattices): (a) triclinic (simple primitive); (b) simple monoclinic; (c) face-centred monoclinic; (d) simple orthorhombic; (e) end-centred orthorhombic; (f) body-centred orthorhombic; (g) face-centred orthorhombic; (h) hexagonal; (i) rhombohedral; (k) simple tetragonal; (l) body-centred tetragonal; (m) simple cubic; (n) body-centred cubic; (o) face-centred cubic.

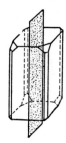

Figure 6 Plane of symmetry. The left and right halves of the crystal are mirror images of one an-other.

Figure 7 Two-fold axis of symmetry. Any face occupies the same position twice on rotation about this axis through 360°.

SPACE-GROUPS (POINT GROUPS)

There exist 230 ways in which all the various possible symmetry operations can be combined. Each of these combinations is termed a space-group, and all crystals belong to one or other of the 230 possible space-groups.

Each space-group is labelled with a special symbol. The cubic holo-hedral class contains 10 space-groups with differing symmetries: $0_h^1, 0_h^2 \ldots 0_h^{10}$

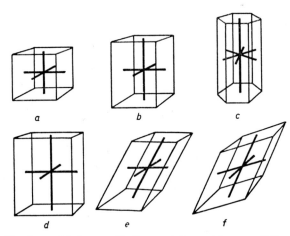

Figure 8 Simple crystal forms with the crystallographic axes of the six crystal systems: (a) cubic; (b) tetragonal; (c) hexagonal; (d) orthorhombic; (e) monoclinic; (f) triclinic.

CRYSTAL CLASSES

A number of point-groups, all of which possess a particular point-group symmetry, comprise each of the 32 crystal symmetry classes.

CRYSTAL SYSTEMS

The 32 crystal classes may, in turn, be arranged in 7 crystal systems. The 32 classes are thereby related to 6(7) different systems of co-ordinates. The sides of the unit cells drawn in Figs. 8 and 9 show the orientation of the axes in these systems.

Combination of all symmetry operations in the space-lattice: 230 point-groups (not externally distinguishable).
Collection together of point-groups with common symmetry relationships: 32 crystal classes (externally distinguishable in some cases).
Consideration of the co-ordinate systems in the 32 crystal classes: 7 crystal systems (often externally distinguishable).

Law of constancy of interfacial angle

The interfacial angles, measured between like faces, are constant for all crystals of a given material under constant physical conditions (e.g. temperature), regardless of the shape of the face. Crystal types may be identified by measuring such interfacial angles.

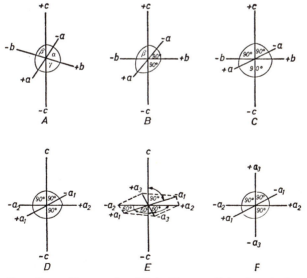

Figure 9 Crystallographic axes; A, triclinic; B, monoclinic; C, orthorhombic; D, tetragonal; E, hexagonal; F, cubic.

Types of crystal face

In order to form faces corresponding to their symmetry, crystals need both space and time. If, for some reason, the crystal grows much faster in one direction than in another, aberrant shapes result in which, although the law of constancy of interfacial angles still holds, the forms of faces of like kind are different.

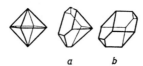

a   b

Figure 10 Normally-developed octahedron: (a), (b) distorted octahedra (the interfacial angles are identical in all cases).

If a face intersects all three crystallographic axes, it is termed a *pyramid face* (Fig. 11). If a face intersects two axes and is parallel to the third, a *prism face* occurs (Fig. 12). Faces which intersect only one axis, lying parallel to the other two, are known as pinacoids. In the cubic system, the pinacoids are termed cube-faces, prism faces are called

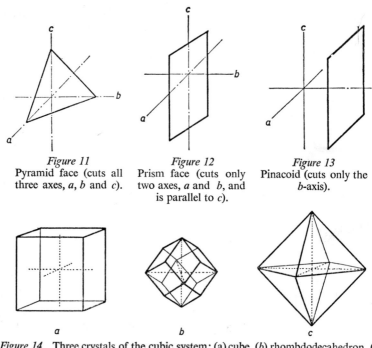

Figure 11
Pyramid face (cuts all three axes, *a*, *b* and *c*).

Figure 12
Prism face (cuts only two axes, *a* and *b*, and is parallel to *c*).

Figure 13
Pinacoid (cuts only the *b*-axis).

a   b   c

Figure 14 Three crystals of the cubic system: (a) cube, (*b*) rhombdodecahedron, (*c*) octahedron.

rhombdodecahedral faces, and pyramid faces are named the octahedral faces (Fig. 14). The notation used to characterize crystal faces is that of 'Miller Indices', e.g. (111), (100), (431) etc., which refer to the reciprocals of the distances at which the faces intercept the crystallographic axes.

Crystal form
The sum of all faces of the crystal. Form may be influenced by the growth environment (for example, composition of the solution).

Crystal habit
Crystals frequently exhibit an external form, which is quite characteristic of their type, e.g. asbestos, fibrous; mica, platy; apatite, columnar. Habit is dependent on growth conditions. Changing conditions can result in a change of crystal habit (Fig. 15).

Habit modification
This is the term used to denote alteration of form and habit by external influences.

Regular intergrowths
Intergrowths of several crystals of the same type, or of different types, may occur according to certain laws.

(A) INTERGROWTHS OF CRYSTALS OF IDENTICAL TYPE

Twinned crystals
Intergrowths of crystals of the same kind and form, which create an additional symmetry element, which does not occur in the single crystal (symmetry plane, axis of symmetry, etc.). Twinning is described by means of certain 'Twinning Laws', for example the 'Spinel Law' means twinning on the octahedral plane (Figs. 16 and 17). Trillings, fourlings and multiple twinning are also possible.

Parallel growths
Intergrowths of crystals of like kind and form, which are oriented parallel, not symmetrically, to one another, e.g. skeletal crystals, dendrites (Fig. 18).

(B) CRYSTALS OF UNLIKE KIND
Oriented overgrowth (epitaxis) is the regular growth of a crystal on a crystalline substrate of another species. It depends on the fact that the

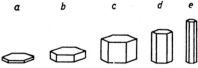

Figure 15 Apatite crystals of varying habit: (a) platy, (b) tabular, (c) stubby prismatic, (d) prismatic, (e) columnar.

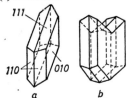

Figure 16 Spinel, twinned on the octahedral plane (111).

Figure 17 (a) Normal gypsum crystal, (b) twinned gypsum crystal.

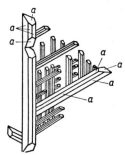

Figure 18 Dendritic intergrowths of copper crystals.

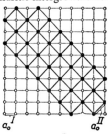

Figure 19 Material with a lattice-spacing a_0^I has grown, on rotation through 45°, on the substrate with lattice-spacing a_0^{II}. In this orientation the two lattice-planes have coincident spacings.

Figure 20 Oriented overgrowth of rutile (TiO_2) on specular iron (= hematite, $\alpha\text{-}Fe_2O_3$) (after H. Seifert).

surface (lattice-plane) of the substrate exerts a directing influence on a lattice-plane of the growing crystal. This influence is particularly strong if the geometrical structure of the lattice-plane of the growing crystal corresponds in two dimensions with the spacing of a lattice-plane of the substrate. The topography of the substrate surface, concentration, temperature, etc. are also important factors. Oriented overgrowths occur among natural and synthetic inorganic and organic substances. They also occur between inorganic and organic substances (Figs. 19 and 20), e.g. many oxide and sulphide films on metals (see 'Metal Surfaces'), as well as products of corrosion.

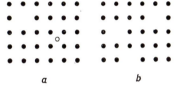

a   *b*

Figure 21   Lattice defects: (a) lattice vacancy and defect due to presence of foreign atom, (b) lattice vacancies.

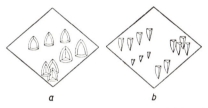

a   *b*

Figure 22   Etch figures showing different symmetries: (a) in calcite, (b) on the same (rhombohedral) face of dolomite.

2.2. *Crystal growth*

Crystals form from melts, solutions or vapours as soon as these reach a certain degree of undercooling or supersaturation. Initially, *nuclei* are formed by the agglomeration of atoms, ions or molecules. When these nuclei reach a certain critical size, they continue growing, spontaneously, into crystals. Foreign particles, impurities, may also act as crystallization centres. In the final stage of growth, the crystal will be bounded by those faces which advance at the slowest rate in free space, that is, those which possess the lowest growth velocity. The growth velocity of faces can be changed by the addition of impurities, e.g. sodium chloride crystallizes from solution normally in the form of cubes, but octahedra form if urea is used as the solvent. Crystal growth is, therefore, also a matter of form and habit modification. Crystal nuclei can also be formed by the condensation of vapour, when small drops of liquid form on a cold surface, and are then frozen out. In the growth of crystals, block upon block (atom, ion, molecule) of building material is deposited successively on the surface of the nucleus, and complete lattice-planes are gradually built up.

IDEAL CRYSTALS – REAL CRYSTALS

No natural crystal possesses a perfect lattice-structure (ideal crystal). All crystals show imperfection to some degree. These structural imperfections may be observable with the naked eye, with an optical microscope or only with an electron microscope. Atomic imperfections, which cannot be detected by these means, are caused by lattice vacancies or by atoms or ions which occur in anomalous unstable or metastable positions in the structure. These atoms or ions may or may not be foreign to the lattice (*structural defects*) (Fig. 21).

CRYSTAL DISSOLUTION AND ETCHING

Both phenomena may be regarded as processes reciprocal to crystal growth. In the earliest stages of etching or crystal dissolution, 'etch pits' form on the surface. These form preferentially at sites with a high concentration of structural imperfections, and on faces with relatively small negative growth velocities. Etch figures express the symmetry of the crystal face concerned (Fig. 22).

2.3 Crystal chemistry

This subject treats the relationships between lattice-structure, lattice-energy, and external form or behaviour of crystals, the latter being determined by the former two factors. Crystal chemistry, in contrast to molecular chemistry, is concerned with the interaction between an infinite number of atoms or molecules.

Each compound has a characteristic crystal structure but substitution of elements by other, related elements similar in size (ionic radius, see below) may occur, with the crystal form being only slightly altered, e.g. KH_2PO_4 and KH_2AsO_4, in which P and As may mutually replace one another. This is isomorphism. If an element is replaced by another of a significantly different size, however the lattice-structure may be changed. This is termed morphotropy.

MIXED CRYSTALS

These are solid phases in which a continuous change of composition occurs, without a change of crystal structure. Further, a chemical substance may, under different physical conditions, form crystals of quite differing types; that is, crystals with differing lattice-structures; e.g. graphite (hexagonal crystal system) and diamond (cubic system) are both forms of carbon (*modifications*). This is polymorphism.

TYPES OF BONDING IN CRYSTALS

Crystals may be classified on the basis of the forces which act between elements, and thus bond the crystal lattice.

Heteropolar bonding (ionic bond, polar bond, electrovalent bond)

In these cases the structural units of the crystals are electrically-charged particles (anion and cations). The smaller the inter-ionic distance and the larger the charge on the ion, the stronger is the ionic bond. Melting and boiling points increase with decrease in inter-ionic spacing, e.g. NaCl, KBr, KCl, NaF, MgO, CaO, CaS, BaS (Figs. 23 and 24).

Figure 23   Unit cell of NaCl with spheres of influence of ions: large spheres = Cl-ions, small spheres = Na-ions.

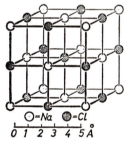

O=Na   ●=Cl

0 1 2 3 4 5Å

Figure 24   NaCl lattice shown schematically.

Polarization

Ions may be deformed by their mutual electrical influence. When two ions of differing charge touch one another, the cation attracts the electron cloud of the anion, i.e. the orbits of the outer electrons will be deformed in the direction of the cations, i.e. polarized (Fig. 25).

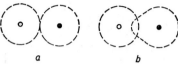

a   *b*

Figure 25   (a) Two unpolarized ions, (b) right-hand ion polarized (transition from ionic to homopolar bonding).

Homopolar bonding (*covalent bonding*)

This type of bonding can occur between electrically-neutral lattice-elements of the same kind. Bonding between these similar atoms is brought about because in some cases two atoms possess a common electron pair. Melts of homopolar crystals are non-conductors, but ionic melts are conductors. Examples: CuBr, CuCl, ZnS, and the C–C, C–Si and –Si bonds.

Metallic bonding

Every metal consists of 'atomic cores', from which have been detached a certain number of valence electrons which move, more or less freely, in the metal lattice. A metal lattice consists, therefore, of a regular arrangement of positively-charged 'electronic cores', immersed in a cloud of free electrons. Bonding is due to the attraction between the positive atomic cores and negatively-charged electrons, e.g. metals and metalloids.

van der Waals bonding (*inter-molecular bonding*)

Electrically-neutral molecules can represent dipoles, owing to non-uniform distribution of positive and negative charges. A dipole may also

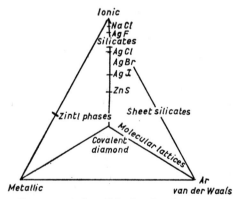

Figure 26   Schematic representation of the four bond-types and several transitional types (after C. W. Correns).

be induced in an intrinsically-neutral molecule, by neighbouring ions or dipoles. Completely-neutral particles, which approach one another, may also form dipoles because of charge mobility. These forces which act between neutral structures are known as van der Waals forces. They are always present in addition to the other bonding forces, but their effect is very limited. The only solids in which bonding is entirely of this type are the crystallized inert gases.

Hybrid (mixed) bonding
Single bond-types occur only rarely in a lattice. Usually, several bond-types are present together in a crystal.

Homodesmic	*Heterodesmic*
(A single bond-type predominates), e.g. diamond	(Several bond-types together), e.g. graphite

In most cases, bonding forces in crystal lattices are of a mixed or transitional type; the four pure bond-types are only limiting cases.

ATOMIC AND IONIC RADII IN CRYSTAL LATTICES

To a first approximation, atoms and ions in crystal lattices may be regarded as spheres which are packed together. Their spacing is the sum of the radii of two touching atoms or ions. The radius of each of these structural units is determined by its atomic number and degree of ionization. Atoms and ions are deformed to a greater or lesser extent because of the mutual influence they exert on one another. Atomic and ionic radii play a significant role in the chemistry of crystals (Figs. 23, 27 and 28). Ionic radii decrease with increasing positive charge.

CLASSIFICATION OF CRYSTAL LATTICES

Crystal lattices are classified according to their conformity to crystal-chemical laws as follows (after Kleber):

(a) M-lattice (lattice with predominantly metallic bonding);
(b) lattices with bonding which resonates between polar and non-polar;
(c) lattices with resonance (or mesomeric) bonding with a metallic tendency (metalloid lattices);
(d) molecular lattice.

(a) *M-lattice*

Crystal lattices of metals try to achieve the greatest possible space-filling of the structural units, and a high symmetry. True metals, almost without exception (over 80%), crystallize in one or more of the following structures:

(i) Close-packing.

  1. Cubic close-packing (face-centred cubic lattice, [Fig. 5(o)]);
  2. Hexagonal close-packing [two hexagonal lattices, one placed within the other, Fig. 5(h)].

(ii) Body-centred cubic packing Fig. 5(n).

In the closest packing of spheres the 'atom spheres' are packed together, from a purely geometrical point of view, as closely as possible. Each atom is surrounded by twelve like neighbours with identical spacing (co-ordination number = 12). Space-filling amounts to 74·1%. In cubic close-packing, each layer (in which the spheres are packed as closely as possible, i.e. with each sphere touching six others) is repeated in exactly the same position, every fourth layer in the stack.

Space-filling in body-centred cubic packing amounts to only about 68%. Each atom, therefore, has eight like neighbours (co-ordination number 8) [Fig. 5(n)], e.g. cubic close-packing: Ag, Au, Cu, Ca, Al, α-Ce, Th, Pb, Nb, γ-Fe, α-Co, Ni, Rh, Pd, Ir, Pt; body-centred cubic: Li, Na, K, V, Ta, α-Cr, Mo, W, α-Fe, δ-Fe; hexagonal close-packing: Be, Mg, Zn, Cd, β-Ce, Te, Ti, Zr, Hf, β-Cr, β-Co, Ru, Os.

Many true metals of identical structural type exhibit isomorphism (vide) and therefore form mixed crystals, which are called alloys. Different types of metal atoms in any lattice may be randomly distributed throughout the lattice-points. If, however, two metals are arranged at regular intervals in the lattice, a *super-lattice* results, e.g. FeAl and Fe_3Al.

(b) *Lattices in which bonding resonates between ionic and homopolar*

Resonance is the alternation of different bonding states, by which the lowest energy state is established (also called mesomerism).

(i) Lattices with ionic-covalent resonance but with predominantly covalent bonding. These are possessed by diamond, zincblende (ZnS), wurtzite (ZnS), SiC, ZnO, BeO, CuI, AgI, greenockite (CdS), CuCl (Fig. 31).

(ii) Simple lattices with ionic-covalent resonance but with predominant polar bonding.

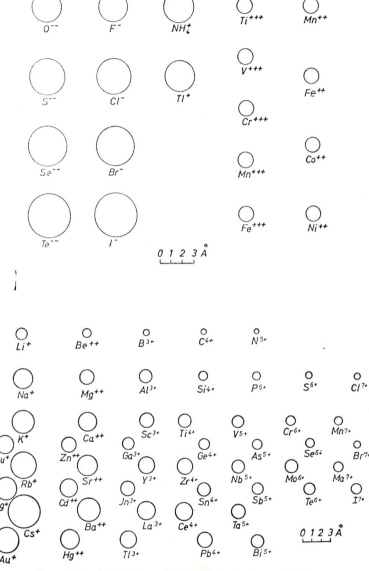

Figures 27 and 28 Ionic radii of important anions and cations.

Figure 29 Cubic close-packing.

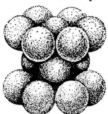

Figure 30 Hexagonal close-packing.

AX-types (1 cation + 1 anion): NaCl, and also the following: SrO, BaO, RbF, CaO, NaF, KCl, CaS, KI, MgO, LiF, NaI, NaBr, LiCl (Fig. 24); CsCl, CsI, CsBr (ZnS-structures are also AX-types).

AX$_2$-types (1 cation + 2 anions): fluorite (CaF_2) and also the following: BaF_2, ThO_2, UO_2, CeO_2 (Fig. 32); rutile (TiO_2), and also PbO_2, SnO_2, MoO_2, WO_2, VO_2, MgF_2; SiO_2-structures (these show characteristic transitions to homopolar bonding); SiO_2, GeO_2, BeF_2.

Simple ternary lattices with ionic-covalent resonance ($A_mB_nX_p$ (single anion type with two different kinds of cation): perovskite ($CaTiO_3$, and the following: KIO_3, $NaNbO_3$, $KNbO_3$; spinel-type (AB_2O_4), e.g. $ZnAl_2O_4$, $FeAl_2O_4$, $NiAl_2O_4$, $CaAl_2O_4$ (normal spinel); $FeMgFeO_4$, $FeTiFeO_4$, $MgTiMgO_4$ (statistical or inverse spinel); Fe_3O_4.

(iii) Complex lattices with ionic-covalent resonance. Certain ionic groups (complexes) form structural units of a higher order within the lattice.

Borates: structural unit is the BO_3-group, which can be bonded in many ways by oxygen atoms.

Silicates: the various types of silicate structure arise through bonding of the SiO_4-groups [SiO_4 tetrahedra, Figs. 33, 34(a), 69(a)]. The ways in which bonding of these groups may occur are as follows (Fig. 34):

1. Silicates with separate groups of one or more SiO_4 tetrahedra: silicates with isolated single SiO_4-groups ('orthosilicates', nesosilicates), e.g. olivine $(Mg, Fe)_2[SiO_4]$; sorosilicates, which are isolated groups of

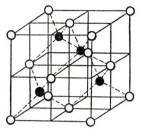

Figure 31   Diamond or zincblende lattice.

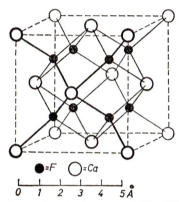

● = F   ○ = Ca

0   1   2   3   4   5 Å

Figure 32   Fluorite lattice. Each cation is surrounded by 8 F-ions and each F-ion by 4 Ca-ions.

Figure 33 SiO_4-group. Si atom (filled circle) surrounded by 4 oxygen atoms (open circles).

two or more SiO_4 tetrahedra thus giving the formula $[Si_2O_7]^{6-}$, e.g. thortveitite, $Sc[Si_2O_7]$; ring silicates (cyclosilicates), with linkage of three SiO_4-groups, and the formula $[Si_3O_9]^{6-}$, e.g. benitoite $BaTi(Si_3O_9)$. There are also ring silicates with linkage of four ($[Si_4O_{12}]^{8-}$) and six ($[Si_6O_{18}]^{12-}$) silica tetrahedra, e.g. beryl, $Al_2Be_3[Si_6O_{18}]$.

2. Chain silicates (inosilicates): the SiO_4-groups are linked to form infinite chains. Nearly all crystals with this structure have, therefore, a columnar, acicular (needle-shaped) or fibrous habit. One-, two-, three-, four-, five-, and seven-chained structures occur, e.g. two laterally-linked single chains with the group $[Si_2O_6]^{4-}$, as in pyroxenes; two double chains with the group $[Si_4O_{11}]^{6-}$ as in the amphiboles.

c

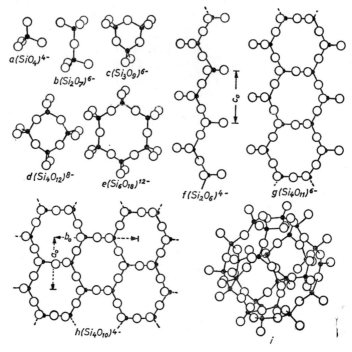

Figure 34   Linkages of SiO_4 tetrahedra: (a) separate SiO_4-groups, (b) sorosilicates, (f) and (g) SiO_4 chains, (h) SiO_4 sheets, (i) SiO_4 framework.

3. Sheet silicates (phyllosilicates): these are formed by the linkage of two double chains in such a way that a two-dimensional network or sheet is built up of $[Si_4O_{10}]^{4-}$-groups, e.g. clay minerals (vide), talc, mica, pyrophyllite.

4. Framework silicates (tectosilicates): these are formed when each SiO_4 tetrahedron is linked by all four corners, so that each oxygen is shared by two tetrahedra. A three-dimensional framework is thus built up, e.g. quartz, felspars, nepheline, sodalite, nosean, leucite. Relatively large open spaces occur in the framework structure, and so foreign ions or molecules can easily become accommodated in it without essential change of the framework, e.g. zeolites, which adsorb H_2O-molecules.

(iv) Ionic-covalent resonance lattices with unlinked complexes: these form isolated groups, which are so strongly bonded that they are able to remain as structural units even in solution, e.g. structures with BX_3-complexes such as calcite $CaCO_3$ (trigonal) (Fig. 35), aragonite $CaCO_3$ (orthorhombic); structures with BX_4-complexes such as anhydrite $CaSO_4$, wolfram $FeWO_4$, scheelite $CaWO_4$, barytes $BaSO_4$.

(c) *M-resonance lattice* (*metalloid lattice*)

Possessed by crystals which exhibit resonance bonding with a characteristic metallic tendency, e.g. graphite (Fig. 36), selenium, many sulphides with isometric structures (galena PbS, niccolite NiAs, iron pyrites FeS_2 [cubic], marcasite FeS_2 [orthorhombic], copper pyrites $CuFeS_2$, stannite Cu_2FeSnS_4), with sheet structures (molybdenite MoS_2), and with chain structures (antimonite SbS_3, SiS_2). The *intermetallic compounds* (Hume–Rothery phases, Zintl phases, Laves phases) also belong to this class.

(d) *Molecular lattices*

These are structures in which chemically-specific molecules, which behave as more or less independent groups, form structural units of the lattices.

Lattices with simple molecules: molecular gases (H_2, O_2, HCl, CO_2), sulphur, simple hydrocarbons.

Lattices with chain-shaped molecules: long-chain aliphatic hydrocarbons, long-chain alcohols, ketones, esters, rubber, cellulose.

Lattices with planar molecules: aromatic hydrocarbons, phenols, quinone, sugars.

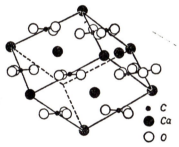

Figure 35 Structure of calcite. The centres of gravity of Ca^{2+} + CO_3^{2-} form a deformed rock-salt lattice.

Figure 36 Graphite lattice.

Lattices with complicated three-dimensional molecules: globular proteins.

2.4 Crystal physics

The physical behaviour of crystals is, in general, dependent on direction.

Scalar properties: physical quantities which have no directional connotation.

Vectorial properties: physical quantities which are direction-dependent.

2.4.1 Scalar properties of crystals

Density of crystals, as measured, usually deviates from the true value, due to the presence of inclusions and impurities. The specific gravities of minerals vary over a wide range. Minerals with the lowest densities are the naturally-occurring organic compounds, e.g. honeystone (mellite), $D = 1 \cdot 6$ g/cm^3. The most important minerals, quantitatively speaking, have densities between $2 \cdot 5$–$3 \cdot 5$ g/cm^3:

Leucite	$D = 2 \cdot 5$	Biotite	$D = 2 \cdot 9$–$3 \cdot 3$
Orthoclase	$D = 2 \cdot 56$	Augite	$D = 3 \cdot 3$–$3 \cdot 5$
Plagioclase	$D = 2 \cdot 61$–$2 \cdot 78$	Hornblende	$D = 2 \cdot 9$–$3 \cdot 5$
Nepheline	$D = 2 \cdot 62$	Olivine	$D = 3 \cdot 3$
Quartz	$D = 2 \cdot 65$		
Muscovite	$D = 2 \cdot 78$–$2 \cdot 88$		

With the exception of quartz, all of these minerals are silicates.

Minerals with densities greater than $2 \cdot 9$ are known as *heavy minerals* when they occur in rocks. They are often used in sedimentology as mineralogical guides to determine the provenance from which sediments have been derived. Minerals which are especially useful in this respect are zircon, tourmaline, garnet and rutile.

The ore-minerals (mineral sources of metals), which are mostly dense metal oxides or sulphides, often possess densities between 4–$7 \cdot 5$. The densest minerals are the native noble metals:

Iridium	$D = 21 \cdot 6$–$22 \cdot 5$	Mercury	$D = 13 \cdot 5$
Platinum	$D = 17$–19	Silver	$D = 10$–12
Gold	$D = 15 \cdot 6$–$19 \cdot 4$		

Specific heat of crystals is always temperature-dependent, and smaller than that of water. The quantity of heat added is converted into vibrational energy of the lattice. Each lattice-unit has a characteristic frequency, and the crystal lattice is accordingly a system of characteristic frequencies. The specific heat of a crystal is related to its *lattice-energy*. (Lattice-energy is the amount of energy released, when one gram-molecule of a particular lattice-structure is formed.)

Specific heats of minerals with a 'metallic' appearance are much lower, in most cases, than those of minerals with a 'stony' appearance (given in cal/g/degree):

Gold	0·031	Sulphur	0·2
Antimony	0·05	Gypsum	0·26
Diamond	0·11		

2.4.2. Vectorial properties of crystals

Hardness is the resistance of the crystal to mechanical attack (scratching, indentation). The resistance to scratching is the easiest to determine. In this test, the crystal is scratched by another material of known hardness. A scale, consisting of 10 standard minerals, was set up by F. Mohs. Other materials (finger-nails for example) can also be used as simple means of testing hardness. A more exact method, which is frequently used, is to determine the resistance to abrasion by grinding the material (after Rosiwal, for example), parallel to a crystal face, with a given quantity of abrasive, until it becomes ineffective.

Mohs' Scale

Hardness number	Standard mineral	Simple testing agent	Resistance to abrasion in water (after Rosiwal) (corundum = 1,000)
1	Talc	Match	0·03
2	Gypsum	Finger-nail	1·25
3	Calcite	Soft-metal coin	4·5
4	Fluorspar		5·0
5	Apatite	Knife-blade	6·5
6	Feldspar	Steel file, hard porcelain	37
7	Quartz		120
8	Topaz		175
9	Corundum	Carborundum (SiC)	1,000
10	Diamond		140,000

The differences in hardness, as shown by the relative resistances to abrasion, from one hardness number to another of the Mohs' Scale, are not identical but increase greatly with increase in hardness number. Both the scratching hardness and resistance to abrasion vary from face to face in all crystals (hardness anisotropy), Fig. 37. Hardness is determined by the lattice-structure; the smaller the spacing in the lattice and the higher the particle valence, the greater is the hardness. Hardness also increases with increasing lattice-energy.

Cleavage. Many crystals, when subjected to mechanical stress, have the property of splitting along distinct planes. These cleavage planes can often be observed, even in unbroken crystals. This is explained by the fact that cleavage planes are those lattice-planes between which the weakest bonding forces are operative. Crystals with a pronounced cleavage often show considerable hardness variation. The hardness is therefore lowest on the cleavage planes (Fig. 38).

Figure 37 Anisotropy of hardness of kyanite. H = 4 parallel to the length, and 7 in the transverse direction.

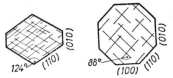

Figure 38 Cleavages in hornblende (at 124°) and augite (at 88°).

DEFORMATION OF CRYSTALS

Crystals undergo changes of shape (deformation) when subjected to mechanical stress (pressure, tension, etc.). *Elastic deformation* means that strain disappears when the applied stress is removed, i.e. the body reverts to its original form. *Plastic deformation* results in a permanent change of shape.

Elastic deformation

The elasticity of crystals is direction-dependent, thus the moduli of elasticity are different in different directions. Elastic behaviour is determined by the lattice-spacing. The hydrostatic compressibility of most crystals is very small. For ionic crystals, hydrostatic compressibility increases with the ionic spacing. With an increase of pressure of one atmosphere, the volume decrease of quartz, felspar, calcite and mica is only about 1–3 millionths. Fracture results if the externally-applied stress exceeds the cohesive forces of the lattice. The strength of a material (tensile-, compressive-, bending-, torsional-, or shear-) denotes, therefore, the resistance to the external forces causing elastic and plastic deformation.

Strengths of quartz

	Parallel to the c-axis	Normal to the c-axis
Compressive strength	25,000 kg/cm²	22,800 kg/cm²
Tensile strength	1,160 kg/cm²	850 kg/cm²
Bending strength	1,400 kg/cm²	920 kg/cm²

Plastic deformation

Two distinct but not mutually-exclusive mechanisms must be differentiated. These are translation gliding and twin gliding. Both mechanisms are included in the term *gliding*. Glide-planes are usually lattice-planes of relatively dense packing. Glide mechanisms first begin to operate when a certain critical shear-stress is reached (about 100 kg/mm²). Mechanical translation gliding produces a parallel displacement of single 'glide packets' along possible, simple crystal planes (= translation planes; the direction of displacement is known on the translation direction). The result is a continuous deformation, without fracturing, at ordinary temperatures. By this mechanism, single crystals may be drawn out considerably into rods or wires ('cold-drawing') (Fig. 39).

Figure 39 Cylinder of a single crystal of zinc, which splits up into 'glide packets' parallel to certain translation planes and becomes elongated.

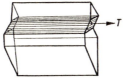

Figure 40 Twin lamellae, produced by pressure, in a calcite crystal (rhombohedron).

Mechanical twinning. In response to mechanical stress, parts of some crystals can be displaced in such a way that they become symmetrically related to the undeformed parts of the lattice (twinning) (Fig. 40).

THERMAL EXPANSION (DILATION) AND THERMAL CONDUCTIVITY OF CRYSTALS

Both phenomena are direction-dependent, with the exception of crystals belonging to the cubic system.

From 0 to 100°C the thermal expansion is generally small, e.g. a rod, 10 cm long, cut from a single quartz crystal expands about 0·9 μ parallel to the c-axis and 1·4 μ normal to the c-axis, on heating 10°C.

$$l_t = l_0(1 + \beta t)$$

l_0 = initial length of the rod, t = increase in temperature in degrees centigrade, l_t = length of the rod after heating to t°C, β = linear coefficient of expansion, which is direction-dependent for all non-cubic crystals.

Examples of coefficients of thermal expansion
(expansion at 0°C per °C per unit length)

Mineral (crystal system)	Coefficient of expansion		
Rock salt, NaCl (cubic)	40×10^{-6} (identical in all directions)		
Fluorite, CaF_2 (cubic)	19×10^{-6} (identical in all directions)		
	β parallel to the c-axis	β normal to the c-axis	
Cadmium, Cd (hexagonal)	49×10^{-6}	17×10^{-6}	
Zinc, Zn (hexagonal)	55×10^{-6}	14×10^{-6}	
Calcite, $CaCO_3$ (trigonal)	26×10^{-6}	6×10^{-6}	
Quartz, SiO_2 (trigonal)	9×10^{-6}	14×10^{-6}	
	β_a parallel to the a-axis	β_c parallel to the b-axis	β_b parallel to the c-axis
Aragonite, $CaCO_3$ (orthorhombic)	10×10^{-6}	16×10^{-6}	33×10^{-6}
Chrysoberyl, $BeO.Al_2O_3$ (orthorhombic)	6×10^{-6}	6×10^{-6}	$5·2 \times 10^{-6}$

Crystals with three axes of equal length (cubic system) possess one coefficient of expansion; crystals with two equal and one unequal axes have two coefficients of expansion (trigonal, hexagonal and tetragonal systems); crystals with three unequal axes possess three coefficients of expansion (orthorhombic, monoclinic, and triclinic systems).

In the cases of calcite (see table above) and graphite, expansion occurs in the direction parallel and a contraction normal to the c-axis. Crystals which have a close-packed lattice or one which is closely related show only very small differences of the thermal expansion in different directions.

THERMAL CONDUCTIVITY

Only cubic crystals and glasses behave in an isotropic manner. Examples of the direction-dependence of thermal conductivity in non-cubic crystals:

Mineral (crystal system)	K_1/K_2
Graphite, C (hexagonal)	4·0
Corundum, Al_2O_3 (hexagonal)	0·85
Calcite, $CaCO_3$ (trigonal)	0·84
Zircon, $ZrSiO_4$ (tetragonal)	0·81

K_1 = thermal conductivity normal to the c-axis.
K_2 = thermal conductivity parallel to the c-axis.

Silicates and quartz are better conductors of heat than water; quartz glass is a poorer conductor of heat than quartz.

ELECTRICAL CONDUCTIVITY

This is very variable in different kinds of crystal. It is possible to differentiate between ionic conductivity and electron conductivity. Conduction in crystals is generally due to a mixture of ionic and electron conduction. Both forms of conductivity are conditioned by lattice imperfections. Ionic conductivity is predominant in rock salt for example, and electron conductivity is predominant in metals (metallic conductivity). Under the influence of an applied electrical field, ions in ionic crystals diffuse in a preferred direction. This leads to a flow of electricity. In electron conductivity mobile electrons are continuously available and under an applied electrical field, these flow in a preferred direction. Examples of specific electrical resistance:

Silver (cubic) $0·016 \times 10^{-4} \Omega/cm$

Quartz (trigonal, parallel to c-axis) $1 \times 10^{14} \Omega/cm$

Quartz (normal to c-axis) $3 \times 10^{16}\Omega/cm$
(Thus the difference between silver and quartz extends
to a factor of 10^{20})

PIEZOELECTRICITY

This phenomenon occurs only in crystals *without a centre of symmetry*. (All faces of a crystal with a centre of symmetry occur as pairs arranged in equivalent positions and parallel orientations on opposite sides of a central point.)

Examples of crystals without a centre of symmetry, which show piezo-electricity, are quartz, tourmaline, tartaric acid, zincblende, sodium chloride, unrefined sugar. In such crystals an electric charge in a specific (polar) direction results from application of pressure or a tensile stress. A polar direction is one in which equivalent faces do not appear on opposite sides of a crystal. The effect can be reversed by application of an electric potential and a contraction or dilation of the crystal results. A fixed cycle of contraction and dilation results from the application of an alternating current. Small rods of single crystals (quartz, for example) are used in this way as high-frequency oscillators. Of the 32 crystal classes, 20 exhibit a polar direction, and thus piezoelectricity.

An explanation of the piezoelectric effect according to lattice-structure is as follows: the spacings between cations and anions in the polar direction are changed by increase in pressure or tensile stress. The electrical neutrality is disturbed by this displacement and the opposing charge occurs at the end of the polar axis [see **Single crystals** (7.15)].

PYROELECTRICITY

This also depends on the absence of a centre of symmetry, and on the polarity of such crystals. In this case however, the polar direction must coincide with a principal crystallographic axis; piezoelectricity does not depend on this condition. Polar principal axes may be recognized by the fact that the kinds of crystal faces at one end of the crystal are different to those occurring at the other end. On heating such crystals at one end, the heated end becomes negatively charged and the other positively charged. Only ten crystal classes occur in which pyroelectricity is possible, e.g. tourmaline, unrefined sugar, tartaric acid, willemite, scolecite.

The lattice-structural explanation is very similar to that for the piezoelectric effect, the only difference being that, in this case, the ionic spacing is changed by heating (Fig. 41).

Figure 41 Tourmaline crystal, electrically excited. Powdered sulphur (negatively charged) attracted to the positively-charged crystal faces, and red-lead powder attracted to the negatively-charged side.

MAGNETISM

Crystals may be classified into three groups on the basis of their magnetic properties: diamagnetic crystals (e.g. rock salt, calcite); paramagnetic crystals (e.g. aluminium, siderite); ferromagnetic crystals (e.g. iron, cobalt, nickel, magnetite, ferrite).

The groups are differentiated, by, among other things, their magnetic susceptibility.

$$K = M/H$$

($H =$ strength of the magnetic field of the crystal; $M =$ magnetic moment per unit volume).

Diamagnetic crystals ($K < 0$) are those which, when suspended in a strong magnetic field, arrange themselves across the lines of force. Their magnetic moment is produced principally by induction. Paramagnetic crystals ($K > 0$) arrange themselves parallel to the lines of force. Atoms and ions of these crystals already possess a magnetic moment; these, however, are disordered due to thermal motion, so that, initially, the crystal as a whole exhibits no magnetic moment. The moments become ordered under the influence of the external magnetic field.

Ferromagnetic crystals ($K > 0$, K attains very high values) are dependent on the external magnetic field. Ferromagnetism is a property of the crystal, not of atoms, and is due to the fact that, in single crystals, domains with strongly-oriented magnetic moments occur. The moments of each of the various crystal domains are oriented in different directions. Under the influence of an external magnetic field, however, the moments become oriented in specific directions.

CRYSTAL OPTICS

With the exception of those of the cubic crystal system, all crystals which transmit light are *doubly-refracting*, i.e. an incident beam of light waves will be split into two beams by the crystal. One beam (composed of ordinary rays) passes through the crystal without being refracted, whereas the other (extraordinary rays) is refracted (Fig. 42).

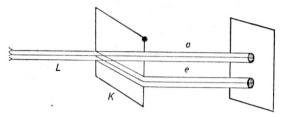

Figure 42 Refraction of a normal light ray (L) by a doubly refracting crystal (K) into an 'ordinary ray' (o) and an 'extraordinary ray' (e). The vibration directions of the rays are mutually perpendicular (polarized light) (after Schumann).

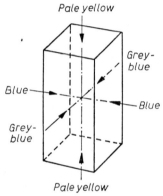

Figure 43 Direction-dependent absorption of light in cordierite (pleochroism).

The vibration directions of both the resultant beams are mutually perpendicular (polarized light), whereas in a normal incident beam all vibration directions occur.

In many coloured, non-cubic crystals, the colour in different directions varies quite distinctly. This is known as *pleochroism*. This depends on the variable kind and intensity of absorption of different wavelengths in different directions in the crystal.

The *refractive index* of a crystal is an intrinsic characteristic. This gives the relationship between the velocity of light in a vacuum to that in the medium (crystal, glass, etc.), e.g. a refractive index of $n = 1·5$ means that the velocity of light in the crystal is 200,000 km/sec:

$$\frac{300,000}{200,000} = 1·5$$

In cubic crystals (singly-refracting) the velocity of light is the same in all directions: a single refractive index (n) is, therefore, characteristic.

Among non-cubic, doubly-refracting crystals, two groups can be differentiated. (1) Optically uniaxial crystals: hexagonal, trigonal and tetragonal crystal systems with *two* refractive indices n_e and n_o (n_e = refractive index of the extraordinary ray, n_o = refractive index of the ordinary ray). (2) Optically biaxial crystals: orthorhombic, monoclinic and triclinic crystal systems with three refractive indices, n_α, n_β, n_γ or n_x, n_y, n_z.

Examples of some refractive indices:

Cubic (isotropic) crystals

Fluorite, CaF_2	$n = 1·4338$
Periclase, MgO	$n = 1·730$
Zincblende, ZnS	$n = 2·396$
Rock salt, NaCl	$n = 1·544$
Sylvine, KCl	$n = 1·490$
Lime, CaO	$n = 1·838$

Optically uniaxial crystals

Rutile, TiO_2	$n_0 = 2·609$	$n = 2·895$
Corundum, Al_2O_3	$n_0 = 1·767$	$n = 1·759$
Quartz, SiO_2	$n_0 = 1·544$	$n = 1·553$
Calcite, $CaCO_3$	$n_0 = 1·658$	$n = 1·486$
Magnesite, $MgCO_3$	$n_0 = 1·700$	$n = 1·509$

Optically biaxial crystals

Anhydrite, $CaSO_4$	$n_x = 1·5700$	$n_y = 1·5757$	$n_z = 1·6138$
Gypsum, $CaSO_4.2H_2O$	$n_x = 1·5205$	$n_y = 1·5226$	$n_z = 1·5296$
Orthoclase, $K_2O.Al_2O_3.6SiO_2$	$n_x = 1·518$	$n_y = 1·522$	$n_z = 1·524$
Albite, $Na_2O.Al_2O_3.6SiO_2$	$n_x = 1·528$	$n_y = 1·532$	$n_z = 1·538$
Anorthite, $2CaO.Al_2O_3.4SiO_2$	$n_x = 1·576$	$n_y = 1·583$	$n_z = 1·589$

LUMINESCENCE

This is the ability of many crystals to change other forms of energy into light energy. Various kinds of luminescence occur.

1. Thermoluminescence: crystals which emit light on heating (e.g. fluorite).

2. Electroluminescence: light emission on subjecting the crystal to the influence of an electric field (semi-conductor phosphors from a type of zincblende, etc.).

3. Chemiluminescence: light emission produced by a chemical reaction.

4. Triboluminescence: light emission produced during mechanical stressing (e.g. zincblende, rock salt, fluorite).

5. Crystalloluminescence: light emission during the crystallization of a compound (e.g. NaOH from the melt).

Luminescence may be caused by lattice imperfections in a crystal ('crystal phosphors' CdS, ZnS, scheelite $CaWO_4$, willemite $ZnSiO_4$, alkaline earth sulphides, etc.). Chemically pure crystals show no light emission. Luminescence is often caused by the presence of particular types of atoms (e.g. the rare earths) in the crystal lattice.

ELECTRON EMISSION

Electron emission of crystals is closely linked with luminescence. It occurs in crystals during and after mechanical stressing, during bombardment with X-ray beams, ultraviolet and visible light, etc. The emission of electrons is always combined with light emission (luminescence).

CRYSTALS AND X-RAYS

The measurements of lattice-planes (spacings of lattice-points) are of the order of magnitude of Ångström units, the same order as that of X-ray wavelengths (for copper anodes, 1·5390 Å; for iron anodes, 1·9360 Å). It is possible, therefore, to use crystal lattice-planes as diffraction gratings for X-rays. When crystals are placed in the path of an X-ray beam, diffraction patterns result from which the lattice-symmetries of the crystals can be determined. The resultant diffraction pattern is called a *Laue diagram*.

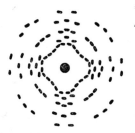

Figure 44 Laue diagram, obtained by passing an X-ray beam through the cube-face of a cubic crystal.

Relationships exist between the lattice-spacing of the crystal and the angle of incidence and wavelength of the X-ray beam used. Rays of a specific wavelength and angle of incidence will be reflected with a specific intensity by lattice-planes of a specific spacing. This is analogous to the reflection of visible light. These relationships are given by the *Bragg equation*:

$$d = \frac{\lambda}{2 \sin \theta}$$

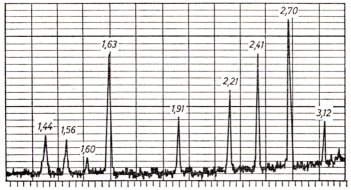

Figure 45 X-ray diffractogram of pyrites. The mineral is identified by the position and intensity of the peaks (the three peaks of greatest intensity occur at 2·70, 2·41 and 1·63 Å).

d = lattice-spacing, λ = wavelength of the X-ray beam used (for copper anode, 1·5390 Å; for an iron anode, 1·9360 Å), θ = diffraction angle.

The lattice-spacings and relative intensities of the diffracted rays are characteristic of the crystal structure, and thus of the particular type of mineral. The Bragg equation makes possible the identification of minerals by means of X-rays (Fig. 45). Glasses and amorphous substances cannot be identified this way, however, because they lack a crystal lattice. Very small particles ($<0.2\,\mu$) also behave increasingly like amorphous substances in their reaction to X-rays, i.e. they cannot be determined by X-ray structural investigation.

In many cases, also, a quantitative interpretation of X-ray diffraction patterns is possible.

CRYSTALS AND ELECTRON BEAMS

A promising method of investigation of extremely minute crystals (crystallites) is one which uses an electron beam, the wavelength of which is much smaller than that of X-rays (wavelength at 40 kV = 0·06 Å). The same laws hold for the diffraction of both electron beams and X-rays by crystal lattice-planes. Neutrons can also be diffracted in the same way.

RADIOACTIVITY

Minerals which contain, for example, uranium, thorium and potassium (K^{40}), are radioactive. Factors of mineralogical importance are the rate of decay, the decay products, the quantity of heat released by the decay process and the radiation involved (α-, β-, γ-radiation). Since uranium and thorium decay ultimately to lead (uranium to Pb^{206} and thorium to Pb^{208}), the age of the rock or mineral can be determined from the relative quantities of lead in uranium or thorium. The basic principle of this *radiometric age determination* (geochronology) is the fact that 1 g uranium decays to form $1\cdot27 \times 10^{-8}$ g Pb^{206} per year.

Large quantities of radioactive substances in a mineral can break down the crystal lattice completely and make it isotropic. Such structurally disordered minerals are amorphous to X-rays and in a state similar to glasses. These are called *metamict* minerals. The original crystal structure of metamict minerals can often be restored by heating.

Naturally-occurring radioactive elements or their isotopes

Element	Atomic weight of the element or isotope	Formation and natural abundance
C	14	Produced by bombardment of nitrogen by cosmic rays
K	40	0·012% of potassium
Rb	87	27·2% of rubidium
Tc	99	Discovered in stars by analysis of their spectra
Pm	147	100% of promethium
Sm	152	26% of samarium
Lu	176	2·5% of lutetium
Re	187	61·8% of rhenium
Th	232	100% of thorium
U	{235	0·71% of uranium (fissionable)
	238	99·28% of uranium
All elements with atomic numbers greater than 93		All isotopes radioactive, but occur in extremely low abundances in the earth's crust

3

GEOCHEMISTRY

Geochemistry is the study of the distribution and relative abundance of the chemical elements and isotopes in minerals, rocks, soils, waters, the atmosphere, and in the cosmos (cosmochemistry); the geochemical cycle in relation to the properties of their ions and atoms.

Practical application of geochemistry in mining, metallurgy, in the chemical industry, agriculture, biology (the circulation and distribution of chemical elements is closely bound up with biochemical processes in organisms), and in the exploration of interstellar space.

Composition of the earth

Estimates of composition rest on fairly reliable data only down to a depth of 20 km (earth's radius = 6377 km). It is generally accepted that the earth consists of spherical shells of differing densities and compositions.

V. M. Goldschmidt proposed the following hypothesis:

Depth	Shell	Density
0–50 km	Sial ⎱ silicate shell = lithosphere	2·8
50–1200 km	Sima ⎰	4·0
1,200–2,900 km	Sulphide–oxide shell = transition shell	5·5
2,900–6,377 km	Nickel–iron core	8–10

Sial: principal elements are silicon and aluminium
Sima: principal elements are silicon and magnesium

Each of the shells show concentrations of particular groups of elements because of their differing affinities for each other under specific physico-chemical conditions.

These elements have a weaker affinity for sulphur and oxygen than for iron and dissolve easily in iron, as elements or alloys. These are

D

Nickel–iron core	Fe	Co	Ni
	Ru	Rh	Pd
	Os	Ir	Pt
	Au	Re	Mo
	Ge	Sn	
	C	P	
	(Pb)	(As)	(W)

known as the *siderophile elements*. The most important of them occur in Group VIII or are neighbouring elements of the periodic table and possess an incomplete outer electron shell.

Sulphide shell	Cu	Ag	
(transitional shell)	Zn	Cd	Hg
	Ca	In	Te
	(Ge)	(Sn)	Pb
	As	Sb	Bi
	S	Se	Te
	(Fe)	(Mo)	(Cr)

These *chalcophile elements* have a strong affinity for sulphur and are soluble in an FeS melt.

They belong to the B subgroups of the periodic table, whose ions have 18 electrons in the outer shells.

Lithosphere	Li	Na	K	Rb	Cs	
(Sial + Sima)	Be	Mg	Ca	Sr	Ba	
	B	Al	Sc	Y		
	Rare earths					
	(C)	Si	Ti	Zr	Hf	Th
	O	Cr	W	U		
	F	Cl	Br	I		
	(Te)	(Ga)	(Ge)	(Sn)		
	(Fe)	Mn				

no such things!

The *lithophile elements* show the strongest affinity for oxygen. They readily form ions with 8 electrons in the outer shell.

Apart from these layers of the solid earth, two further geochemical divisions – the *biosphere* and the *atmosphere* – can be regarded as belonging to the earth. In the biosphere (the domain of plant and animal organisms on the earth's surface, in the water and air), the following elements predominate: H, C, N, O, P, V, I, K, S, = *biophile elements*. In the atmosphere (*atmophile elements*), the following occur: H, N, (C), (O), He, Ne, Ar, Kr, Xe, Rn.

The *uppermost part of the crust* (to a depth of 16 km) consists of:

95% igneous rocks (chiefly granite)

4% shales
0·75% sandstones } 5% sedimentary rocks
0·25% limestones

Chemical analyses (average compositions) of these rocks are:

	Igneous rocks (wt per cent)	Sedimentary rocks (wt per cent)
SiO_2	59·12	55·64
Al_2O_3	15·43	14·44
Fe_2O_3	3·08	6·87
FeO	3·80	—
MgO	3·49	2·93
CaO	5·08	4·69
Na_2O	3·82	1·21
K_2O	3·13	2·87
TiO_2	0·73	0·69
P_2O_5	0·18	0·17
H_2O^+	1·15	3·50
H_2O^-		2·04
CO_2		3·86
SO_3		0·32
C		0·65
	99·04	100·00

(H_2O^+: water driven off above 105°C; H_2O^-: water driven off below 105°C)

The mean composition of the earth's crust in grams per ton (German = 1,000 kg):

O	466,000	Rb	120	Hf	5	Hg	0·5
Si	277,200	V	110	Dy	5	I	0·3
Al	81,300	Ni	80	Sn	3	Sb	0·2
Fe	50,000	Zn	65	B	3	Bi	0·2
Ca	36,300	N	46	Yb	3	Tm	0·2
Na	28,300	Ce	46	Er	3	Cd	0·2
K	25,900	Cu	45	Br	3	Ag	0·1
Mg	20,900	Y	40	Ge	2	In	0·1
Ti	4,400	Li	30	Be	2	Se	0·09
H	1,400	Nd	24	As	2	Ar	0·04
P	1,180	Nb	24	U	2	Pd	0·01
Mn	1,000	Co	23	Ta	2	Pt	0·005
F	700	La	18	W	1	Au	0·005
S	520	Pb	15	Mo	1	He	0·003
Sr	450	Ga	15	Cs	1	Te	0·002
Ba	400	Th	10	Ho	1	Rh	0·001
C	320	Sm	7	Eu	1	Re	0·001
Cl	200	Gd	6	Tl	1	Ir	0·001
Cr	200	Pr	6	Tb	0·9	Os	0·001
Zr	160	Sc	5	Cp	0·9	Ru	0·001

This table shows that oxygen and silicon make up nearly 75%, by weight, of the entire crust of the earth. The eight most abundant elements (O, Si, Al, Fe, Ca, Na, K, Mg) comprise almost 99% of the weight of the crust, and oxygen amounts to nearly half the total weight. When the volume per cent of elements is calculated from the ionic radii it may be seen that over 90%, by volume, of the earth's crust is formed by oxygen. The earth's crust can be regarded, therefore, as a dense packing of oxygen ions with metal ions occurring in the interstitial spaces. Volume percentages for the most important elements have been calculated as follows:

	Wt per cent	Atom per cent	Ionic radius (Å)	Volume per cent
O	46·60	62·55	1·40	93·77
Si	27·72	21·22	0·42	0·86
Al	8·13	6·47	0·51	0·47
Fe	5·00	1·92	0·74	0·43
Mg	2·09	1·84	0·66	0·29
Ca	3·63	1·94	0·99	1·03
Na	2·83	2·64	0·97	1·32
K	2·59	1·42	1·33	1·88

Ga, Ge, Hf, rare earths and other elements have ionic radii closely similar to one another and to important rock- and ore-forming elements. For this reason they are often incorporated in the lattice ('camouflaged') in small quantities, and to a certain extent substitute for the major constituents, e.g. Ti replaces Fe, Hf replaces Zr, Ge replaces Si, Rb replaces K, etc. These predominantly camouflaged elements form, there-fore, few or no minerals of their own. Although they are distributed everywhere only in minute quantities, their total abundance is often greater than that of many elements of economic importance which have been concentrated in mineral deposits, as, for example, Hg, I, Sb, Bi, As, etc.

Geochemical balance for some elements of the earth's crust

Igneous rocks are weathered and fractions of the constituent elements become incorporated into sedimentary rocks and sea water, e.g. 4·55 kg Na occur for each 1 cm^2 of the earth's surface composed of igneous rocks. Of this amount, 1·55 kg cm^2 is incorporated into sedimentary rocks and sea water contains 3 kg cm^2, i.e. with respect to 1 cm^2 of the earth's surface, only 66·2% of the sodium contained in igneous rocks is contained in sea water. The geochemical balance-sheets for several elements are given in the following table (after Correns).

Element	Amount in igneous rocks (kg/cm^2)	Amount from magmatic source incorporated into sediments (kg/cm^2)	Amount in sea water (kg/cm^2)	% of the magmatic element in the sea
Na	4·55	1·55	3	66·2
K	4·16	4·05	0·11	2·6
Ca	5·81	5·69	0·12	2·1
Mg	3·36	3·00	0·36	10·7
Ba	4×10^{-2}	4×10^{-2}	3×10^{-6}	0·0075
Sr	$2·4 \times 10^{-2}$	$2·14 \times 10^{-2}$	$3·6 \times 10^{-3}$	15
Cl	$7·68 \times 10^{-2}$	—	0·53	6,900
Br	$3·2 \times 10^{-1}$	—	$1·8 \times 10^{-2}$	56,250
F	$1·28 \times 10^{-2}$	$1·24 \times 10^{-2}$	$3·9 \times 10^{-4}$	3
I	$3·2 \times 10^{-6}$	—	$1·4 \times 10^{-5}$	440
S	$8·32 \times 10^{-2}$	—	0·25	3,005
B	$4·8 \times 10^{-4}$	—	$1·34 \times 10^{-3}$	2,792
C	$5·1 \times 10^{-3}$	—	$8·5 \times 10^{-3}$	167

Composition of the hydrosphere which is formed almost exclusively of sea water with only a negligible fraction of fresh water is;

$$85·8\% \ O_2 \quad \text{and} \quad 10·67\% \ H_2$$

One ton of sea water also contains (mostly in an ionic state):

18,980 g Cl	380 g K	0·01–7	g SiO_2
10,561 g Na	65 g Br	4·6	g B
1,272 g Mg	28 g C (inorganic and CO_2)	1·2–3	g C (organic)
884 g S	22 g Fe (predominantly colloidal)	0·16–1·9 g Al	
400 g Ca	13 g Sr	1·4	g F

The composition of the atmosphere to a height of 60 km (vol. per cent):

78·09	N_2	0·93	Ar	$1·8 \times 10^{-3}$	Ne
20·95	O_2	0·03	CO_2	$5·24 \times 10^{-4}$	He

The cosmic abundance of the elements:

Spectrographic measurements of the *sun* gave the values shown below (in atoms per 100 atom Si) for the most abundant elements:

H	1,800,000	Fe	165	Ni	1·8
He	320,000	Mg	110	Cr	1·2
Ne	2,000	Si	100	Mn	0·9
O	1,750	S	26·5	K	0·6
N	950	Al	6·8	Co	0·3
C	450	Ca	5·4		

The abundance of the elements in meteorites (in atoms per 100 Si) show different relationships:

O	347	Ca	5·7	Mn	0·66
Si	100	Ni	4·6	P	0·58
Fe	89·1	Na	4·4	Ti	0·47
Mg	87·2	Cr	1·1	Co	0·35
S	11·4	K	0·69	C	0·33
Al	8·8				

Since meteorites are celestial bodies which presumably originated in the solar system, it is assumed that the overall composition of the earth approximates that of meteorites.

Organic geochemistry is concerned with all organic materials (compounds of carbon, hydrogen, and also in certain cases of oxygen, nitrogen, sulphur, etc.), which occur in rocks (predominantly sedimentary rocks) and meteorites.

The total amount of organic material in rocks of the earth's surface is distributed as follows:

Shales	3×10^{15} tons
Limestones	$0·15 \times 10^{15}$ tons
Coals	6×10^{12} tons

Half the total organic matter of the earth is, therefore, bound up in these rocks.

4

PETROLOGY

Rocks are formed by geological processes in which chemical reactions, pressure, temperature, place of formation in the crust, and the length of time involved in the formation, all play decisive roles. The genesis of rocks is conditional on the formation of minerals. Petrogenesis (study of the origin of rocks) cannot be regarded, therefore, as separate from the study of mineral genesis. The following types can be differentiated according to their mode of formation (genetic classification):

(*1*) *Igneous* (*magmatic*) *rocks* [eruptive (volcanic) rocks, intrusive (plutonic) rocks], which have formed by the solidification of a melt.

(*2*) *Sedimentary rocks* (stratified rocks), which represent consolidated chemical or mechanical deposits of material derived from the destruction of pre-existing rocks.

(*3*) *Sediments* are unconsolidated deposits.

(*4*) *Metamorphic rocks* (altered rocks), which may be formed from either magmatic or sedimentary rocks by transformation under a variety of conditions.

AGE AND AGE-CLASSIFICATION OF ROCKS

It is possible to arrange rocks into age-divisions (eras, systems, etc.) on the basis of fossils (animal and plant remains) which occur in sedimentary rocks, and by geochemical age-dating. Fossils characteristic of a geological age-division are termed type-fossils (see table on p. 44).

THE ROCK-FORMING MINERALS

Relatively few minerals play an important part in rock composition. Each is differentiated according to the amount present and the role it plays in the rock:

principal constituents (essential minerals), which determine the nature of the rock (e.g. quartz in granite);
subsidiary constituents, which occur in small quantities in any rock (e.g. apatite, zircon, etc.);

minor constituents (accessories), which are significant if they are characteristic of specific geological processes (e.g. topaz in granite), or if they substitute for principal constituents (e.g. sodalite and hauyne may substitute for nepheline in phonolites).

Geological era	Main subdivision		Duration in millions of years
Archaean			3,000
Algonkian			400
Palaeozoic (time of ancient life)	⎧ Cambrian ⎪ Ordovician ⎨ Silurian ⎪ Devonian ⎪ Carboniferous ⎩ Permian	100 ⎫ 60 ⎪ 40 ⎬ 50 ⎪ 80 ⎪ 50 ⎭	380
Mesozoic (time of middle life)	⎧ Triassic ⎨ Jurassic ⎩ Cretaceous	40 ⎫ 45 ⎬ 65 ⎭	150
Cainozoic (time of recent life)	⎧ Tertiary ⎨ ⎩ Quaternary ⎰ Pleistocene = ice age ⎱ Holocene = recent (present time)	69 ⎫ ⎬ 70 0·8 ⎭	

In the three main groups of rocks, the following minerals (arranged in order of abundance) are the most common:

igneous (magmatic) rocks – felspars, quartz, mica (biotite and muscovite), augite, hornblende, olivine, nepheline, leucite, glass (parts of the magma which are chilled so quickly that no crystallization occurs),
sedimentary rocks – mica and clay minerals, quartz, carbonates; felspars (in places also rock salt, gypsum, anhydrite);
metamorphic rocks – felspars, quartz, mica (biotite and muscovite), augite, hornblende, chlorite, garnet, epidote, zoisite, serpentine.

Two broad groups of minerals may be differentiated: the low-density, light-coloured, sialic minerals (*felsic* minerals) such as felspar, quartz, felspathoids, muscovite, etc., and the dark-coloured minerals of somewhat higher density (the *femic* minerals). Light-coloured rocks which contain up to only about 25% of dark constituents are called leucocratic rocks; dark-coloured rocks containing more than 25% dark constituents are called melanocratic rocks.

TABLE GIVING THE PRINCIPAL ROCK-FORMING MINERALS
(see also under 6.2 and 6.3)

Elements:	carbon, graphite
Sulphides:	pyrites, pyrrhotite, copper pyrites
Halides:	rock salt, fluorspar
Oxides:	hematite, magnetite, ilmenite, limonite, corundum quartz, chalcedony, opal, rutile, zircon
Carbonates:	calcite, dolomite, siderite, ankerite
Titanate:	perovskite
Sulphates:	gypsum, anhydrite
Phosphates:	apatite, phosphorite, monazite
Silicates:	felspars (orthoclase, microcline, plagioclase), felspathoids (leucite, nepheline, sodalite, nosean, hauyne), mica, augite, hornblende, scapolite, melilite, gehlenite, chlorite, olivine, serpentine, talc, kaolinite, illite, montmorillonite, epidote, garnets, zoisite, sphene (titanite), orthite, cordierite, tourmaline, andalusite, sillimanite, kyanite (disthene), topaz, staurolite, zeolites

Magmatic mineral- and rock-formation

Magma is a predominantly silicate melt of the earth's interior in which are dissolved metals and volatiles such as water, sulphur, chlorine, fluorine, boron, etc. The fluid state is produced by the high temperature prevailing in the earth. In this way, a silicate melt, which in most cases is moderately homogeneous, is formed from the solid rock of the earth's crust. The viscosity is determined mainly by the pressure of the overlying rock. The higher the pressure the greater the viscosity of the rock magma, which on release of pressure becomes correspondingly more fluid.

Through mountain-building movements and fractures in the earth's crust, the magma forces its way to the earth's surface. In this way a release of pressure and simultaneous chilling results (at a depth of 16,000 m a temperature of about 1,800 °C occurs). On a slight temperature decrease, large quantities of various crystal types begin to separate out from the magma; from these crystals igneous (magmatic) rocks are formed. Because the temperature decreases only slowly if the magma flows slowly on to the earth's surface, relatively large crystals are formed, which form massive deposits.

The crystallization of silicate melts proceeds in a distinct sequence (magmatic differentiation) (Fig. 46).

1. *Early crystallization* in a liquid magmatic phase at temperatures of 1,600 °C to 1,000 °C. During this early phase, Mg–Fe silicates (olivine) and oxides or sulphides of Fe, Ti, P, Cr, V, Bi and Cu separate out from

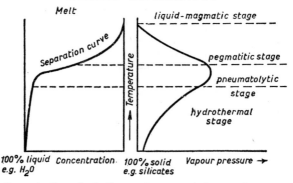

Figure 46   Concentration of volatile constituents and change of vapour pressure in solidification of magmas.

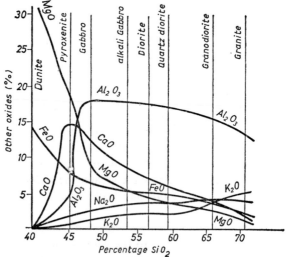

Figure 47   Graphic representation of chemical compositions of the most important igneous rocks.

the magma. The relatively dense, newly-formed crystals sink to the bottom of the melt (gravitative differentiation, gravity-settling) and there form masses of basic and ultra-basic rocks as well as mineral deposits.

Rocks with $<52\%$, by weight, SiO_2 are termed basic;
Rocks with 65–52%, by weight, SiO_2 are termed intermediate;
Rocks with $>65\%$, by weight, SiO_2 are called acid.
Basic and ultra-basic rocks are melanocratic (Fig. 47).

2. In the succeeding *main crystallization* stage, the melt has become

enriched in silicon and aluminium. Crystals associated with light-coloured intermediate and acid rocks separate out between 1,200°C and 600°C, and form rocks. Next to silicon and aluminium, the minerals of these rocks contain principally Ca, Mg, Fe, Na, and K.

3. In the *residual crystallization* stage, the melt has, by this time, a quite different composition to that of the original liquid. The concentration of rare elements (Li, Be, B, rare earths, Y, Zr, Hf, Th, Nb, W, Mo, Sn, etc.) is considerably increased. There is also a high concentration of volatiles (H_2O, H_2S, F, Cl, CO_2, SO_2, etc.).

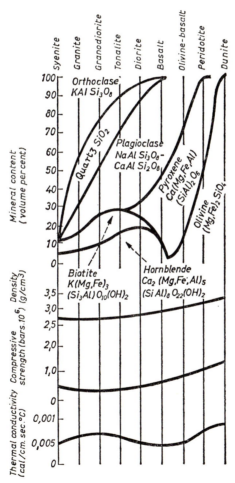

Figure 48   Mineral components and physical data of important igneous rocks.

Silicates again separate out preferentially in the temperature range between 600 and 400 °C. This crystallization occurs mostly in joints developed in rocks which have already solidified. These sharply-defined, newly-formed rocks (pegmatites, from Greek *pegma* = bond, framework) often contain very large crystals of felspar, tourmaline, beryl, topaz, etc. (*pegmatitic stage*). After the pegmatitic crystallization, the vapour pressure of the melt increases greatly, because, by this time, gases and liquid solutions determine the composition. Owing to the high pressure, the readily volatile metal compounds of chlorine, fluorine, boron and metal and non-metal hydroxides fugitive in water vapour, are distilled off and diffuse into pre-existing cracks (joints) in the solid rock. The temperatures of this *pneumatolytic mineral formation* lie approximately between 500 °C and 300 °C. Tin, tungsten and molybdenum mineral deposits, especially, result from this process, but no rocks are formed.

4. In the succeeding *hydrothermal stage*, dilute, pure or colloidal, aqueous solutions at temperatures of between 400 °C and 50 °C, occur as the residual magmatic fluids. No more rocks are formed but in addition to quartz, felspar and other non-ores, the chief minerals are ores (sulphides, thioantimonides, thioarsenides, and oxides of the heavy metals). They form very important mineral deposits, developed mostly as veins filling joints in the formerly barren cover.

The formation of igneous (magmatic) rocks occurs during magmatic differentiation, and predominantly during the early- and main-crystallization stages.

The most important minerals of these rocks separate out with decreasing temperature approximately in the following order (Fig. 48):

olivine → augite → hornblende → biotite → potash felspar → muscovite → quartz

calc (lime) felspar → soda-lime felspar
(continuously decreasing lime content)

——————————————————————————————→

decreasing temperature

——————————————————————————————→

basic   increasing SiO_2 content   acid

As a consequence of magmatic differentiation four great magma groups with their corresponding minerals may be differentiated:

1. peridotite magmas (olivine, augite or hornblende);
2. gabbroic magmas (lime-soda felspar, augite, olivine);

3. dioritic magmas (soda-lime felspar, augite, hornblende);
4. granitic and syenitic magmas [alkali felspar, hornblende, biotite, quartz in some cases (granites)].

The igneous rocks can be further subdivided, according to their chemical composition, into *calc-alkaline (Pacific-type*. e.g. in the Andes), and *alkali* types. Among the alkali rocks those with dominant soda (*Atlantic-type*, e.g. in the Azores) and those with dominant potash (*Mediterranean-type*, e.g. in central Italy) are differentiated.

After their formation, minerals can react with the enclosing magma during the differentiation process and their composition is thus changed (e.g. originally-formed olivine can become converted to augite). In many cases, too, fragments of the country rock may be incorporated into the magma; these may then be melted and assimilated, so that the chemical and mineral composition of the magma is altered (*hybrid magma*). The mean mineral composition of all igneous rocks has been computed as:

Felspars	59
Augite and Hornblende	17
Quartz	12
Mica	4
Other minerals	8
	100%

(*Felspars are, therefore, the most abundant minerals in the earth's crust*)

ROCK FORMATION AND PHASE-RULE EQUILIBRIA

All processes, including those of rock formation, attempt to attain a state of equilibrium. If the chemical or physical conditions change, new equilibria become established. In rocks, true equilibria are seldom achieved, usually only false- or metastable-equilibria occur, i.e. metastable states, which closely approach true equilibria, e.g. granite, which is formed at depth under definite conditions of presure and temperature, reaches the earth's surface through weathering and erosion of the overlying rock. The minerals are here only in apparent equilibrium and the result is further weathering. The *mineralogical phase-rule*, which also holds for false-equilibria, states:

The number of phases (P) in a rock equals the number of independent components (C) present, e.g. if a system is composed of 5 components, say, CaO, MgO, Al_2O_3, K_2O and SiO_2, the maximum number of minerals which can stably co-exist is 5 (a mineral assemblage is stable at a given temperature and pressure, if no reaction occurs between any of the minerals even in the presence of a common solvent).

The mineralogical phase-rule is derived from the Gibbs phase-rule:

Number of phases + number of degrees of freedom

= number of independent components + 2

Phases: physically and chemically distinct and homogeneous kinds of aggregate matter, such as gaseous, liquid and solid phases. In the solid state, there are several phases if chemically different, crystalline or amorphous materials occur, or if the material has several modifications. Degrees of freedom: in rocks, temperature and pressure are normally the two degrees of freedom; the third degree of freedom, viz. concentration, can often be regarded as constant. Applied to rocks, therefore, the phase rule states that

$$P + 2 = C + 2 = \underline{P = C}$$

REVIEW OF THE IGNEOUS ROCKS

Classification: *plutonic rocks, hypabyssal (dyke) rocks,* and *extrusive (effusive, volcanic) rocks* are recognized. This differentiation is determined by the geological environment in which solidification occurs. Plutonic rocks crystallize several kilometres below the earth's surface. Hypabyssal rocks solidify at shallower depths, since they intrude the crust through fissures, and extrusive rocks flow from volcanoes on to the earth's surface, where they solidify.

Accordingly, plutonic rocks solidify slowly under high pressure, hypabyssal rocks solidify somewhat faster under high pressure, and extrusive rocks solidify quickly at a lower pressure. Any type of magma can, therefore, form plutonic, hypabyssal or volcanic rocks depending on the geological environment in which solidification occurs. The extrusive rocks are sometimes subdivided (unnecessarily) into ancient (Palaeozoic and older) and young (Tertiary and post-Tertiary) groups.

STRUCTURES OF IGNEOUS ROCKS

In addition to mineral composition, the mutual arrangement of the constituent minerals (fabric) also provides information about the genesis of rocks. The concept of rock fabric (petrofabrics, structural petrology) includes structural arrangement measured in the mm–cm range (*texture*) and also the structural arrangement of larger units, e.g. of the order of metres (*structure*).

Plutonic and some hypabyssal rocks are completely crystalline (holocrystalline or eucrystalline) and fine- to coarse-grained. The crystals may, in part, possess their characteristic forms (idiomorphic) or be anhedral

Important igneous rocks

Mineral composition	Plutonic rocks Calc-alkali	Alkali	Extrusive rocks Ancient	Young	Hypabyssal rocks
orthoclase + quartz + biotite *et al.*	granite	alkali- granite	quartz porphyry	rhyolite pitchstone obsidian perlite pumice	granite porphyry aplite pegmatite
+ hornblende *et al.* orthoclase + alkali hornblende *et al.*	syenite	alkali- syenite	porphyry	trachyte	syenite porphyry
+ plagioclase + quartz hornblende + nepheline ± orthoclase	diorite quartz diorite granodiorite tonalite eleolite syenite		porphyrite andesite dacite phonolite		diorite porphyry
+ plagioclase + bronzite augite + nepheline ± olivine	gabbro norite		basalt felsparphyric basalt melaphyre	nepheline basalt olivine basalt	dolerite
olivine ± augite	peridotite dunite		picrite basalt		

(xenomorphic) (Fig. 49); this depends partly on the order of crystallization. In addition to crystals, extrusive rocks contain mainly glass (dyscrystalline, cryptocrystalline, vitrophyric); in specific cases the rock consists almost entirely of glass (hyaline, vitreous). A porphyritic texture commonly occurs in and is typical of extrusive rocks, in which large, perfectly-formed crystals (phenocrysts) are set in a fine-grained, often glassy groundmass (Fig. 50). Hypabyssal rocks also may often contain phenocrysts set in a fine-grained, glass-free, groundmass.

Evidence of flow in magmas may be seen by the preferred orientation of most lath-shaped crystals (e.g. felspars). This is flow-structure (Fig. 51).

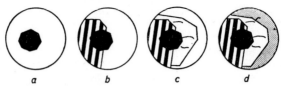

Figure 49   Order of crystallization and characteristic forms of minerals in granite: (a) biotite = euhedral; (b) biotite + plagioclase (subhedral); (c) biotite + plagioclase + orthoclase (subhedral); (d) biotite + plagioclase + orthoclase + quartz (anhedral, filling the interstices). [Thin section, ×50 (schematic)]

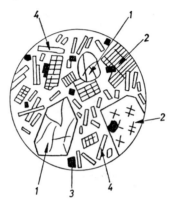

Figure 50   Porphyritic texture (plagioclase basalt). Phenocrysts: 1 = olivine 2 = augite, 3 = magnetite (black), 4 = plagioclase (laths). White: glassy groundmass. [Thin section, ×50 (schematic)]

Because nearly all rocks contract during their formation, cracks or zones of limited cohesion occur, often forming a regular pattern. These zones are called joints. Quartz porphyries and granites form laminar or sheet-like jointing; basalts form polygonal columns.

Rocks are classified and named on the basis of: (i) mineral constituents, (ii) chemical composition, (iii) fabric.

DESCRIPTION OF IMPORTANT IGNEOUS ROCKS

The most important means of rock description and mineral determination is provided by thin sections. These are slices of the rock, about 3 cm² in area and 20–30 μ thick, which can be examined in transmitted polarized light.

GRANITIC MAGMAS

Plutonic rocks. **Granite:** directionless granular fabric. Composed of felspar, quartz and mica. Felspar is predominantly orthoclase, with variable amounts of soda-rich plagioclase (oligoclase). Microline often

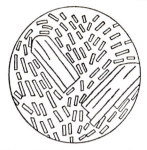

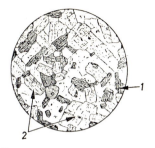

Figure 51 Flow-structure in an andesite. Large plagioclase crystals surrounded by oriented felspar laths. [Thin section, ×50 (schematic)]

Figure 52 Granite (biotite-granite): 1 = biotite, 2 = felspar, 3 = quartz (colourless interstitial material). [Thin section, ×50]

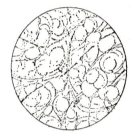

Figure 53 Perlite with typical cracks. [Thin section, ×50]

occurs instead of orthoclase. Mica mostly biotite, often in addition to variable amounts of muscovite. Sometimes with hornblende or augite. Zircon, apatite, magnetite, ilmenite, always in small quantities. **Rapakiwi:** Finnish hornblende–biotite–granite (Figs. 49, 52, 63).

Hypabyssal rocks. **Granite porphyry:** corresponds to granite in composition, but with porphyritic instead of granular texture. Phenocrysts of quartz, orthoclase, plagioclase and biotite set in fine-grained groundmass. **Aplite** and **pegmatite:** light-coloured, granitic dyke rocks, which are composed almost entirely of orthoclase and quartz (Fig. 63).

Extrusive rocks. **Quartz porphyry** (an ancient volcanic rock): porphyritic texture, phenocrysts of orthoclase and pagioclase (oligoclase) set in holocrystalline groundmass. Chemically, closely similar to granite. **Rhyolite (liparite);** the volcanic rock corresponding to granite. Glassy volcanic rocks. **Pitchstone** (with 5–9% H_2O), **perlite** (with about 3% H_2O), **obsidian** (almost water-free), **pumice** (frothy texture (Figs. 53, 63).

SYENITIC MAGMAS

Plutonic rocks. **Syenite;** unoriented, granular rock composed of orthoclase, hornblende, with little or no quartz (Fig. 54). Occasionally also

E

mica (biotite) and augite. Subsidiary constituent: commonly sphene. *Larvikite:* alkali syenite containing feldspar showing a blue iridescence (schillerization).

   Extrusive rocks. **Orthoclase porphyry:** ancient volcanic rock with porphyritic texture. Phenocrysts: orthoclase and hornblende. **Trachyte:** porphyritic texture: phenocrysts of sanidine, plagioclase (oligoclase), hornblende and biotite in a groundmass, which contains small amounts of glass. Trachyte glasses also common: **trachytic pumice, trachytic obsidian.**

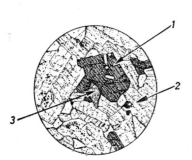 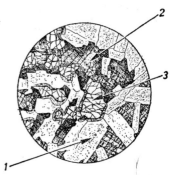

Figure 54   Syenite (hornblende-syenite): 1 = hornblende, 2 = orthoclase, 3 = sphene. [Thin section, × 50]

Figure 55   Gabbro (olivine gabbro): 1 = plagioclase, 2 = augite, 3 = olivine. [Thin section, × 50]

DIORITIC MAGMAS

Plutonic rocks. **Diorite** with directionless granular texture. Constituents: plagioclase, hornblende, and in small quantities, biotite, augite, orthoclase and quartz. **Quartz diorites:** quartz-rich diorites. Transitional types from granite to quartz-diorite: **granodiorite (tonalite** is a quartz-diorite rather closely related to granite). **Eleolite syenite (foyaite):** alkali rock composed of potash felspar and eleolite (nepheline) with augite, hornblende or biotite.

   Extrusive rocks. **Porphyrite:** a volcanic rock composed of plagioclase, hornblende, biotite or augite. Quartz may be an essential constituent; orthoclase decreases. Phenocrysts of plagioclase in a dense groundmass. 'Porfido rosso antico', porphyrite from the Red Sea region, much used in antiquity. – **Andesite:** volcanic rock composed of plagioclase, hornblende, augite and mica. No orthoclase. Phenocrysts of plagioclase, hornblende and biotite set in grey or brown groundmass. **Dacite:** andesite with essential quartz content (transitional to granite). **Phonolite:**

alkali volcanic rock, corresponding to nepheline syenite. Porphyritic texture: phenocrysts of nepheline, orthoclase and augite (Fig. 51).

GABBROIC MAGMAS

Plutonic rocks. **Gabbro:** directionless granular fabric, composed of lime-rich plagioclase felspar (labradorite) and clino- and rhombic-pyroxenes. **Norite:** rock with dominant rhombic-pyroxene. Olivine may also be present **(olivine gabbro)** (Fig. 55).

Extrusive rocks. Volcanics corresponding to gabbro are very diverse. **Diabase:** ancient, mostly granular volcanic rock, which has been subjected to fold movements. Constituents: plagioclase (labradorite) and augite, besides olivine (olivine diabase), hornblende and biotite. Green-coloured. **Melaphyre:** olivine diabase, which is younger than the characteristic diabase, but, however, still of Palaeozoic age. **Basalts:** young basic volcanic rocks of Tertiary or post-Tertiary age. The rock masses often form huge polygonal columns. **Felspar basalt:** porphyritic texture. Composed of plagioclase, augite, olivine and magnetite. If nepheline substitutes for plagioclase = **nepheline basalt,** if leucite substitutes for plagioclase = **leucite basalt** (Fig. 50).

PERIDOTITIC MAGMAS

Plutonic rocks. **Peridotite:** felspar-free granular rock composed of olivine (peridot) and augite (matrix of South African diamond-bearing rocks). **Dunite:** pure olivine-rock.

Extrusive rocks. **Picrite:** almost felspar-free rock composed of olivine and augite.

Sedimentary rocks

Origin. Sedimentary rocks are derived from disintegration products which are formed by the weathering of igneous, sedimentary and metamorphic rocks. The sedimentary rocks cover about 75% of the earth's surface, but they form only 5% of the total volume of the earth's crust. The mean mineral composition of all sedimentary rocks is (per cent):

quartz	30	felspars	9	chlorite	2
mica	23	carbonates	8·5	water	2
clay minerals	17·5	Fe_2O_3 *et al.*	5·5	remainder	2·5

Weathering. The name given to the transformation processes occurring on the earth's surface, which are caused by geological agents of denudation (e.g. oxygen, water, pressure and temperature variation). Weathering products form soils in their place of origin, and sedimentary rocks after subsequent transport.

Weathering processes are subdivided into *chemical* and *mechanical* types.

MECHANICAL WEATHERING PROCESSES

(a) Weathering due to heating and cooling of the rock surface; (b) frost-action by volume increase of water freezing in cracks and pores of the rock; (c) salt-action through volume increase caused by crystallization of salts in cracks and pores of the rock or by the hydration of anhydrous or water-deficient salts.

CHEMICAL WEATHERING PROCESSES

Rocks are reduced to small particles by mechanical weathering and chemical attack is thus promoted. The most important type is the *weathering of silicates*, because silicates compose more than three-quarters of the earth's crust. Of this, felspars comprise 58% (40% plagioclase and 18% potash felspar). Felspars gradually dissolve in water, so that first the alkalis, SiO_2 and Al_2O_3, are removed in true solution, since they are the most soluble. Muscovite, leucite, olivine and tremolite are dissolved in a similar way. Quartz has a very low solubility and is only slightly attacked by water. The solubility of silicon, aluminium and iron is dependent on the pH of the solution (Fig. 56). Silica is only slightly soluble in acid or neutral solution, but strongly soluble in alkaline solution (at pH >9). The salt content of the sea is too low to precipitate the SiO_2 which gets carried into it by rivers.

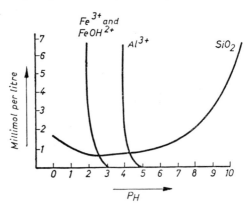

Figure 56   Solubility of silica, alumina and iron in relation to pH (modified after Correns).

Aluminium is soluble in acid (pH <4) and alkaline (pH >9) solutions.

In the absence of oxygen, iron is soluble only in acid (pH <3) solutions, but in the presence of oxygen is soluble also in neutral and alkaline solutions. Solutions of the alkalis and alkaline earth elements are very stable and, for the largest part, are carried away from the weathered region, whereas most of the Si, Al and Fe becomes precipitated again (mostly in soil). The latter migrate predominantly in a colloidal state.

FORMATION OF NEW MINERALS BY CHEMICAL WEATHERING

In the course of weathering, hydroxides of iron, aluminium and silicon are formed. Through further reactions the following minerals can originate, e.g.:

from ferric hydroxide: hematite (α-Fe_2O_3), siderite ($FeCO_3$), magnetite (Fe_3O_4), goethite (α-FeOOH, 'needle iron ore'), lepidocrocite (γ Fe-OOH);
from silicon hydroxide: opal, chalcedony (silicification), quartz;
from aluminium hydroxide: gibbsite (γ-$Al(OH)_3$), diaspore (α-AlOOH), boehmite (γ-AlOOH);
from silicon hydroxide and aluminium hydroxide: formation of aluminium silicates such as kaolinite, halloysite, montmorillonite and muscovite.

CLASSIFICATION OF SEDIMENTARY ROCKS

(a) Mechanically-formed sediments (clastic sediments)
Rock particles formed by mechanical weathering are transported from their place of origin by running water (fluviatile), ice (glacial) and wind (aeolian), and deposited elsewhere, when the velocity and turbulence of the transporting medium falls below a certain value.

(b) Chemical and biogenic sediments
The elements dissolved in the weathering process and transported over large distances may be precipitated by the introduction of other substances, by evaporation, or by the action of organisms.

CLASSIFICATION AND DESCRIPTION OF THE SEDIMENTARY ROCKS

(a) Clastic sediments and sedimentary rocks
Sediments may be subdivided, according to grain size of the constituent particles, into **pelites** or **argillites** (clays – in this context, the word also implies a size grade), **psammites** or **arenites** (sands) and **psephites** or

rudites (gravels). Uncompacted deposits are *sediments*; consolidated deposits are *sedimentary rocks* where consolidation has occurred through diagenesis without extensive physical and chemical changes. *Diagenesis* refers to geological processes (for example, a relatively small increase in pressure due to the weight of overlying sediments) which lead to the consolidation of loose sediments and the formation of a rock, without any great chemical or physical changes (mineral composition remains essentially the same, with the exception, e.g., of the formation of pyrites and/or concretions).

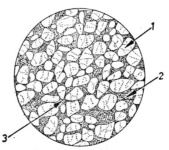

Figure 57   Sandstone: 1 = small quartz grains (white), 2 = calcite, 3 = clay matrix acting also as a cement. [Thin section, × 100]

Group	Mean grain size	Name		
		Unconsolidated	Unconsolidated	Consolidated
Pelites	0·2 μ 2 μ	colloidal clay fine clay coarse clay	clay, calcareous mud, loess (in part)	shales, mudstones, some limestones
	0·02 mm			
Psammites	0·2 mm	fine sand coarse sand	silt, sand, fine gravel	sandstone, arkose, greywacke
	2 mm			
Psephites	20 mm 200 mm	fine gravel coarse gravel pebbles, boulders, blocks	gravel, scree	rounded fragments: conglomerate, angular fragments: breccia
Pyroclastics (volcanic fragments)	<2 μ to 200 mm	ash, volcanic agglomerate		tuffs

Fabric of sedimentary rocks

The most typical characteristic is *bedding* (*layering*) which is produced by variation in the supply of material during deposition. If the direction of flow changes during deposition, *cross-bedding* results.

Pelites. Clay minerals are the principal constituents of **clays.** Quartz, felspar, iron compounds, carbonates, etc., may also occur. In exceptional cases other minerals may also predominate in the clay grain size grade ($<4 \mu$), for example, extremely fine-grained calcium carbonate in some muds. **Loam** is argillaceous (clayey) sand, **clunch** is the miner's term for plastic clay, **loess** is an aeolian deposit of extremely fine-grained quartz powder with some clay and carbonates. **Shales** are consolidated clays with a distinct lamination (bedding) and small compositional variation, in contrast with clays (rocks occurring in association with European coal seams). They also contain organic substances such as amino-acids, metal porphyrin complexes, hydrocarbons, purine and pyridene.

Psammites. Sandstones consist essentially of small quartz grains with subordinate amounts of mica, clay minerals, felspar, carbonates and in some cases glauconite. The constituent particles are often cemented by clay, silica or carbonates. **Calcareous sandstones:** sandstones with much calcite; **arkose:** felspar- and mica-rich sandstones; **greywacke:** sandstones with relatively fresh, unweathered particles (Fig. 57).

Psephites, conglomerates. Rounded pebbles or boulders cemented together by a clay, calcareous, or siliceous cement. **Breccias:** similar to conglomerate with, however, predominantly angular fragments.

Tuffs. Consolidated volcanic ashes and agglomerates. Possess the composition of the rock from which they originate (e.g. basaltic tuffs, melaphyric tuffs, trachytic tuffs, quartz-porphyritic tuffs, etc.) Clay minerals are often formed by the weathering of tuffs and the country rock, e.g. montmorillonite ('bentonite').

(*b*) *Chemical and biogenic sediments and sedimentary rocks*
Classification:

(A) Precipitates (in part through the action of organisms).

Unconsolidated	*Consolidated*
Calcareous mud (in part)	limestone (predominant)
Dolomitic mud (in part)	marl (in part),
	dolomite (in part),
	dolomitic limestone (in part),
	dolomitic marl (in part)

(B) Rocks formed almost entirely of organic remains.

Unconsolidated	*Consolidated*
(1) Calcareous: calcareous mud (in part), foraminiferal mud	limestone (in part), chalk, coral limestone, reef limestone
(2) Siliceous: radiolarian mud, kieselguhr, diatomaceous earth, flinty earth (tripoli)	radiolarite, hornstone siliceous shale
(3) Bituminous: peat, sapropel, petroleum (natural gas)	lignite (brown coal), coals, oil shales

(C) Evaporites.

Gypsum, anhydrite
sulphates and chlorides
calcareous sinter
siliceous sinter

IMPORTANT CHEMICAL AND BIOGENIC SEDIMENTARY ROCKS

Limestones are usually formed of greater or lesser amounts of organic material. Only a small proportion of limestones are formed as clastic sediments or as **calcareous sinter,** which originates in a purely chemical way, from fresh-water springs. Limestone consists predominantly of $CaCO_3$, and is soluble in cold HCl. *Impervious* limestone is very fine-grained and consists mainly of fossil remains (Fig. 58). Often with admixtures: **argillaceous-, dolomitic-, siliceous-** and **bituminous-**limestone. **Oolitic** limestone is formed of spherical grains of calcite, up to the size of a pea, which are bonded by a dense calcareous cement. **Roe-stone:** oolitic limestone with a sandy cement – **travertine, calcareous tufa,** and **fresh-water limestones** are porous limestones, in part with a proportion of organic matter. **Chalk:** fine-grained, soft limestone, composed almost exclusively of the calcareous shells of micro-fossils.

Dolomites. Similar to limestone, but formed predominantly of CaMg $(CO_3)_2$ (limestone hardness $= 3$, dolomite hardness $= 4$; density of limestone $= 2.7$, dolomite $= 2.9$). Dolomite in a coarse, fragmentary form is scarcely soluble in cold HCl.

Marls. Variable mixtures of clay and calcium carbonate (also dolomite, in some cases) are covered by this term (Fig. 82).

Marly clay	95–85% clay	5–15% calcite
Marl–clay	85–75% ,,	15–25% ,,
Clay–marl	75–65% ,,	25–35% ,,
Marl	65–35% ,,	35–65% ,,
Calcareous marl	35–25% ,,	65–75% ,,
Marl–limestone	25–15% ,,	75–85% ,,
Marly limestone	15– 5% ,,	85–95% ,,

Siliceous rocks originate principally from the siliceous shells and skeletons of plants and animals. **Siliceous shales** (lydites) are black hornstone-like rocks, which are very hard and consist of the remains of siliceous organisms. They show a distinct bedding. **Polishing earth** (tripoli) is a rock originating from the remains of diatoms. **Siliceous sinter** is an inorganic deposit from hot springs and geysers.

Fossil fuels, coals. Coal formation takes place under reducing conditions (carbonization, coalification) established after the subsidence of marshy swamps, filled with wood and other plants, under a sedimentary cover.

$$\text{Peat} \longrightarrow \text{Lignite} \longrightarrow \text{Coal}$$

increasing coalification

With increasing coalification the carbon content increases and the volatile content decreases. Coals are classified on the basis of their volatile content:

	Volatile content (wt %)	C-content* (wt %)
Wood	∼80	50
Peat	65	55–60
Lignite	60–50	65–72
Sub-bituminous	50–45	72–77
High-volatile bituminous C	45–40	75–80
High-volatile bituminous B	40–35	80–83
High-volatile bituminous A	35–28	83–84·5
Medium-volatile bituminous	28–19	86·5–90·0
Low-volatile bituminous (coking-steam)	19–14	90–91·5
Semi-anthracite	14–10	91·5–93
Anthracite	<10	93
Graphite	0	100

* Calculated on an ash- and water-free basis.

Coals may be readily subdivided into lustrous, dull and fibrous varieties on their external appearance. Inorganic constituents are the following: clay minerals, pyrites, marcasite, carbonates and quartz.

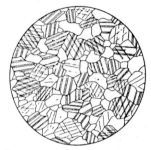

Figure 58   Limestone with fossil remains. [Thin section, ×100]

Figure 59   Marble [thin section]. Calcite crystals with sutured grain boundaries (most show pressure-induced twinning: parallel and intersecting lines). [×50]

Further subdivision of coals may be made microscopically, since, like other rocks, they are formed of *fabric-constituents* (macerals):

vitrinite → exinite group → inertinite group

These fabric-constituents may form mono-, bi-, and tri-maceral aggregates = types of banded coal (microlithotypes).

Microlithotype	Number of macerals	Type of maceral
Vitrite	1	Vitrinite
Fusite	1	Inertinite (fusinite)
Clarite	2	Vitrinite + exinite
Durite	2	Exinite + inertinite
Vitrinertite	2	Vitrinite + inertinite
Duroclarite (intermediate stage)	3	Vitrinite + inertinite + exinite
Clarodurite (intermediate stage)	3	Inertinite + vitrinite + exinite

Oil shales (sapropelites) originate by the consolidation of marine sapropel. They contain 20–40% bitumen.

Petroleum and natural gas. Formed under reducing conditions from animal and plant material in sediments. Crude oil consists of varying mixtures of paraffins, naphthalenes, olefines and aromatic compounds. Natural gas is formed mostly of about 90% methane, nitrogen and carbon dioxide. Ethane may occur in exceptional cases.

Natural asphalt. Mixture of bitumen, sand, clay and volcanic ash, e.g. Trinidad; natural asphalt there is composed of 40% bitumen, 30% sand and clay, 30% H_2O.

Gypsum. Forms compact, granular masses in salt deposits. Quartz, boracite, rock salt, sulphur and clay minerals may occur as impurities.

Anhydrite. Mostly medium to fine-grained, occurring as layers and 'plugs' or 'stocks'. Impurities: rock salt, dolomite and boracite.

Rock Salt. Occurs in granular aggregates with impurities of clay, iron oxides, $MgCl_2$ and $CaCl_2$.

Potassium Salts. Mineral deposits consist of rock-forming chlorides and sulphates of potassium and magnesium. Principal constituents of these deposits are:

Carnallite ($KCl.MgCl_2.6H_2O$)
Kainite ($KCl.MgSO_4.3H_2O$)
Kieserite ($MgSO_4.H_2O$)
Polyhalite ($2CaSO_4.MgSO_4.K_2SO_4.2H_2O$)
Sylvine (KCl)

Metamorphic rocks

Origin. Metamorphic rocks are formed by the transformation (metamorphism) of igneous and/or sedimentary rocks. Weathering (including diagenesis) and the complete remelting of a rock (palingenesis) are not included in the term metamorphism. Various types of metamorphism may be distinguished, and more than one kind may be involved in the formation of a metamorphic rock.

Load metamorphism: recrystallization due to the pressure of the overlying rock mass. Normally, temperature increases 3 °C and pressure about 27 kp/cm^2 per 100 m depth.

Contact metamorphism: transformation of the surrounding country rock by heat supplied from an intrusive magma (thermal metamorphism, pyrometamorphism). The country rock may also be altered by permeating magmatic gases and solutions, which thus also change the composition of the rock (contact metasomatism).

Autometamorphism: volatiles emanating from a consolidating magma react with and modify the already-formed solid phases of this magma.

Dynamic metamorphism (kinetic-, mechanical-, dislocation- metamorphism): metamorphism through the action of mountain-building forces, in which movement, fracturing and plastic deformation of rocks occur.

Regional metamorphism: term applied to large-scale transformations affecting considerable regions of the crust, due to temperature increase, pressure (including directed-pressure) and possible metasomatism.

Metamorphism occurs through the recrystallization of existing crystals and mechanical deformation.

Recrystallization may be isochemical (without change of chemical composition) or allochemical (with addition of new material).

ISOCHEMICAL RECRYSTALLIZATION

(a) Isophase recrystallization (the pre-existing phases are preserved; no new phase is formed), e.g.

unconsolidated sediment → sedimentary rock → metamorphic rock

calcareous mud → limestone → marble
= calcite = calcite = calcite
quartz sand → sandstone → quartzite
= quartz = quartz = quartz

Riecke's principle: crystals under unidirectional pressure (stress) dissolve; crystals which are not under stress grow at the expense of the stressed minerals

(b) Allophase recrystallization (new phases formed). These reactions occur predominantly in the solid state, chemical transformations, etc., e.g.

$$\text{calcite} + \text{quartz} \xrightarrow{\sim700°C} \text{wollastonite} + \text{carbon dioxide}$$
$$CaCO_3 \quad SiO_2 \quad CaSiO_3 \quad CO_2$$

$$\text{calcite} + \text{kaolinite} \xrightarrow{\text{heating}} \text{anorthite} + \text{water} + \text{carbon dioxide}$$
$$CaCO_3 \quad Al_2(OH)_4[Si_2O_5] \quad CaAl_2SiO_8 \quad H_2O \quad CO_2$$

ALLOCHEMICAL RECRYSTALLIZATION

Addition or subtraction of material may occur, e.g.

Metasomatism: pre-existing calcite, dolomite and silicates are converted into other compounds by addition of magmatic gases and solutions.

$$2FeCl_2 + 3CaCO_3 \rightarrow Fe_2O_3 + CaCl_2 + 3CO_2$$
from magma   calcite   hematite

$$2H_2O + 2KAlSi_3O_8 \rightarrow Al_2(OH)_4[Si_2O_5] + K_2O + 4SiO_2$$
from magma   potash felspar   kaolinite

Coral reefs composed of calcite may be dolomitized by sea water:

$$2CaCO_3 + MgCl_2 \rightarrow CaMg(CO_3)_2 + CaCl_2$$
calcite   from sea water   dolomite

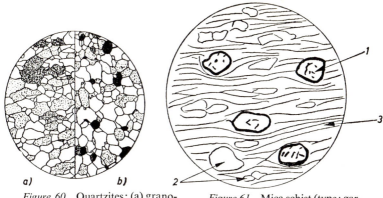

Figure 60   Quartzites: (a) granoblastic texture, (b) mosaic texture.
[Thin sections, ×50]

Figure 61   Mica schist (type: garnet mica schist). 1 = garnet, 2 =
quartz, 3 = elongate flakes of sericite. [Thin section, ×50, sche-
matic]

Recrystallization results in the development of a particular *fabric* in
the rock, although the original fabric and individual minerals may be
partly preserved as relics. Recrystallization also promotes the development of new crystalline phases (*crystalloblastic structures*) (Greek *blastos*
= sprout). *Granoblastic structures* are equigranular structures without
any recognizable older structure [Fig. 60(a)]. *Porphyroblasts* are newly-
formed, large, single crystals in a finer-grained matrix.

Crystals have a varying ability to grow with their characteristic forms,
when in contact with simultaneously growing crystals of other kinds.
Minerals can be arranged, therefore, in an *idioblastic series* according
to their increasing tendency to grow as idiomorphic crystals:

sphene,   → augites, → breunnerite, → mica,   → calcite → quartz,   → orthoclase
rutile,   horn-   dolomite,   chlorite   plagioclase   microcline
magnetite,   blendes   albite
ilmenite,
hematite,
garnet,
tourmaline,
staurolite,
kyanite

decreasing tendency to form idiomorphic crystals in metamorphic rocks

Mechanical deformation of rocks results from burial by a sedimentary
cover (raising of the hydrostatic pressure and temperature) and through
tectonic movements in the earth's crust (vertical and, particularly,

tangential movements of rock masses under the influence of directed pressure, stress). If the strength of the rock is exceeded during deformation, fracturing results, with the development of joints (shear and tension joints). Under certain conditions, the material may be completely granulated and broken into small fragments. This is *cataclasis*. Pulverized rocks are **mylonites.** A regular arrangement (preferred orientation) of both pre-existing and newly-formed minerals may result under the influence of stress. A foliation (schistosity) is often formed by the parallel orientation of flaky minerals (mica, chlorite); this foliation should not be confused with layering occurring in sedimentary rocks.

The combined action of recrystallization and mechanical deformation determines the mineral composition and the fabric of the majority of metamorphic rocks.

In predominantly mechanically-deformed rocks, the following *stress minerals* occur: kyanite, chloritoid, staurolite, mica, talc, chlorite, epidote, zoisite and several hornblendes.

The following *anti-stress minerals* never occur in deformed rocks: leucite, nepheline, sodalite, scapolite, andalusite and cordierite.

Paragneisses are metamorphic rocks formed from sediments.

Orthogneisses are metamorphic rocks formed from igneous rocks.

Both the fabric and mineral composition are controlled to a large extent, by the *depth in the crust at which metamorphism occurs.*

Epizone (upper part of the earth's crust): recrystallization occurs at low temperature and hydrostatic pressure, but under a very high directed-pressure. Mechanical deformation is the predominant process; recrystallization phenomena more weakly developed. The typical minerals contain hydroxyl groups: chlorite, mica, talc. The rocks always possess a well-developed foliation.

Mesozone (middle part of the crust): formation at moderate temperatures and hydrostatic pressures and high directed-pressure. Typical minerals with, at most, small quantities of (OH)-groups are mica, hornblendes, staurolite.

Katazone (lower part of the crust): recrystallization at high temperatures. Hydrostatic pressure dominant over directed-pressure; foliation much weaker and a directionless, granular fabric often developed in these rocks. Typical minerals are anhydrous and with a small molecular volume, e.g. garnet, cordierite, sillimanite, wollastonite.

CLASSIFICATION AND DESCRIPTION OF METAMORPHIC ROCKS

Metamorphic rocks are subdivided into:

(a) rocks originating by contact metamorphism,

(b) crystalline schists (predominantly formed by regional metamorphism).

CONTACT METAMORPHIC ROCKS

Original rock	⟶ Metamorphic rock
sandstones, argillaceous sandstones	quartzites
limestone	marble
marly limestone, marly clay, marl clays, arenaceous clays	hornfels
marly clay, clays, arenaceous clays	spotted hornfels 'Knotenschiefer'
bauxite	emery

CRYSTALLINE SCHISTS

Original rock	Epizone	Mesozone	Katazone
sandstones, quartz veins	quartzites	quartzites	quartzites
calcite, limestones	marbles	marbles	marbles
granites, syenites,	sericite gneisses	muscovite-biotite gneisses	biotite gneiss
arenaceous clays	phyllites	mica schists	granulite
diorites, gabbros	epidote-chlorite-schists	hornblende-gneiss	plagioclase-gneiss augite gneiss
marly clays, marls	(greenschists), talc schists, serpentines	talc schists	olivine gneiss
clays	slates phyllites	mica schists mica schists	gneisses garnet-biotite-gneiss
marls	calc-phyllites	calc-mica-schists	diopside gneiss

IMPORTANT CONTACT-METAMORPHIC ROCKS

Hornfelses: form from impure limestones and clays. Hard, translucent at the edges. Fine-grained, in places still weakly layered. Constituents: orthoclase, albite, cordierite, andalusite, garnet and staurolite. Forms near the magma/sedimentary rock interface.

Spotted hornfelses: foliated rocks with dark, lentil-sized spots. Form in the outer zones, somewhat removed from the magma/clay, shale interface. Constituents: quartz, muscovite, felspar, chlorite, graphitic material. The dark spots consist of cordierite, often altered and with many inclusions of graphitic material.

Marble: some marbles originate as contact-metamorphic products. Constituents: interlocking calcite crystals. Most crystals show strong twinning due to pressure (Fig. 59).

Quartzites: some quartzites result from contact-metamorphism. Constituents: predominantly interlocking quartz crystals (Fig. 60).

Important crystalline schists

Slates: intermediate between sedimentary and metamorphic rocks. Extremely well foliated and very fine-grained. Constituents: quartz, chlorite, graphitic material, rutile, sericite, pyrites. Pencil slate results when two foliation directions (cleavages) occur, (breaks in thin elongate masses). Epizonal rock. Clays are transformed in the following sequence:

$$\underbrace{\text{Clay} \longrightarrow \text{Shale}}_{\substack{\text{Sedimentary} \\ \text{rocks}}} \longrightarrow \underbrace{\text{Slate} \longrightarrow \text{Phyllite} \longrightarrow \text{Mica schist} \longrightarrow \text{Gneiss}}_{\text{Metamorphic rocks}}$$

Phyllite: epizonal rock. Foliation extremely well developed. Composed predominantly of sericite and quartz. Sometimes calcareous **(calc-phyllite).**

Talc schists: epi- and mesozonal rocks. Constituents: talc; quartz and felspar also common.

Chlorite schists: epizonal rocks, composed almost entirely of chlorite. Green colour. With epidote: epidote-chlorite schist.

Mica schists: mesozonal group of rocks, consisting of mica and quartz with usually a little felspar. The mica may be biotite and/or muscovite. Tourmaline, garnet, hornblende, chlorite, talc, kyanite, epidote, etc., may also occur. With abundant calcite: **calcareous-mica schist;** with abundant quartz: **quartz-mica schist;** predominant quartz: schistose quartzites (Fig. 61).

Gneisses: predominantly katazonal rocks. Constituents: felspar

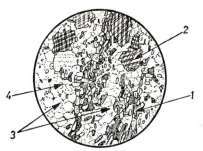

Figure 62 Gneiss (type: epidote gneiss). 1 = biotite, 2 = calcite, 3 = quartz-felspar mosaic, 4 = epidote (small, columnar grains). [Thin section, × 30]

(mostly orthoclase), quartz and mica. According to the fabric, the following types are differentiated: granular-, flaser-, flaky-, schistose- and pencil-gneisses. Both ortho- and para-rocks represented (ortho-gneiss, para-gneiss). **Mica gneisses: muscovite-, biotite-, muscovite-biotite-,** and **sericite gneiss** with dominant sericite. **Hornblende gneiss** with hornblende, **epidote gneiss** with epidote (Fig. 62) and augen-gneiss with eye-shaped felspar crystals.

Granulites: fine-grained, light-coloured rocks, with a granitic composition. Often with large garnet crystals.

F

5

MINERAL DEPOSITS

Mineral deposits are mineral concentrations in the earth's crust, which are economically workable (economically unworkable deposits are termed occurrences or localities). Besides *ore-deposits* there are also *deposits of non-metallic raw materials* (fossil fuels, non-ores, rocks, earths, etc.). The nomenclature of mineral deposits follows the name of the principal mineral or element extracted from the deposit ('magnetite-', 'zinc-', 'clay-deposits'). Particularly in the case of ore-deposits, the extracted mineral usually forms only a very small part of the total mass. Mineral deposits are only parts of larger rock-units; they are therefore geological bodies, whose origin, form, composition and kind are determined by geological relationships and conditions.

Exploration for mineral deposits. After the requisite geological mapping of the surface, geophysical surveying of the area, with, in some cases, geochemical and bio-geological examination also, is carried out, in order to establish a mineral deposit as definitely as possible. By means of sampling, attempts are made to gain extensive knowledge of the location, content, amount, and the grade of the minerals, as well as of the geological relationships (e.g. through bore-holes). Estimation of the workability then provides a basis for assessing the economics of working and recovery of the mineral raw material. The estimation is particularly concerned with the grade and quantity of the deposit, technical considerations involved in working it, and with economic factors (demand, etc.) (see the chapter on Engineering Geology, Geotechnics, Mining).

The origin of mineral deposits is closely bound up with the origin of rocks and minerals (see Chapter 4). Accordingly, the following classification may be made:

> magmatic mineral deposits,
> sedimentary mineral deposits,
> metamorphic mineral deposits.

Further subdivision may be made into *primary mineral deposits*, in which the deposit has been formed directly as such, with no intermediate stage, and *secondary mineral deposits*, which originate by the alteration of already-existing minerals (weathering, diagenesis, etc.).

5.1. Magmatic mineral deposits

Developed predominantly as material separating from a magma. The following subdivision is made (see Chapter 4):

5.1.1. Magmatic ore deposits (segregations)
5.1.2. Pegmatites
5.1.3. Pneumatolytic veins and impregnations
5.1.4. Contact mineral deposits
5.1.5. Hydrothermal mineral deposits
5.1.6. Exhalation mineral deposits
5.1.7. Submarine exhalative – sedimentary ore deposits

Transitional forms occur between most types of mineral deposit.

5.1.1. Magmatic ore-deposits

Originate as ore-minerals crystallizing from a magma – in part after crystallization of the silicates. They sink to the bottom of the melt and in many cases become concentrated in this way. In part, they may also arise by being 'squeezed out' of the remaining melt by tectonic forces. In these deposits occur metals such as chromium, titanium and the platinum group, the latter being confined exclusively, as economically-workable deposits, to this type of mineral deposit. Copper, nickel and iron also occur as workable deposits.

Chromite deposits [Urals, Turkey (south-east Anatolia), Philippines, Southern Rhodesia, South Africa (Bushveld), Cuba, Balkans, etc.].

Platinum alloys in ultrabasic rocks [Urals, South Africa (Bushveld)].

Ilmenite and titanomagnetite deposits in gabbroic rocks [Sweden (Routivara, Taberg), Urals, South Africa (Bushveld), north-west States of the U.S.A. (Adirondacks), Canada (Lake Allard)]. These ores often contain considerable amounts of V in addition to Ti.

Nickeliferous pyrrhotite – copper pyrites deposits in gabbros. Principal minerals: pyrrhotite, pentlandite, copper pyrites [Canada (Sudbury), Sweden, Norway, U.S.S.R. (Kola peninsula, Urals), U.S.A. (Montana), South Africa (Bushveld)].

Nickeliferous pyrrhotite deposits with important contents of platinum and palladium [South Africa (Bushveld: Merensky Reef), Southern Rhodesia, U.S.A. (Montana), U.S.S.R. (Jenessai region)].

Primary diamond occurrences in micaceous peridotites (kimberlites) should probably be placed here [South Africa (Kimberley near Pretoria), Katanga, East Africa].

5.1.2. Pegmatites

Quartz-felspar-muscovite rocks occurring mostly in veins (filled joints in country rock) and as schlieren (streaks) in country rocks, are younger than the granite whose intrusion they usually follow. They contain, principally, Be, Ti, B, Li, Mo, W, P, F, rare earths, U, Th, etc. (Fig. 63).

Tin pegmatites, tungsten pegmatites, molybdenum pegmatites [e.g. Italy (Elba), south-west Africa, South Africa] (Fig. 63).

Uranium and thorium pegmatites (e.g. Norway, Sweden).

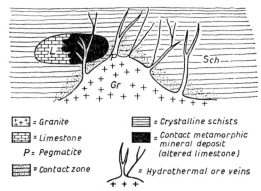

Figure 63 Schematic sketch of an ore-forming granite with pegmatite veins, contact-metamomatized limestone strata and hydrothermal ore veins.

Gold pegmatites [Brazil, U.S.S.R. (Urals), U.S.A. (Colorado)].

Rare earth pegmatites: niobate-tantalate pegmatites (South Scandinavia, Madagascar, Nigeria, Western Australia), zirconate-tantalate pegmatites [South Norway, Greenland, U.S.S.R. (Urals)].

Light-metal pegmatites: lithium-mica pegmatites [ore masses in England (Cornwall), Sweden], spodumene pegmatites [U.S.A. (South Dakota), New Mexico], amblygonite pegmatites (Spain), beryl pegmatites [Brazil, U.S.A. (South Dakota), Argentina, south-west Africa], cryolite pegmatites (Ivigtut in Greenland).

Gemstone pegmatites: tourmaline, topaz, beryl, rose quartz (south-west Africa, Urals, Madagascar, Brazil, Ceylon, etc.).

Mica pegmatites (Bengal, Ceylon, East Africa).
Felspar pegmatites (e.g. Bavarian Forest, Bohemian Forest, Norway).
Phosphate pegmatites with apatite (Norway).
Garnet pegmatites (south-east States, U.S.A.).
Aluminium silicate pegmatites with kyanite, sillimanite, andalusite
and dumortierite (U.S.A., India).
Graphitic pegmatites (Ceylon).

5.1.3. Pneumatolytic veins and impregnations

Formed by crystallization in veins from super-critical magmatic solutions, or by diffusion into country rocks (see Chapter 4). The solutions
contain H_2O, heavy metal fluorides and chlorides, large quantities of
SiO_2 and volatile constituents with B, Li, P, etc. Ore formation occurs
according to the following scheme, for example:

$$\underbrace{SnF_4 + 3H_2O}_{\substack{\text{from pneumatolytic} \\ \text{solutions}}} \longrightarrow \underbrace{SnO_2}_{\text{cassiterite}} + 4HF + H_2O$$

Tin deposits [England (Cornwall), Malaga, Brazil, Spain, China, Congo,
Nigeria, South Africa, U.S.S.R. (Siberia), Burma, Siam, Tasmania,
Australia].
  Wolframite deposits [England (Cornwall), Central Africa, North-
West Spain, Portugal, China, Burma, Argentina].
  Molybdenite deposits [U.S.A. (Colorado: Climax mine), Norway,
Morocco, Chile, Peru, Mexico, Korea, Canada].
  Tourmaline-bearing gold and copper-quartz veins – native gold
[U.S.A. (Southern Appalachians), Canada, Brazil, India, U.S.S.R.
(Siberia), South Korea] – copper (Brazil, Japan, British Columbia).

5.1.4. Contact mineral deposits (contact-pneumatolytic replacement deposits)

Very volatile constituents escaping from a magma can react with limestones and dolomites of the country rock and thus become deposited
(see Chapter 4), e.g.

$$\underbrace{ZnCl_2 + H_2S}_{\text{from the magma}} \leftrightarrow \underbrace{ZnS}_{\substack{\text{zinc} \\ \text{blende}}} + 2HCl \rightarrow CaCO_3 \overset{\nearrow CaCl_2}{\underset{\searrow CO_2}{\rightarrow H_2O}}$$

(Because calcite reacts with HCl, the reaction proceeds towards the
right-hand side.)

In this type of deposit, the metals W, Mo, Fe, Cu, Au and Sn occur. Scheelite deposits, which are always connected with granite (Central Sweden, Morocco, Yugoslavia, Turkey, U.S.A., Chile, Brazil).

Molybdenite deposits [Canada, Morocco, U.S.A. (North Carolina]).

Magnetite deposits [Rumania, Italy (Piedmont, Elba), Spain, Morocco, U.S.S.R. (Urals, Siberia), China, Japan, Central Sweden].

Copper deposits with copper pyrites, bornite, pyrites and zincblende [Japan, Korea, U.S.A. (south-west States), Australia.

Gold deposits [Mexico, U.S.A. (Montana), British Columbia, Borneo, Sumatra, Brazil, Japan] (Fig. 63).

5.1.5. Hydrothermal mineral deposits

These are formed through separation from hydrothermal solutions (see Chapter 4). Predominant deposits are ores of the following metals: Cu, Pb, Zn, Au, Ag, Fe, Co, B, U, Ni, Sb, As and Hg. The commonest non-metals are quartz, calcite, dolomite, siderite, barytes and fluorite. Deposition occurs in veins, tectonically-disturbed zones in the cover and in stockworks (a mass of single small veins in the rock). The mineral associations of the veins are known as 'formations'. Associated non-metallic minerals in the veins are called 'gangue minerals' (Fig. 63).

Gold and gold–silver formations with native gold, silver ores, gold-bearing pyrites, quartz, etc. (e.g. Fichtelgebirge, Hohe Tauern, Siebenge-birge, South Africa, U.S.S.R., Canada, U.S.A., Australia).

Pyrites and copper formations with iron and copper pyrites [e.g. Spain, Portugal, Rheinisches Schiefergebirge, Kupferberg in Silesia, U.S.S.R. (Urals), Italy (Tuscany), North Albania].

Lead–zinc–silver formations with silver-bearing galena, zincblende, pyrites, tetrahedrite, bournonite, copper pyrites, and the following gangue minerals; quartz, calcite, dolomite, brown spar, rhodochrosite, barytes, fluorite [(Erzgebirge, Freiberg), Harz, Black Forest, Rhine Mountains, Lower Lahn region, U.S.A., Canada, Australia, Mexico, U.S.S.R., Congo, Peru, Morocco].

Silver–cobalt–nickel–bismuth–uranium formations with silver and cobalt ores and pitchblende [Sweden (Kongsberg), Harz (Andreasberg), Schwarzenberg, Aue, Schneeberg, Czechoslovakia (Joachimsthal), Black Forest (Wittichen), Morocco, Sardinia, Siegerland] (Fig. 64).

Tin–silver–bismuth–tungsten formations with cassiterite, stannite, etc. (Bolivia, Japan, U.S.A.).

Antimony–mercury–arsenic–selenium formations with antimonite, cinnabar, realgar, orpiment, etc. – antimony (China, Mexico, Brazil) – mercury [Spain (Almaden), Italy (Tuscany), Carniola, Landsberg, i.d.

Pfalz, U.S.A. (California)] – arsenic (Croatia, Persia, Caucasus, Carpathians) – selenium (Harz, Argentina, Mexico, Bolivia).

Oxidic iron–manganese–magnesium formations: siderite (Siegerland, Styria, North Spain, Algiers, Tunis) – specular iron (Black Forest, Thuringian Forest, Erzgebirge) – manganese ores with pyrolusite, psilomelane, cryptomelane (Black Forest, Thuringian Forest, California, Sardinia) – magnesite deposits [Austria (Veitsch, Trieben, Radenthein), Carpathians, Urals, South Manchuria, U.S.A.].

Ore-free formations: fluorite deposits [Harz, Thuringian Forest,

Figure 64 Hydrothermal vein occurring in crystalline schists. Black = gel-like precipitate of pitchblende, D = vein filled with dolomite.

Vogtland, Oberpfalz, Black Forest, France (Central Plateau), U.S.A. (Illinois)] – barytes deposits (Harz, Werra region, Thuringian Forest, Rhine mountains, Black Forest, Spessart, Sardinia, U.S.A.) – quartz veins [e.g. the 'Pfahl' (stake), a quartz-enriched fault-zone extending 150 km through the Palatinate Forest, Bavarian Forest and Spessart].

5.1.6. Exhalation deposits

These originate from gas or vaporiform exhalations from active or recently-extinct volcanoes. Sulphur deposits and boron exhalations occur in particular. Sulphur [Italy (near Rome), Chile, Japan] – boron [Italy (Tuscany)].

5.1.7. Submarine exhalative–sedimentary deposits

Form as a result of submarine eruptions of basic magmas in marine basins. The accompanying exhalations of iron bicarbonates, copper chlorides and, in certain cases, H_2S react with the sea water with the formation of iron oxides, quartz or copper–iron sulphides. The minerals formed are deposited as layers on the ocean floor, interbedded with lavas, tuffs and marine sediments. Hematite ores formed of siliceous hematite, magnetite, siderite, chlorites and pyrites (Lahn-Dill region, Sauerland, Switzerland, Croatia) – sulphidic ores with pyrites and copper pyrites (Meggen, Rammelsberg, Turkey) – manganese ores (Kellerwald, Switzerland).

5.2. Sedimentary mineral deposits

Mineral deposits of the sedimentary type are formed by processes analogous to those which form sedimentary rocks (see Chapter 4). They may be subdivided into:

5.2.1. Secondary enrichment produced by the weathering of pre-existing ore-deposits
5.2.2. Alluvial, detrital or placer deposits
5.2.3. Continental deposits formed by weathering
5.2.4. Precipitated deposits from inland waters or seas (terrestrial evaporites)
5.2.5. Marine salt deposits (marine evaporites)
5.2.6. Fuel deposits
5.2.7. Descendent deposits

5.2.1. Secondary enrichment produced by the weathering of pre-existing ore-deposits

Deposits of sulphide and oxide ores become weathered in the surface regions of the earth. The uppermost zone of these deposits is the oxidation zone (gossan or 'iron hat' because of the coloration by iron compounds), in which difficultly-soluble compounds (oxides, hydroxides, carbonates, sulphates and phosphates) of the heavy metals, as well as native silver, gold and copper are concentrated. If the metal-bearing solutions produced by weathering reach deeper, oxygen-free regions of the deposit, reaction with the undecomposed sulphides results and the noble metals (e.g. sulphides of copper and silver) become concentrated at the expense of the non-noble metals (e.g. iron) to give a zone of secondary enrichment (cementation zone).

The following oxidized ores of individual metals are formed:

Iron: limonite   Lead: anglesite and cerussite
Copper: malachite and azurite   Manganese: manganese oxides
                                        and Mn-hydroxides

In the zone of secondary enrichment the following minerals are common: chalcocite, bornite, argentite, complex silver sulpho-salts.

5.2.2. Alluvial and detrital (placer) deposits

On weathering, metallic (gold, platinum, cassiterite, ilmenite, chromite, etc.) and non-metallic ores (zircon, garnet, monazite, quartz, diamond, sapphire, ruby) which are highly resistant to weathering, become sepa-

rated from their more-easily weathered parent rock and become transported by rivers, marine currents and, more rarely, wind. The minerals
are then deposited, in the order of their densities, in localities where the
current velocity has decreased. *Placer deposits* are thus formed. Fluviatile placers, marine placers, and aeolian placers (wind placers) are
recognized. They may be formed at the present time (recent placers) or
as 'fossil placers' in ancient geological formations.

RECENT PLACERS

Gold placers [U.S.S.R. (Lena), California, Australia, Canada, India];
    Platinum placers (Urals, Columbia).
    Cassiterite placers (Tasmania, Malaga, Vietnam, Siam, China).
    Ilmenite sands (Baltic coast, Argentina, Brazil).
    Magnetite sands (west coast of Italy, New Zealand).
    Rutile and zircon sands (Australia, India, West Africa).
    Monazite placers [Brazil, U.S.A. (Carolina), India].

FOSSIL PLACERS

Gold deposits [in Witwatersrand and Transvaal (South Africa) occurring together with uranium ores].

Detrital mineral deposits are formed by concentration of fragments of
ore in the vicinity of a weathered mineral deposit. Iron ore deposits
(Salzgitter, Peine-Ilsede).

5.2.3. Continental deposits formed by weathering

Formed by deposition from solutions resultant on weathering, whereby
a concentration of metallic and non-metallic compounds occurs (see
Chapter 4).

Clay deposits: deposits of particular economic use occur as weathered
crusts of felspar-rich volcanic rocks: kaolin [e.g. Meissen, Halle, Oberpfalz, Zettlitz (U.S.S.R.)]. Bentonite: results from the weathering of
tuffs [Wyoming (U.S.A.)]. There is also an increasing use of alluvial
clays, which have formed in basins: kaolin [Westerwald, Vogelsberg
(Hessen), lignitic clays of various localities].

Bauxite and laterite deposits: bauxite (calc-bauxite) is associated with
limestones and dolomites, which cause the precipitation of dissolved
aluminium hydroxide [South France (Le Beaux), Italy, Yugoslavia,
Hungary, Rumania, Greece, Turkey, Urals, Vietnam]. Laterites (sili-
cate-bauxites) form on the surfaces of felspar-rich rocks as a result
of tropical weathering (Guiana, Brazil, U.S.A., Jamaica, Cuba, East
Africa).

Deposits of nickel silicates: formed by the weathering of nickel-bearing ultra-basic rocks and serpentinites. Principal minerals are: pimelite, garnierite, schuchardtite (Urals, New Caledonia, Frankenstein in Silesia).

Deposits of iron and manganese ores formed by weathering: the types of deposit formed are dependent on climatic conditions during formation. Principal minerals are limonite, goethite and manganese oxides.

(a) Hydroxides of Fe and Mn are precipitated from solution by electrolytes or oppositely-charged colloids. In this way ores form in limestones and shales [Hunsrück, Lahn region, Eifel, Spessart, Odenwald, Kellerwald, Upper Silesia, Amberg, Urals, U.S.A. (Texas, Arkansas), West Africa, Cuba, South Africa].

(b) Evaporation in dry periods of solutions containing iron and manganese compounds: lateritic iron ores and incrustation ironstones. Lateritic iron ores (basalt-ironstones) occur principally as residual deposits connected with iron-rich basic igneous rocks such as dunite, gabbro and basalt (Cuba, East India, Philippines, Brazil, West Africa).

Enrichment of non-ferrous heavy metals in detrital deposits of arid regions. Heavy metal-bearing solutions, resultant on weathering, impregnate and evaporate in terrestrial detrital deposits, principally sandstones and conglomerates, where metallic compounds separate or become precipitated. Grains of former ore-deposits are also found as constituents of these detrital masses.

Copper-enriched deposits: principal minerals are chalcocite, pyrites, copper pyrites and bornite [Lower Silesia, Pfalz, Alps, Saar, Urals, U.S.A. (Utah, etc.)].

Silver-enriched deposits: principal minerals are argentite and native silver [U.S.A. (Utah)].

Uranium–radium–vanadium-enriched deposits (carnotite deposits): principal mineral is carnotite [U.S.A. (Colorado Plateau), U.S.S.R. (West Urals)].

Lead and zinc-bearing sandstones formed by hydrothermal activity: principal minerals are galena, pyrites, copper pyrites, zincblende, cerussite, anglesite, pyromorphite (Commern, Mechernich).

Copper ores from Zambia and Katanga.

Terrestrial salt deposits have more or less the same origin as the other deposits due to weathering. They precipitate from fresh water in regions with pronounced dry and rainy seasons (salt incrustations, salt marshes, salt lakes). Glauber's salt [U.S.S.R. (Caspian Sea), U.S.A. (Great Salt Lake, Utah), Canada, Mexico, Argentina, Chile] – Epsom salt [U.S.S.R. (Lake Aral), Tibet, South Iran, U.S.A. (western States)].

Sodium carbonates, principally trona [East Africa, Western U.S.A., U.S.S.R. (Siberia), Tibet, Manchuria]. Borates [Peru, Chile, Argentina, Italy (Tuscany), south-western North America, Asia Minor]. Saltpetre (Chile).

5.2.4. Precipitated deposits from inland waters and seas

(A) BIOCHEMICAL IRON DEPOSITS FROM FRESH WATER

Iron dissolved in groundwater and inland lakes may be precipitated at the earth's surface by oxygen and micro-organisms (e.g. in swamps, marshes and damp meadows: meadow ore, bog iron ore [e.g. Denmark (Jutland), Belgium, formerly also in North Germany]. Lake ores are precipitates of iron formed through the action of micro-organisms either from groundwater where it enters the oxygen-rich water near the banks of lakes or directly from lake-water (through annual variation of the Fe-content) in the middle of the lake bottoms (Sweden, Finland, Canada).

(B) OOLITIC IRON DEPOSITS FROM SEA WATER

Small concentrically-layered spheres of iron ore (oolitic ironstone) are precipitated under appropriate geological conditions on the extensive supply of iron-bearing weathering solutions to enclosed lagoons. Extensive iron deposits may thus be formed. This process, too, probably involves the action of micro-organisms. These deposits consist of phosphorus-rich iron hydroxides with siliceous, marly and calcareous constituents or of iron silicates (chamosite ores): oolitic iron ores [Southern U.S.S.R. (Crimea, Kertsch, Ukraine), Egypt, Allgäu, Algiers, Tunis, Central England, Lorraine, Luxembourg, Baden-Württemberg, Franken, North Germany, Newfoundland]; oolitic iron silicates (Thuringia, Bohemia, Brittany); oolitic manganese ores [U.S.S.R. (Caucasus, Ukraine)] are formed in a similar way to oolitic iron ores.

(C) BIOCHEMICAL MARINE PYRITES – COPPER DEPOSITS OF THE SULPHUR CYCLE

Bacteria maintain a constant sulphur-cycle in the sapropelites formed on the bottoms of seas or deep inland lakes. The resultant hydrogen sulphide causes the precipitation of iron and copper in the form of their sulphides. The following deposits are formed: sedimentary pyrites deposits, in part with volcanic material, which occur in marls, shales, oil shales, etc.; lead, zinc and copper sulphides are also common in these rocks (Rammelsberg near Goslar, Meggen, Australia, Turkey); copper shales (Mansfeld, Hettstedt, Eisleben, Lower Silesia, North of England); coals with abundant pyrites, which have a similar origin (Moscow Basin); sedimentary sulphur and sulphate deposits, which form from sulphate-bearing solutions through bacterial action [South Italy, Siberia, Poland (Galicia), U.S.A. (Texas and Louisiana)].

5.2.5. Marine salt deposits

Formed in the flat coastal regions of oceans through geological processes occurring in a dry environment. These regions become increasingly cut off from the main body of the ocean by evaporation of the water and precipitation of salts in the sequence: calcite, gypsum, rock salt, potassium salts, magnesium salts. The deposits are later subjected to slow tectonic subsidence. Two main types of marine salt deposits are differentiated among German deposits:

(i) With predominant rock salt and anhydrite, without potassium and magnesium salts (Heilbronn, Schwäbisch Hall, Berchtesgaden, Reichenhall).

(ii) With rock salt, anhydrite and potassium–magnesium salts (Südbaden, Elsass, Nordhausen, Salzdetfurth, Vienenburg, Stassfurt).

5.2.6. Fuel deposits

(a) Coals originate in tropical to sub-tropical regions with luxuriant plant growth and a high water table (swamps, coastal regions of lakes and seas). Through subsidence, the plant remains gradually become embedded in an oxygen-free environment and are decomposed by physico-chemical and biochemical action, with consequent carbon concentration (see Chapter 4). According to the degree of coalification (carbon content), peat, lignite and coal are differentiated. Peat deposits (North Germany, Alpine foreland); lignite deposits (Rhineland, Central Germany, Czechoslovakia, Austria, Australia); coal deposits (Ruhrgebiet, Aachen region, Upper Silesia, Lower Saxony, Saar, Saxony, France, Belgium, Holland, North America, U.S.S.R., etc.).

(b) Petroleum and natural gas originate from sapropelite rich in organisms, after the deposition of overlying sediments and the consequent exclusion of air. The weight of overlying sediment forces the oil-forming substances out of the source rock in many cases and it then becomes concentrated in porous reservoir rocks. Petroleum (e.g. Venezuela, U.S.A., Near East, Sahara, U.S.S.R., Rumania, Austria, Italy, North-West Germany). Natural gas [e.g. in Southern France (Lacq), Italy, Holland, U.S.S.R., North German coastal area].

5.2.7. Descendent mineral deposits

Formed by the precipitation of minerals from metal-bearing solutions which descend in the earth, e.g. siderite deposits (Osnabrück, Amberg, Eifel, U.S.A.), uranium–vanadium ores in cave-deposits [U.S.S.R. (Turkestan)], blackband ironstones (Ruhrgebiet). Ore formation by *ascending* solutions is also possible (e.g. strontianite in Westphalia).

5.3. Metamorphic mineral deposits

Metamorphic deposits originate by the alteration of pre-existing deposits. The metamorphism results from change of temperature and pressure, addition and subtraction of material and through mechanical stress. The following types are differentiated:

5.3.1. Ore-deposits transformed into crystalline schists by load, dynamic and regional metamorphism.

5.3.2. Complex polymetamorphic ore-deposits with the addition of magmatic and palingenetic material.

5.3.1. Ore-deposits transformed into crystalline schists by load, dynamic and regional metamorphism

Ferruginous quartzites and hematite mica schists (itabirites) with magnetite, specular iron and martite. The deposits originated as sedimentary iron ores (Norway, Sweden, Brazil, Ukraine, Venezuela, South Africa, Australia). Banded iron-jaspilites are finely-banded, siliceous iron ores or ferruginous siliceous rocks (Central Sweden, India).

Iron ores of Lake Superior (U.S.A.), which represent multiply-altered ores, derived predominantly from originally basic, extrusive rocks.

Metamorphic manganese ore-deposits, such as manganese quartzites, manganese shales, manganese silicate and manganese carbonate deposits; these are particularly workable in the oxidation-zone (Czechoslovakia, South Africa, West Africa, Brazil, India.

Dynamic metamorphic pyrites deposits [Bavarian Forest, Fichtelgebirge, Oberpfalz, Erzgebirge, Riesengebirge, Eastern Alps, France, Carpathians, Norway (very important deposits)].

5.3.2. Complex polymetamorphic ore-deposits with the addition of magmatic and palingenetic material

Swedish and Finnish skarn ores. Ore-minerals predominantly magnetite, hausmannite, braunite, pyrites, pyrrhotite, copper pyrites, zincblende, galena, bournonite, cubanite, chalcocite. Skarn minerals are the associated non-ore minerals, e.g. actinolite, diopside, epidote, augite, garnet, etc.

Leptite iron ores and magnetite skarn ores in Central Sweden.

Manganese skarn ore in Central Sweden.

Sulphide skarn ores in Sweden and Finland.

Copper–gold deposits in Canada and the U.S.A. which are, in part, layered and in part occur as veins – principal minerals are gold-bearing pyrites, pyrrhotite, copper pyrites, zincblende, magnetite.

Zinc–manganese deposits in Franklin (N.J., U.S.A.), principal minerals: franklinite and willemite. Lead–zinc deposits in Broken Hill (Australia), principal minerals: galena, zincblende, tetrahedrite, pyrrhotite, copper pyrites and arsenopyrite.

6

SYSTEMATIC MINERALOGY

6.1. The classification of minerals

The classification is based on the chemical composition and crystal structure of minerals. Grouping is therefore essentially according to crystallochemical factors.

- I. Class: elements
- II. Class: sulphides and related compounds (sulphur, arsenic, antimony, bismuth, selenium and tellurium compounds).
- III. Class: haloids
- IV. Class: oxides and hydroxides
- V. Class: nitrates, carbonates, borates (oxy-salts with O in 3-fold co-ordination)
- VI. Class: sulphates, chromates, molybdates, tungstates (hexavalent cation with O in 4-fold co-ordination)
- VII. Class: phosphates, arsenates, vanadates (pentavalent cation with O in 4-fold co-ordination)
- VIII. Class: silicates (Fig. 34)
  SiO_4-structures with single tetrahedra (nesosilicates)
  SiO_4-structures with groups of tetrahedra (sorosilicates)
  SiO_4-chain structures (inosilicates)
  SiO_4-sheet structures (phyllosilicates)
  SiO_4-framework structures (tectosilicates)
- IX. Class: organic compounds

6.2. Summary of important ores and their uses

(arranged according to metals; H = hardness on the Mohs' Scale, D = density, Cl. = mineral class).

Aluminium

Principal ore is bauxite, a mixture of the minerals diaspore, boehmite, hydrargillite, and alumogel. Al_2O_3-content: 46–70%. *Occurrence:* terrestrial deposits due to weathering. *Uses:* Al-production, Al-salts, abrasives, cement, oil-refining, refractory diaspore and bauxite bricks.

Diaspore γ-AlOOH, Cl. IV, orthorhombic, H: 6·5, D: 3·4, 45% Al. *Occurrence:* sedimentary, metamorphic, contact metamorphic, hydrothermal and pegmatitic rocks.

Boehmite γ-AlOOH, Cl. IV, orthorhombic, H: 3·5, D: 3·05, 45% Al. *Occurrence:* sedimentary rocks.

Hydrargillite (Gibbsite) γ-Al(OH)$_3$, Cl. IV, monoclinic, H: 2·5–3·5— 3·0, D: 2·4, 35% Al. *Occurrence:* sedimentary rocks.

Alumogel (Kliachite) AlOOH.nH_2O, Cl. IV, amorphous, H: ?, D: 2·55, variable Al-content. *Occurrence:* sedimentary rocks.

Cryolite α-Na$_3$[AlF$_6$], Cl. III, monoclinic, H: 2·5–3·0, D: 2·95, 13% Al. *Occurrence:* pegmatites.

Antimony

Uses: in alloys, flame-proofing agent for textiles, dyes, lacquer, ammunition.

Antimonite (stibnite, antimony glance) Sb_2S_3, Cl. II, orthorhombic, H: 2·0, D: 4·6, 71% Sb. *Occurrence:* ore veins.

Tetrahedrite Cu_3SbS_{3-4}, Cl. II, cubic, H: 3·5, D: 4·4–4·9, 24% Sb. *Occurrence:* ore veins.

Jamesonite $4PbS.FeS.3Sb_2S_3$, Cl. II, monoclinic, H: 2·5, D: 5·6, 29% Sb. *Occurrence:* ore veins.

Bournonite (wheel ore) $PbCuSbS_3$, Cl. II, orthorhombic, H: 3·0, D: 5·8, 25% Sb. *Occurrence:* ore veins.

Cervantite (Roméite) $Sb_2O_4.nH_2O$, Cl. IV, cubic, H: 4·5, D: 5·8–6·6, 75% Sb. *Occurrence:* weathered zones of ore veins.

Valentinite (antimony bloom), Sb_2O_3, Cl. IV, orthorhombic, H: 2·5– 3·0, D: 5·6–5·8, 83% Sb. *Occurrence:* weathered zones of ore veins.

Arsenic

Uses: pesticides, protective coating of timber, enamels, alloys. Most of the As produced is extracted from gases formed by the smelting of lead, copper, gold and tin ores, which contain arsenides or thioarsenides.

Arsenopyrite (arsenical pyrites) FeAsS, Cl. III, monoclinic, H: 5·5– 6·0, D: 5·9–6·2, 46% As. *Occurrence:* ore veins, pneumatolytic, contact metasomatic.

Löllingite $FeAs_2$, Cl. III, orthorhombic, H: 5·0, D: 7·3, 73% As. *Occurrence:* ore veins, contact metasomatic, pegmatitic, pneumatolytic.

Orpiment As_2S_3, Cl. II, monoclinic, H: 1·5–2·0, D: 3·4–3·5, 61% As. *Occurrence:* ore veins, volcanic, thermal, secondary.

Realgar AsS, Cl. II, monoclinic H: 1·5–2·0, D: 3·5–3·6, 69% As. *Occurrence:* ore veins, volcanic, thermal, secondary.

Beryllium

Uses: steel processing, rocket and jet aircraft materials, moderators in nuclear reactors, supersonic-missile material, copper–beryllium alloys, gemstones.

Beryl $Al_2Be_3[Si_6O_{18}]$, Cl. VIII, hexagonal, H: 7·5–8·0, D: 2·63, 5% Be. *Occurrence:* pegmatitic, hydrothermal. The sole economically-workable Be-ore.

Bismuth

A large proportion of the Bi produced comes from the smelting of Pb-, Zn-, Au-, W- and Sn-ores, in which it occurs in small quantities. *Uses:* pharmacy, dyes, enamels, glazing, low-melting alloys.

Native bismuth Bi, Cl. I, trigonal, H: 2·0–2·5, D: 9·8, 100% Bi. *Occurrence:* veins, pegmatitic–pneumatolytic.

Bismuthinite (bismuth glance) Bi_2S_3, Cl. II, orthorhombic, H: 2·0, D: 6·8–7·2, 81% Bi. *Occurrence:* veins.

Bismutite $Bi_2[O_2/CO_3]$, Cl. V. tetragonal, H: 3·0–4·5, D: 6·1–7·6, up to 80% Bi. *Occurrence:* secondary veins.

Bismite (bismuth ochre) α-Bi_2O_3, Cl. IV, monoclinic, H: 4·5, D: 8·6, up to 90% Bi. *Occurrence:* secondary veins.

Cadmium

The sole mineral formed independently by cadmium, greenockite, does not occur in economic quantity. Cd is produced by extraction from gases formed by the smelting of zinc, lead and copper ores, which contain small amounts of the metal (about 0·1% in zinc, and about 0·02–0·05% in lead). *Uses:* low-melting alloys, glass industry, reactor material, dyes, rust-preventive coating of iron.

Greenockite CdS, Cl. II, hexagonal, H: 3·0–3·5, D: 4·9. *Occurrence:* hydrothermal, product of weathering.

Caesium

Pollucite is the sole economically-important caesium mineral; also obtained from lepidolite (up to 0·7% CsO_2) and beryl (up to 3% CsO_2), which may contain caesium. *Uses:* photocells, thermoelectric processes.

G

Pollucite (Cs,Te,Na)[AlSi$_2$O$_6$],H$_2$O, Cl. VII, cubic, H: 6·5, D: 2·9, 36% Cs$_3$O. *Occurrence:* granite pegmatites [see Lithium (lepidolite)].

Chromium

Only extracted from one ore, chromite. *Uses:* chrome-nickel steels, chrome-tungsten steels, chromium plating, nickel-chrome wires, refractory bricks and bodies, wood preservation, tanning, dyes.

Chromite (chrome iron ore) Cr$_2$FeO$_4$, Cl. IV, cubic H: 5·5, D: 4·2, 15–60% Cr$_2$O$_2$. *Occurrence:* magmatic, contains varying amounts of Mg, Al, etc., in addition to Fe.

Cobalt

Uses: high-grade and high-speed steel manufacture, ceramic pigments, catalysts.

Cobaltite (cobalt glance) CoAsS, Cl. II, cubic H: 5·5, D: 6·0–6·4, 35% Co. *Occurrence:* veins.

Smaltite (tin white cobalt) CoAs$_{2-3}$, Cl. II, cubic, H: 5·5, D: 6·4–6·6, up to 28% Co. *Occurrence:* veins.

Safflorite CoAs$_2$, Cl. II, orthorhombic, H: 4·5–5·0, D: 7·2–7·4, 28% Co. *Occurrence:* veins.

Carrolite Co$_2$CuS$_4$, Cl. II, cubic, H: 5·0–6·0, D: 4·8, about 12% Co. *Occurrence:* veins.

Linnaeite (cobalt pyrites) Co$_3$S$_4$, Cl. II, cubic, H: 4·5–5·5, D: 4·8, 53% Co. *Occurrence:* veins.

Heterogenite (stainierite) Co$_2$O$_3$.H$_2$O, H: 3·0, D: 2·0–4·0, 63% Co. *Occurrence:* veins, weathering product.

Asbolite (earthy cobalt) mixture of cobalt and manganese oxides, which may contain from 4% to 30% Co. *Occurrence:* product of the weathering of ore-deposits.

Copper

The most important non-ferrous metal. Extensive use as metal, alloys and salts (copper sulphate: pesticide, dyes).

Native copper Cu, Cl. I, cubic, H: 2·5–3·0, D: 8·5–9·0, 100% Cu. *Occurrence:* hydrothermal, weathering zones.

Chalcocite (copper glance) Cu$_2$S, Cl. II, orthorhombic, H: 2·5–3·0, D: 5·5–5·8, 79% Cu. *Occurrence:* veins, pegmatitic, pneumatolytic, sedimentary.

Copper pyrites (chalcopyrites) CuFeS$_2$, Cl. II, tetragonal, H: 3·5–4·0, D: 4·1–4·3, 34% Cu. *Occurrence:* magmatic, pegmatitic–pneumatolytic, veins.

Covellite CuS, Cl. II, hexagonal, H: 1·5–2·0, D: 4·68, 66% Cu. *Occurrence:* veins, sedimentary, weathering zones.

Bornite (variegated copper ore) Cu_5FeS_4, Cl. II, cubic, H: 3·0, D: 4·9–5·3, 56–69% Cu. *Occurrence:* veins, magmatic, contact metasomatic, pegmatitic.

Cuprite (red oxide of copper) Cu_2O, Cl. IV, H: 3·5–4·0, D: 5·8–6·14, 88% Cu. *Occurrence:* oxidation zone of Cu-deposits, sedimentary, veins.

Malachite $Cu_2[(OH)_2/CO_3]$, Cl. V, monoclinic, H: 4·0, D: 4·0, 57% Cu. *Occurrence:* veins, chemically-formed sediments (impregnation).

Azurite (blue carbonate of copper) $Cu_3[OH/CO_3]_2$, Cl. V, monoclinic, H: 3·5–4·0, D: 2·7–3·9, 55% Cu. *Occurrence:* veins, chemically-formed sediments (impregnation), weathered deposits.

Chrysocolla $CuSiO_3.nH_2O$, Cl. VIII, orthorhombic (?), H: 2·0–4·0, D: 2·0–2·3, variable Cu-content. *Occurrence:* veins (products of weathering).

Gallium

Extracted from zincblende, iron pyrites, bauxite and germanite, in which it occurs in trace quantities. Only one, rare and economically-insignificant gallium mineral is known, **Gallite**, $CuGaS_2$ (tetragonal). *Uses:* in dental alloys, in high-temperature thermometers.

Germanium

Occurs in only a few minerals, of which germanite is the most important. In recoverable quantities in coal ashes. *Uses:* transistors (sem-conducting properties), photocells, special glasses, luminous materials.

Germanite $Cu_3(Fe,Ge)S_4$, Cl. II, cubic, H: 2·5–3·0, D: 4·6, 5–10% Ge. *Occurrence:* veins (only Tsumeb in South-West Africa). **Renierite** is iron-rich germanite.

Argyrodite $4Ag_2S.GeS_2$, Cl. II, orthorhombic, H: 2·5, D: 6·2, 6·5% Ge. *Occurrence:* veins.

Stottite $FeH_2[GeO_4].2H_2O$, Cl. VI, tetragonal, H: 4·5, D: 3·6, 28% Ge. *Occurrence:* weathering of germanium deposits.

Gold

About 33% is derived from magmatic, 44% from sedimentary (placers) and 13% from metamorphic deposits. *Uses:* basic currency, precious-metal alloys, jewellery, dyes, dental fillings, apparatus.

Native gold Au, Cl. I, cubic, H: 2·5–3·0, D: 14·56–19·3, 100% Au, usually with silver content, however. *Occurrence:* pegmatitic, hydrothermal veins, placer deposits.

Mountain gold: gold occurring in primary deposits in contradistinction to placer gold.

Free gold: gold visible in ores with the naked eye.

Sylvanite (Au,Ag)Te$_4$, Cl. II, orthorhombic, H: 1·5–2·0, D: 8·0–8·2, 25–27% Au. *Occurrence:* veins.

Krennerite (Au,Ag)Te$_2$, Cl. II, orthorhombic, H: 2·3, D: 8·63, 40% Au. *Occurrence:* veins.

Calaverite AuTe$_2$, Cl. II, monoclinic, H: 2·5–3·0, D: 9·04–9·39, up to 44% Au. *Occurrence:* veins.

Nagyagite Pb$_5$Au(Te,Sb)$_{5-8}$, Cl. II, tetragonal, H: 1·0–1·5, D: 6·8–7·5, varying Au-content. *Occurrence:* veins.

Hafnium

Forms no independent minerals, but is almost invariably present in zircon (up to 16% HfO$_2$) (q.v.). Hf absorbs electrons very strongly (reactor construction).

Indium

Forms no economically-important minerals of its own. Extracted from lead, zinc, tin, tungsten, manganese and copper ores, in which limited quantities occur (traces $\sim 0.1\%$ In). *Uses:* protection of metal surfaces, as a component of high-melting alloys.

Iridium

See Platinum metals.

Iron

About 47% of the ores come from metamorphic, 29·5% from sedimentary, and 23·5% from magmatic rocks (1938). *Uses:* well known.

Magnetite (magnetic iron ore) Fe$_3$O$_4$, Cl. IV, cubic, H: 5·5, D: 5·2, 72% Fe. *Occurrence:* magmatic, metamorphic, hydrothermal.

Maghemite Fe$_2$O$_3$, magnetic, cubic; titanomagnetite is titanium-bearing magnetite.

Hematite (specular iron, kidney ore), α–Fe$_2$O$_3$, Cl. IV, trigonal, H: 6·5, D: 5·2–5·3, 70% Fe. *Occurrence:* hydrothermal, pneumatolytic, metamorphic, sedimentary, exhalative.

Martite: hematite pseudomorphic after magnetite.

Goethite (needle iron ore) α-FeOOH, Cl. IV, orthorhombic, H: 5·0–5·5, D: 4·3, 62% Fe. *Occurrence:* sedimentary Fe-ores such as limonite (brown iron ore). Constituent of rust.

Lepidocrocite γ-FeOOH, Cl. IV, orthorhombic, H: 5·0, D: 4·09, 62% Fe. *Occurrence:* as for goethite. Constituent of rust.

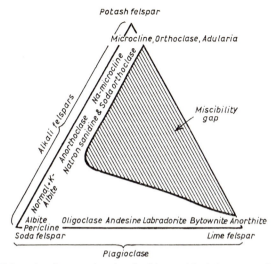

Figure 65   Triangular diagram showing the felspars (shaded area = miscibility gap).

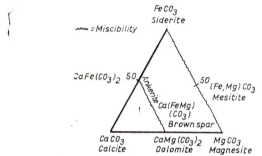

Figure 66   Triangular diagram showing the phases occurring in the $CaCO_3$–$FeCO_3$–$MgCO_3$ system.

Siderite (spathose iron, chalybite) $FeCO_3$, Cl. V, trigonal H: 4·0–4·5, D: 3·89, 48% Fe. *Occurrence:* metasomatic, pegmatitic, hydrothermal, sedimentary (Fig. 66).

Ankerite: mixed crystal of siderite and dolomite (Fig. 66), in which Mg and Fe may replace one another, but with a constant Ca-content.

Ilmenite (titanic iron ore) $FeTiO_3$, Cl. IV, tri-rhombohedral, H: 5·0–6·0, D: 4·5–5·0, 36% Fe. *Occurrence:* magmatic, pegmatitic, metamorphic, hydrothermal, placer deposits. Important titanium ore.

Chamosite $(Fe^{3+},Mg,Fe^{2+},Al)_6[(OH)_8/AlSi_3O_{10}]$, Cl. VIII, monoclinic, H: 3·0, D: 3·2, 30–40% Fe. *Occurrence:* metamorphic.

Thuringite $(Fe^{2+},Mg,Fe^{3+},Al)_6[(OH)_8/Al_{1-2}Si_{2-3}O_{10}]$, Cl. VIII, monoclinic, H: 1·0–2·0, D: 3·2, 30–40% Fe. *Occurrence:* metamorphic.

Pyrites (iron pyrites) FeS_2, Cl. II, cubic, H: 6·0–6·5, D: 5·0–5·2, 46% Fe, often contains Au, Cu and As. *Occurrence:* all formations; important source of sulphur.

Pyrrhotite (magnetic pyrites) FeS, Cl. II, hexagonal, H: 4·0, D: 4·6, 61% Fe. *Occurrence:* magmatic, pegmatitic, hydrothermal, sedimentary. Often contains nickel (Sudbury).

Lead

Uses: cables, accumulators, pipes, screens for protection from radiation, glass, dyes, alloys.

Galena (lead glance) PbS, Cl. II, cubic, H: 2·5, D: 7·2–7·6, 86% Pb. *Occurrence:* ore veins, contact metasomatic, chemically-deposited sediments.

Cerussite $PbCO_3$, Cl. V, orthorhombic, H: 3·0–3·5, D: 6·4–6·6, 77% Pb. *Occurrence:* oxidation zone in lead deposits.

Anglesite $PbSO_4$, Cl. VI, orthorhombic, H: 3·0, D: 6·3, 68% Pb. *Occurrence:* oxidation zone in lead deposits.

Bournonite $PbCuSbS_3$, Cl. II, orthorhombic, H: 3·0, D: 5·8, 42% Pb. *Occurrence:* ore veins.

Boulangerite $Pb_5Sb_4S_{11}$, Cl. II, monoclinic, H: 2·5–3·0, D: 6·0–6·3, 55% Pb. *Occurrence:* ore veins.

Lithium

Uses: in alloys, manufacture of lubricating greases, ceramics, glasses and enamels, reactor materials, catalysts in the chemical industry.

Amblygonite $LiAl[F/PO_4]$, Cl. VII, triclinic, H: 6·0, D: 3·0–3·1, 8–10% Li_2O. *Occurrence:* pegmatitic–pneumatolytic.

Spodumene (triphane) $LiAl[Si_2O_6]$, Cl. VIII, monoclinic, H: 6·5– 7·0, D: 3·1–3·2, 5–7% Li_2O. *Occurrence:* pegmatitic.

Lepidolite $KLi_2Al[(F,OH)_2/Si_4O_{10}]$, Cl. VIII, monoclinic, H: 2·5–4·0, D: 2·8–2·9, 2–4% Li_2O. *Occurrence:* pegmatitic–pneumatolytic (see Micas).

Petalite $Li[AlSi_4O_{10}]$, Cl. VIII, monoclinic, H: 3·6–6·5, D: 2·42, 8% Li_2O. *Occurrence:* pegmatitic.

Zinnwaldite $KLiFeAl[(F,OH)_2/AlSi_3O_{10}]$, Cl. VIII, monoclinic, H: 2·5–3·0, D: 2·9–3·1, small variable Li-content.

Triphylite $Li(Fe,Mn)[PO_4]$, Cl. VII, orthorhombic, H: 4·5–5·0, D: 3·4–3·6, 8% Li_2O. *Occurrence:* pegmatitic.

Lithiophylite Li(Mn,Fe)[PO$_4$], Cl. VIII, orthorhombic, H: 3·0–4·5, D: 3·4–3·6, 8% Li$_2$O. *Occurrence:* pegmatitic.

Magnesium

See Magnesite and Dolomite. *Uses:* Mg-salts in pharmacy, tanning, and in the manufacture of artificial silk and rayon, sorel cement, alloys. Produced in part from the waste liquor of the potassium industry, from seawater, salt lakes and salt marshes.

Manganese

Nearly 90% of the manganese ores are obtained from sedimentary and only about 10% from metamorphic deposits. *Uses:* manufacture of special steels, dry batteries, glass manufacture, ceramics.

Pyrolusite (polianite) MnO$_2$, Cl. IV, tetragonal, H: 2·0–6·0, D: 4·7–5·0, 60–65% Mn. *Occurrence:* sedimentary. Impure MnO$_2$: psilomelane, cryptomelane.

Manganite MnOOH, Cl. IV, monoclinic, H: 4·0, D: 4·3–4·4, 63% Mn. *Occurrence:* oxidation zone of ore veins.

Braunite 3Mn$_2$O$_3$.MnSiO$_3$, Cl. IV, tetragonal, H: 6·0–6·5, D: 4·7–4·9, 64% Mn. *Occurrence:* metasomatic.

Hausmannite Mn$_3$O$_4$, Cl. IV, tetragonal, H: 5·5, D: 4·7–4·8. *Occurrence:* metasomatic.

Rhodochrosite MnCO$_3$, Cl. V, trigonal, H: 4·0, D: 3·3–3·6, 48% Mn. *Occurrence:* hydrothermal, zone of oxidation.

Rhodonite (manganese spar) (Mn,Fe,Ca)[SiO$_3$], Cl. VIII, triclinic, H: 5·5–6·5, D: 3·4–3·7, 42% Mn. *Occurrence:* metamorphic, contact metasomatic, hydrothermal.

Mercury

Uses: electrical industry, catalysts, mercury electrodes in chlorine and sodium manufacture, medicaments, weedkillers.

Cinnabar HgS, Cl. II, trigonal, H: 2·0–2·5, D: 8·1, 86% Hg. *Occurrence:* veins.

Metacinnabarite HgS, Cl. II, cubic, H: 3·0 D: 7·7–7·8, 86% Hg. *Occurrence:* hydrothermal, weathering product.

Calomel HgCl$_2$, Cl. III, tetragonal, H: 1·0–2·0, D: 6·4–6·5, 75% Hg. *Occurrence:* veins, impregnations.

Mercury-bearing tetrahedrite (schwazite, hermesite) (Cu$_2$Hg)$_3$. Sb$_2$S$_6$, Cl. II, cubic, H: 3·0–4·0, D: 4·4–5·4, up to 17% Hg. *Occurrence:* veins.

Mercury Hg, Cl. I, liquid, D: 13·6, 100% Hg. *Occurrence:* hydrothermal, hot springs.

Molybdenum

Uses: manufacture of special steels, incandescent filaments and heating coils, reactor materials, enamels, lubricants.

Molybdenite (molybdenum glance) MoS_2, Cl. II, hexagonal, H: 1·0–1·5, D: 4·6–4·7, 60% Mo. *Occurrence:* veins, pegmatitic.

Molybdite (ferrimolybdite, molybdic ochre) $Fe_2(MoO_4)_3.7H_2O$, Cl. VI, orthorhombic, H: 1·0–2·0, D: 4·5, 39% Mo. *Occurrence:* veins.

Wulfenite (yellow lead ore) $PbMoO_4$, Cl. VI, tetragonal, H: 3·0, D: 6·5–6·9, 26% Mo. *Occurrence:* oxidation zones.

Nickel

Uses: manufacture of special steels, alloys, surface-protection of metals, enamels, rocket and nuclear reactor technology, batteries, catalysts.

Pentlandite $(Fe,Ni)_9S_8$, Cl. II, cubic, H: 3·5–4·0, D: 4·6–5·0, 10–45% Ni. *Occurrence:* magmatic (invariably associated with pyrrhotite).

Garnierite (nickel chrysotile) $(Ni,Mg)_6[(OH)_6/Si_4O_{11}].H_2O$, Cl. VIII, monoclinic, H: 2·0–4·0, D: 2·2–2·7, up to 25% Ni. *Occurrence:* product of weathering, hydrothermal alteration.

Pimelite (nickelian montmorillonite) $(Ni,Mg)_3[(OH)_2/Si_4O_{10}].nH_2O$.

Schuchardtite (nickelian chlorite) $(Ni,Mg,Al)_6[(OH)_8(Al,Si)Si_3O_{10}]$.

Niccolite (kupfernickel) $NiAs$, Cl. II, hexagonal, H: 5·5, D: 7·7, 44% Ni. *Occurrence:* veins, magmatic.

Chloanthite (white nickel) $NiAs_{3-2}$, Cl. II, cubic, H: 5·5, D: 6·5–6·9, about 28% Ni. *Occurrence:* veins.

Niobium

Uses: manufacture of special steels, catalysts, reactor materials, manufacture of extremely hard materials (Nb-carbide). Nb-minerals contain tantalum in many cases.

Niobite $(Fe,Mn)(Nb,Ta)_2O_6$, Cl. IV, orthorhombic, H: 6·0, D: 5·3–7·9, 40–75% Nb_2O_5 and 1–42% Ta_2O_5. *Occurrence:* pegmatitic.

Tantalite $(Fe,Mn)(Ta,Nb)_2O_6$, Cl. IV, orthorhombic, H: 6·0–6·5, D: 7·9–8·0, 3–40% Nb_2O and 42–84% Ta_2O_5. *Occurrence:* pegmatitic.

Columbite: name of the continuous series of mixed crystals between niobite and tantalite.

Pyrochlore $(Ca,Na)_2Nb_2O_6(F,OH,O)$, Cl. IV, cubic, H: 5·0–5·5, D: 4·3–4·5, 47–70% Nb_2O_5 and 0·2–2% Ta_2O_5. *Occurrence:* pegmatitic.

Osmium

See Platinum metals.

Palladium

See Platinum metals.

Platinum and the platinum metals

Apart from Pt, the metals palladium, iridium, rhodium, ruthenium and osmium are also included in this group. *Uses:* platinum: jewellery manufacture (with small amounts of Os and Ir), electrical industry (contacts), catalysts in the chemical industry, laboratory ware. *Palladium:* electrical industry, jewellery manufacture, laboratory ware, spinning nozzles. *Iridium:* alloyed with Pt, fountain-pen nibs, catalysts. *Rhodium:* plating, thermocouples, resistance wire. *Ruthenium:* salts used for staining organic tissues, platinum alloys. *Osmium:* alloyed with Ir for pen nibs, staining organic tissues.

Native platinum Pt, Cl. I, cubic, H: 4·0–4·5, D: 13·3–19·75, 100% Pt, however mostly alloyed with Fe, Sn, etc. *Occurrence:* magmatic, placer deposits.

Sperrylite Pt As_2, Cl. II, cubic, H: 6·0–7·0, D: 10·6, 57% Pt. *Occurrence:* magmatic, zone of weathering.

Cooperite PtS, Cl. II, tetragonal, H: 4·0–5·0, D: 9·5, 86% Pt. *Occurrence:* magmatic.

Braggite (Pt,Pd,Ni)S, Cl. II, tetragonal, H: 2·0, D: 10·0, varying Pt- and Pd-content. *Occurrence:* magmatic.

Laurite RuS_2, Cl. II, cubic, H: 7·5, D: 7·0, 77% Ru. *Occurrence:* magmatic.

Osmiridium (newjanskite) OsIr, Cl. I, hexagonal, H: 7·0, D: 19·0– 21·0, 100% Os and Ir. *Occurrence:* magmatic, placer deposits.

Potassium

Extracted from potassium salts (see Salt Minerals).

Radium

See Uranium.

Rare earths

See Thorium.

Rhodium

See Platinum metals.

Ruthenium

See Platinum metals.

Selenium

Uses: electrical engineering (selenium rectifiers, selenium cells), glass manufacture, rubber manufacture, dye-making, catalysts. Natural occurrence is mostly in the form of the selenides of Cu, Pb, Ag, Au, Hg, Bi and Pt, which are mainly contained in small quantities in copper ores and pyrites. Produced as a by-product of copper extraction and of the manufacture of sulphuric acid from pyrites.

Silver

Uses: alloyed with copper in jewellery, electrical industry (contacts), photographic emulsions, electroplating, coinage, catalysts.

Native silver Ag, Cl. I, cubic, H: 2·5–3·0, D: 10·1–11·1, 100% Ag. *Occurrence:* hydrothermal veins, zone of cementation.

Argentite (β-silver glance) Ag_2S, Cl. II, cubic, H: 2·0, D: 7·3, 87% Ag. *Occurrence:* veins, α-silver glance (monoclinic) forms above 179°C.

Stephanite $5Ag_2S.Sb_2S_3$, Cl. II, H: 2·5, D: 6·2–6·3, 68% Ag. *Occurrence:* veins.

Pyrargyrite (dark-red silver ore) Ag_3SbS_3, Cl. II, trigonal, H: 2·5–3, D: 5·85, 60% Ag. *Occurrence:* veins.

Proustite (light-red silver ore) Ag_3AsS_3, Cl. II, trigonal, H: 2·5, D: 5·57, 65% Ag. *Occurrence:* veins.

Polybasite $8(Ag,Cu)_2S.Sb_2S_3$, Cl. II, cubic, H: 2·0–3·0, D: 6·1–6·3, 64–72% Ag. *Occurrence:* veins.

Silver-bearing tetrahedrite $(Cu_2Ag_2Hg)_3(Sb,As)_2S_6$, Cl. II, cubic, H: 3·0–4·0, D: 4·4–5·4, 0·5–5% Ag. *Occurrence:* veins.

Sodium

Extracted from salt minerals (q.v.).

Tantalum

Nearly always associated with niobium in natural occurrences. Extracted from the same minerals. *Uses:* laboratory ware, electron and X-ray tubes, manufacture of special steels, high-melting compounds.

Tellurium

Occurs naturally as tellurides (cf. selenium as selenides) of Au, Cu, Pb, Ag, Mg and Bi. Present in a finely-divided state in these ores. Recovered principally as a by-product of the smelting of tellurium-bearing gold. *Uses:* metallurgy, rubber industry, thermoelectric effects.

Calaverite $AuTe_2$, Cl. II, monoclinic, H: 2·5–3·0, D: 9·0–9·3, 55% Te. *Occurrence:* subvolcanic veins.

Thorium and rare earths

Uses: Th is the fuel used in breeder reactors. Th- and Ce-oxides were once used in the manufacture of gas mantles. Rare earths used in alloys, as additives in the manufacture of special glasses and in carbon electrodes.

Monazite $(Ce,Th)[PO_4]$, Cl. VII, monoclinic, H: 5·0–5·5, D: 4·8–5·5, 0–30% ThO_2, 39–74% CeO_2, 0–5% oxides of the yttrium group. *Occurrence:* placers, pegmatites.

Thorite (orangite) $(Th,Ce)[SiO_4]$, Cl. VIII, tetragonal, H: 4·5–5·0, D: 4·4–4·8, 48–72% ThO_2, 0–7% oxides of the cerium group. *Occurrence:* pegmatites.

Thorianite $(Th,Ce,U)O_2$, Cl. IV, cubic, H: 5·5–6·0, D: 8·0–9·7, 70–80% Th, 12–28% oxides of the cerium group, variable uranium content. *Occurrence:* pegmatites, placers.

Cerite $(Ca,Fe)Ce_3H[H_2O/SiO_4)_3]$, Cl. VIII, orthorhombic, H: 5·5, D: 4·9, 38–72% CeO_2, 0–7% oxides of the yttrium group. *Occurrence:* contact metasomatic, pneumatolytic.

Allanite (orthite) $(Ca,Ce,La,Na)_2(Al,Fe,Be,Mg,Mn)_3[OH/SiO_4)_3]$, Cl. VIII, H: 5·5–6·0, D: 3·0–4·2, 0–3% ThO_2, 2–34% oxides of the cerium group, 0–4% oxides of the yttrium group. *Occurrence:* magmatic, contact metasomatic, pneumatolytic, metamorphic, pegmatitic.

Tysonite (cerfluorite) $(Ce,Pr,Nd,Sm,La)F_3$, Cl. III, hexagonal, H: 4·5–5·0, D: 6·1, 81–83% oxides of the cerium group, 1–4% oxides of the yttrium group. *Occurrence:* pneumatolytic, contact metasomatic, pegmatitic.

Samarskite $(Ce,Y,Er)_4(Nb,Ta)_2O_7$, Cl. IV, orthorhombic, H: 5·0–6·0, D: 5·7–6·2, 0–6% ThO_2, 2–5% oxides of the cerium group, 5–21% oxides of the yttrium group.

Xenotime YPO_4, Cl. VII, tetragonal, H: 4·0–5·0, D: 4·5, 54–64% Y_2O_3, 0–11% oxides of the cerium group, 0–3% ThO_2. *Occurrence:* granite pegmatites, placers.

Gadolinite $Y_2Fe[O/BeSiO_4]_2$, Cl. VIII, monoclinic, H: 6·5–7·0, D: 4·0–4·7, 32–46% Y_2O_3, 0–50% oxides of the cerium group.

Eschynite $(Ce,Th,U,Ca,Fe)(Nb,Ta,Ti)_2O_6$, Cl. IV, orthorhombic, H: 5·0–6·0, D: 5·2, 12–23% ThO_2, 15–23% oxides of the cerium group. *Occurrence:* pegmatitic.

Tin

Uses: tin plate, bronze, gun-metal, solder, tin foil, zinc oxides in enamels.

Cassiterite (tinstone) SnO_2, Cl. IV, tetragonal, H: 6·0–7·0, D: 6·8–7·1, 78% Sn. *Occurrence:* pegmatitic–pneumatolytic, veins, placers.

Stannine (tin pyrites) $CuFeSnS_4$, Cl. II, tetragonal, H: 4·0, D: 4·3–4·5, 27% Sn. *Occurrence:* veins, pegmatitic and hydrothermal.

Frankeite $Pb_5Sn_3Sb_2S_{14}$, Cl. II, monoclinic, H: 2·0, D: 5·5–5·9, 17% Sn. *Occurrence:* subvolcanic veins.

Teallite $PbSnS_2$, Cl. II, orthorhombic, H: 1·0–2·0, D: 6·4, 30% Sn. *Occurrence:* veins.

Titanium

Uses: aircraft construction, as a substitute for steel, steel alloys, pigments (titanium white), textile industry, paper making, leather manufacture, cosmetics, glasses.

Ilmenite (menaccanite) $FeTiO_3$, Cl. IV, trigonal, H: 5·0–6·0, D: 4·74, 30% Ti. *Occurrence:* magmatic, veins, placers, pegmatitic.

Rutile TiO_2, Cl. IV, tetragonal, H: 4·6, D: 4·2, 60% Ti. *Occurrence:* magmatic, placers, pegmatites, metamorphic.

Titanomagnetite (titanium-bearing magnetite) $Fe_3O_4 + FeTiO_3$ (see under Iron, *magnetite*).

Sphene (titanite) $CaTi[O/SiO_4]$, Cl. VIII, monoclinic, H: 5·0–5·5, D: 3·4–3·6, 25% Ti. *Occurrence:* magmatic, metamorphic, contact metamorphic, pegmatitic.

Tungsten

Uses: manufacture of special steels, hard materials (tungsten carbide), alloys, shell casing, electrical engineering, rocket technology, electric filaments.

Wolframite $(Fe,Mn)WO_4$, Cl. VI, monoclinic, H: 5·0–5·5, D: 7·1–7·5, 76% WO_3. *Occurrence:* pegmatitic–pneumatolytic. Wolframite is a continuous mixed crystal series between **ferberite** $(FeWO_4)$ and **hübnerite** $(MnWO_4)$.

Scheelite $CaWO_4$, Cl. VI, tetragonal, H: 4·5–5·0, D: 5·9–6·1, 80% WO_3. *Occurrence:* pegmatitic–pneumatolytic, contact metasomatic.

Uranium and radium

Uses: uranium is used as reactor fuel, catalysts, pigments for glass and enamels. Radium (about 3·4 g radium is contained in 10 tons uranium) is used as a source of radiation (medicine), in luminous paints and in the testing of materials (see also Thorium and the Rare earths).

Pitchblende (uraninite) UO_2, Cl. IV, cubic, H: 4·0–6·0, D: 9·0–10·0, 46–88% U. *Occurrence:* pegmatitic, hydrothermal veins (Fig. 64).

Uraninite UO_2 with good crystalline form; usually in pegmatites.

Bröggerite: uraninite with a high Th-content.

Cleveite: uraninite with a high content of Ar, He and rare earths.

Pitchblende: uranium oxide ($\sim U_3O_7$) with a botryoidal form, often containing Th and Ce. Mostly occurs in hydrothermal veins.

Gummite: alteration product of pitchblende.

Uranotile (uranophane) $CaU_2[(OH)_3/SiO_4]_2.4H_2O$, Cl. VIII, monoclinic, H: 2·0–3·0, D: 3·8–3·9, 67% UO_3. *Occurrence:* pegmatitic, hydrothermal, veins, zone of oxidation.

Carnotite $K[UO_2/VO_4].1·5H_2O$, Cl. VII, monoclinic, H: 4·0, D: 4·5, 63–65% UO_3. *Occurrence:* impregnation deposits.

Autunite $Ca[UO_2/PO_4]_2.10H_2O$, Cl. VII, tetragonal, H: 2·0–2·5, D: 3·0–3·2, 58–63% UO_3. *Occurrence:* pegmatites, secondary veins.

Torbernite $Cu[UO_2/PO_4]_2.nH_2O$, Cl. VII, tetragonal, H: 2·0–2·5, D: 3·4–3·6, 57–61% UO_3. *Occurrence:* veins, hydrothermal.

Tujamunite $Ca[UO_2/VO_4]_2.3–8H_2O$, Cl. VII, orthorhombic, H: 2·0, D: 3·7–4·3, 57–58% UO_3. *Occurrence:* biochemical sediments.

Vanadium

Deposits containing less than 2% are economically workable. A considerable portion of the amount produced is recovered from blast furnace slag, since it occurs in traces in iron ores. *Uses:* manufacture of special steels, alloys, catalysts.

Patronite VS_4, Cl. II, cryst. system? H: 2·0–3·5, D: ?, about 30% V. *Occurrence:* biochemical sediments? veins?

Vanadinite $Pb_5Cl(VO_4)_3$, Cl. VII, hexagonal, H: 3·0, D: 6·8–7·1, 11% V. *Occurrence:* ore-deposits (secondary).

Descloizite $Pb(Zn,Cu)[OH/VO_4]$, Cl. VII, orthorhombic, H: 3·5, D: 5·5–6·2, 13% V. *Occurrence:* ore-deposits.

Mottramite: descloizite with a high Cu-content.

Carnotite $K[UO_2/VO_4].1·5H_2O$, Cl. VII, monoclinic, H: 4·0, D: 4·5, 12% V. *Occurrence:* impregnation deposits.

Roscoelite $K(Al,V)_2[(OH,F)_2AlSi_3O_{10}]$, Cl. VIII, monoclinic, H: 2·5, D: 2·9, 14–16% V. *Occurrence:* hydrothermal veins, sedimentary, impregnations (see Micas).

Zinc

Uses: brass manufacture, alloys, galvanizing, sheet zinc, pigments (lithopone), pesticides.

Zincblende (sphalerite) $(Zn,Fe)S$, Cl. II, cubic, H: 3·5–4·0, D: 3·9–4·2, up to 67% Zn and 3% Cd. *Occurrence:* veins, metasomatic and contact metasomatic, chemical sediments.

Wurtzite (Zn,Fe)S, Cl. II, hexagonal, H: 3·0–4·0, D: 4·0, up to 67% Zn and 3% Cd. *Occurrence:* veins, chemical sediments.

Smithsonite (zinc spar) $ZnCO_3$, Cl. V, trigonal, H: 5·0, D: 4·3–4·5, 52% Zn. *Occurrence:* secondary veins, metasomatic.

Hemimorphite (silicate of zinc) $Zn_4[(OH)_2/Si_2O_7].H_2O$, Cl. VIII, orthorhombic, H: 4·5–5·0, D: 3·3–3·5, 54% Zn. *Occurrence:* metasomatic, chemical-sedimentary.

Zincite (red oxide of zinc) ZnO, Cl. IV, hexagonal, H: 4·5–5·0, D: 5·4–5·7, 80% Zn. *Occurrence:* contact metasomatic, metamorphic.

Willemite $Zn_2[SiO_4]$, Cl. VIII, trigonal, H: 5·5, D: 4·0–4·2, 58% Zn. *Occurrence:* contact metasomatic, metamorphic, hydrothermal.

Franklinite $(Zn,Mn)Fe_2O_4$, Cl. IV, cubic H: 6·0–6·5, D: 5·1–5·2, 7–20% Zn. *Occurrence:* contact metasomatic, metamorphic.

Zirconium

Uses: reactor material, highly-refractory materials, tanning, glazing, special alloys, gemstone.

Zircon $ZrSiO_4$, Cl. VIII, tetragonal, H: 6·5, D: 3·9–4·8, 67% ZrO_2, with Hf, Th, Y, etc. *Occurrence:* pegmatitic, metamorphic, placers.

Baddeleyite ZrO_2, Cl. IV, monoclinic, H: 6·5, D: 5·4–6·02, 71–93% ZrO_2. *Occurrence:* pegmatitic, volcanic. **Brazilite:** fibrous variety of baddeleyite.

Zircite: mixture of zircon and brazilite.

6.3. Summary of important non-ores, stones and earths
(arranged in alphabetical order)

Apatite and phosphorite (mineral phosphates)

Uses: fertilizer manufacture (superphosphate), matches, phosphor bronze, phosphor-organic compounds, cattle feed.

Apatite $Ca_5[(F,Cl,OH)/PO_4)_3]$, Cl. VII, hexagonal, H: 5·0, D: 3·1–3·2. 40–42% P_2O_5. *Occurrence:* magmatic, pegmatitic–pneumatolytic, biochemical-sedimentary.

Fluor-apatite, chlor-apatite and **hydroxyl-apatite** are differentiated on the basis of whether F, Cl or OH, respectively, are dominant.

Phosphorite is cryptocrystalline apatite which is mostly formed from amorphous calcium phosphate. The most important source of phosphorus. *Occurrence:* biochemical-sedimentary. **Collophane** is amorphous calcium phosphate.

Asbestos

Asbestos represents a group of fibrous silicates. *Uses:* fireproof fabrics, heat and electrical insulators, sheets, boards in the building industry, additive in cement (pipes), brake linings, paper industry, plastics, rubber industry, filter material. The following types are included in the term *commercial asbestos*: **chrysotile** (fibrous serpentine) and **amphibole** (hornblende) asbestos (actinolite, crocidolite, anthophyllite, amosite and tremolite) (see p. 180).

Chrysotile (fibrous serpentine, serpentine asbestos) $Mg_6(OH)_8(Si_4O_{10})$, Cl. VIII, monoclinic, H: 2·5–4·0, D: 2·36–2·50. *Occurrence:* hydrothermal veins, contact metasomatic. Most important type of asbestos.

Actinolite (asbestos) $Ca_2(Mg,Fe)_5[(OH)_2/Si_8O_{22}]$, Cl. VIII, monoclinic, H: 5·0–6·0, D: 3·0–3·2. *Occurrence:* epizonal regional metamorphism, hydrothermal veins.

Crocidolite $(Na,K)_2Mg_2Fe_5^{2+}Fe_4^{3+}[(OH)_4/Si_{16}O_{44}]$, Cl. VIII, monoclinic, H: 4·0, D: 3·3–3·2. *Occurrence:* hydrothermal veins, regional metamorphic.

Anthophyllite $(Mg,Fe)_7[(OH)_2Si_8O_{22}]$, Cl. VII, monoclinic, H: 5·5–6·0, D: 2·9–3·2, iron-poor to iron-free. *Occurrence:* regional metamorphism, contact metamorphism.

Amosite (iron-anthophyllite) is iron-rich anthophyllite.

Tremolite $Ca_2Mg_5Si_8O_{22}(OH)_2$, Cl. VIII, monoclinic, H: 5·0–6·0, D: 2·9–3·1. *Occurrence:* contact metamorphic, contact metasomatic, regional metamorphic.

Barytes and witherite

Uses: barytes is used principally in heavy materials (as a mix component in heavy concrete, added to the mud used in oil-drilling, shield plates for protection from X-rays and radioactivity, additive in lacquers and pigments, manufacture of lithopone, paper industry, filler for gramophone records and in the textile industry).

Barytes (heavy spar) $BaSO_4$, Cl. VI, orthorhombic, H: 3·0–3·5, D: 4·48. *Occurrence:* veins, chemical-sedimentary, contact metasomatic, deep hydrothermal veins.

Witherite $BaCO_3$, Cl. V, orthorhombic, H: 3·0–3·5, D: 4·25. *Occurrence:* veins.

Boron minerals

Uses: as a diamond substitute (boron nitride), reactor material, enamels, rocket propellants, glass manufacture (kernite), pharmacy, cosmetics, detergents. A large part of the boron produced is obtained from salt marshes and volcanic emanations, in which it occurs as dissolved salts.

Kernite (rasorite) $Na_2B_4O_7.4H_2O$, Cl. V, monoclinic, H: 3·3–5·0, D: 1·95, 51% B_2O_3. *Occurrence:* contact metamorphic, chemical-sedimentary.

Colemanite $Ca_2B_6O_{11}.5H_2O$, Cl. V, monoclinic, H: 3·5–4·5, D: 2·4, 51% B_2O_3. *Occurrence:* chemical-sedimentary.

Ulexite $NaCaB_5O_9.8H_2O$, Cl. V, triclinic, H: 1·0, D: 1·7, 43% B_2O_3. *Occurrence:* chemical-sedimentary.

Pandermite (priceite) $Ca_5B_{12}O_{23}.9H_2O$, Cl. V, triclinic, H: 3·0, D: 2·45, 50% B_2O_3. *Occurrence:* chemical-sedimentary.

Borax (tincal) $Na_2B_4O_7.10H_2O$, Cl. V, monoclinic, H: 2·0–2·5, D: 1·7–1·8, 36% B_2O_3. *Occurrence:* chemical-sedimentary.

Sassoline (native boric acid) H_3BO_3, Cl. IV, triclinic, H: 1·0, D: 1·48, 56% B_2O_3. *Occurrence:* volcanic sublimate.

Boracite $Mg_3B_7O_{13}Cl$, Cl, V_β orthorhombic, H: 7·0, D: 2·9–3·0, 62% B_2O_3. *Occurrence:* chemical-sedimentary.

Tincalconite (mohavite) $Na_2B_4O_7.5H_2O$, Cl. V, trigonal, H:?, D: 1·88, 48% B_2O_3. *Occurrence:* chemical-sedimentary.

Bromine minerals

Uses: anti-knock agent, pharmacy, photography, insecticides. The world demand for bromine cannot be satisfied by the few rare bromine minerals which occur: most is obtained from sea water, salt marshes and potassium salt deposits.

Bromargyrite $AgBr$, Cl. III, cubic, H: 2·0, D: 5·8–6·0. *Occurrence:* ore veins, zone of weathering.

Calcite, magnesite and dolomite (spathic carbonates)

Uses: calcite in the manufacture of soda, calcium carbide, (crude) calcium cyanamide, ammonia, bleaching powder, glass and sugar, as a flux in blast furnaces, polarizing prisms in optical apparatus (microscopes, range-finders). Magnesite is used in the manufacture of highly-refractory constructional materials, glass and sorel cement. Dolomite is used for highly-refractory constructional materials, glass, and, like limestone, in the building industry and for road metal. Magnesite and dolomite are also sources of magnesium. Magnesite forms a continuous mixed crystal series with siderite, dolomite with ankerite (Fig. 66), see Iron.

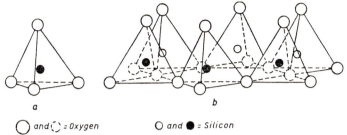

a b

◯ and ⟨⟩ = Oxygen   ○ and ● = Silicon

Figure 67   Diagrams showing the spacial arrangement of SiO_4-tetrahedra: (a) single SiO_4-tetrahedron, (b) sheet formed by linked SiO_4-tetrahedra.

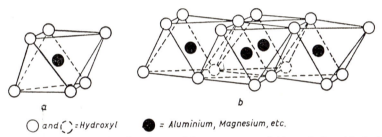

a b

◯ and ⟨⟩ = Hydroxyl   ● = Aluminium, Magnesium, etc.

Figure 68   Diagrams showing the spacial arrangement of Al-octahedra: (a) single octahedron, (b) layer formed by linked octahedra.

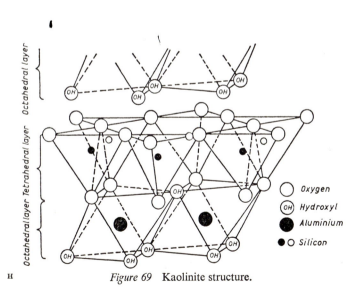

○ Oxygen
(OH) Hydroxyl
● Aluminium
●○ Silicon

H   *Figure 69*   Kaolinite structure.

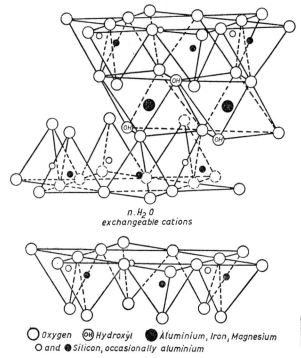

$n.H_2O$
exchangeable cations

○ Oxygen   ⓞₕ Hydroxyl   ● Aluminium, Iron, Magnesium
○ and ● Silicon, occasionally aluminium

Figure 70   Structure of montmorillonite.

Calcite (calc spar) $CaCO_3$, Cl. V, trigonal, H: 3·0, D: 2·6–2·7. *Occurrence:* chemical-sedimentary, hydrothermal, organic.

Aragonite $CaCO_3$, Cl. V, orthorhombic, H: 3·5–4·0, D: 2·95. *Occurrence:* metasomatic, chemical-sedimentary. Changes to calcite between 400° and 500°C.

Magnesite $MgCO_3$, Cl. V, trigonal, H: 3·5–4·5, D: 3·0. *Occurrence:* metamorphic, metasomatic.

Dolomite $CaMg(CO_3)_2$, Cl. V, trigonal, H: 3·5–4·0, D: 2·85–2·95. *Occurrence:* chemical-sedimentary, metasomatic, veins, hydrothermal.

Clay minerals (see 7.1.4)

Clay minerals are hydrated aluminium silicates, which may also contain other components such as Ca, Mg, Fe, Na, K, etc. The basic structure of all the clay minerals is a composite sheet composed of a layer of linked SiO_4-tetrahedra (see Fig. 67), and a layer of octahedrally coordinated aluminium in which each Si-atom is surrounded by 4 O-atoms and each Al by 6 O-atoms or (OH)-molecules (see Fig. 68). Two-layered minerals (1 SiO_4-sheet and 1 Al-octahedral layer) and three-layered minerals, in which one Al-octahedral layer is sandwiched between two SiO_4 sheets, occur (see Figs. 71 and 72). These sheet structures, consisting of two or three single layers, are stacked one on top of the other. The following mineral groups belong to the clay minerals.

Kaolinite group: —(T + O)—(T + O)—(T + O)—
Montmorillonite group: —(T + O + T)—(T + O + T)—
(T + O + T)—
Illite group: —(T + O + T)—(T + O + T)—(T + O + T)—
Chlorite group
Clay minerals with a double chain structure
Vermiculite
Clay minerals with a variable layering structure.

KAOLINITE GROUP

Two-layered minerals with composite sheets, which consist of SiO_4-tetrahedral layers (T) and Al-octahedral layers (O). The single composite sheets are electrically neutral. Bonding between the sheets is effected by the attractive forces between the O-ions of the base of the SiO_4-tetrahedral layer of one composite sheet and the OH-ions of the octahedral layer of the underlying sheet (see Fig. 69). The thickness of a two-layered sheet (T + O) amounts to 7 Å. The kaolinite group is comprised of kaolinite, dickite, nacrite, halloysite and metahalloysite.

Halloysite consists of kaolinite sheets with H_2O layers at variable intervals in the structure. The interspersal of water layers weakens the bonding between the sheets. This presumably causes a bending of the sheets and leads to the formation of tubes.

Kaolinite (kaolin, china clay) $Al_2O_3.2SiO_2.2H_2O$, Cl. VIII, triclinic, H: 2·0–2·5, D: 2·58. *Occurrence:* weathering product occurring in argillaceous sediments, hydrothermal alteration of felspars and felspathoids in granites, gneisses, etc. *Uses:* ceramics, china, pottery, stoneware, fillers in paper, textiles, rubber, asbestos, linoleum, absorbent, base for insecticides. Most important mineral of the Kaolinite group (Fig. 71). Kaolin is a clay consisting predominantly of kaolinite.

Dickite $Al_2O_3.2SiO_2.2H_2O$, Cl. VIII, monoclinic, H: 2·5–3·0. D: 2·62. *Occurrence:* hydrothermal, not in sediments. *Uses:* partly as a substitute for kaolinite.

Nacrite $Al_2O_3.2SiO_2.2H_2O$, Cl. VIII, monoclinic, H: 2·5–3·0, D: 2·58. *Occurrence:* pneumatolytic and hydrothermal. Not in sediments.

Halloysite (endellite) $Al_2O_3.2SiO_2.4H_2O$, Cl. VIII, monoclinic,

H: 1·0–2·0, D: 2·0–2·6. *Occurrence:* weathering product, ore veins. *Use:* occasionally used in place of kaolinite.

Metahalloysite $Al_2O_3.2SiO_2.2H_2O$, Cl. VIII, monoclinic, H: 1·0–2·0, D: 2·2. *Occurrence:* product of weathering.

MONTMORILLONITE GROUP

Three-layered minerals, whose basic structure is formed by the super-position of the three layers, tetrahedral–octahedral–tetrahedral (T + O + T). Because part of the Si of the SiO_4-tetrahedral layer is often replaced by Al, and the aluminium of the Al-octahedral layers is always partly replaced by Mg^{2+}, Fe^{3+}, etc., the bonding between the three-layered sheets is weakened and the lattice is no longer electrically neutral. As a result, variable quantities of water molecules and ex-changeable ions may be taken up in the interstices between the layers (see Fig. 70). The ideal formula of montmorillonite is specified as $(OH)_4Si_8Al_4O_{20}.11H_2O$, but because part of the Al^{3+}, in montmoril-lonite is replaced by Mg^{2+}, a formula corresponding more closely to the actual naturally-occurring mineral is: $(Na,Ca)(Mg,Al)_2[(OH)_2/Si_4 O_{10}]$. $11H_2O$, Cl. VIII, monoclinic, H: 1·0, D: 2·25. *Occurrence:* chemical-sedimentary, weathering product, hydrothermal. When the Al^{3+} of the octahedral layers is completely replaced by Mg^{2+}, the mineral is called **saponite,** and if Al is replaced by Fe^{3+}, **nontronite.** Magnesium-poor montmorillonite with extensive substitution of Si by Al is termed **beidellite.**

Bentonite is a clay composed predominantly of montmorillonite, which results from the weathering of volcanic ash. **Fuller's earth** is also a clay containing montmorillonite. Bole is an iron oxide-stained clay composed predominantly of montmorillonite or halloysite. *Uses* of montmorillonite: thickening of drilling muds in sinking oil wells (especially bentonite, see 7.6.4(a)), binding agent for moulding sands in the iron industry, ceramics, fillers for rubber and synthetic materials, pharmacy, cosmetics, removal of organic stains (especially Fuller's earth), absorbents, base for insecticides.

ILLITE GROUP (CLAY MINERALS SIMILAR TO THE MICAS)

Three-layered minerals, whose basic structural unit is formed of an Al-octahedral layer sandwiched between two SiO_4-tetrahedral layers. This structure is the same as that of montmorillonite, with the exception that some Si of the SiO_4-tetrahedral layers is always replaced by Al, thus disturbing the electrical neutrality. The net negative charge which results from this substitution is balanced by K^+. Part of the Al of the octahedral layer, also, is always replaced by Mg^{2+}, Fe^{3+}, etc. A formula for illite may be given as $K_{0.5}(Al_2,Fe_2,Mg_3)[(OH)_2/Al_{0.5}Si_{3.5}O_{10}]$, Cl. VIII, monoclinic. *Occurrence:* weathering product. *Uses:* constituent of many brick clays, fertilizer ($\sim6\%$ K_2O).

CHLORITE GROUP

The structure is built up by repetition of one three-layered and one brucite sheet [brucite is a trigonal mineral with the formula $Mg(OH)_2$].

$\left\{\begin{array}{l}\text{SiO}_4\text{-tetrahedral layer}\\\text{Al-octahedral layer}\\\text{SiO}_4\text{-tetrahedral layer}\end{array}\right\}$ Three layered sheet $(OH)_4(Si,Al_8)(Mg,Fe)_6O_{20}$

{Brucite layer} $\qquad (Mg,Al)_6(OH)_{12}$

$\left\{\begin{array}{l}\text{SiO}_4\text{-tetrahedral layer}\\\text{Al-octahedral layer}\\\text{SiO}_4\text{-tetrahedral layer}\end{array}\right\}$ Three-layered sheet

{Brucite layer}

The chlorite group contains a large number of minerals, e.g. **penninite** $Mg_3(Mg,Al)_3[(OH)_8/Al_2Si_2O_{10}]$, **prochlorite** $(Mg,Fe)_5Al[(OH)_8/AlSi_3O_{10}]$, **clinochlore** $(Mg,Al,Fe)_6[(OH)_8/AlSi_3O_{10}]$, **amesite** $(Mg_4Al_2[(OH)_8 Al_2Si_2O_{10}]$.

Clay minerals with a double chain structure

A small number of clay minerals, such as attapulgite and sepiolite, possess a chain structure.

Attapulgite (palygorskite) $Mg_{2.5}[(H_2O)_2/OHSi_4O_{10}].2H_2O$, Cl. VIII, orthorhombic, H: 2.0–2.5, D: 2.0. *Occurrence:* hydrothermal, weathering product. *Use:* absorbent.

Sepiolite (meerschaum) $Mg_4[(H_2O)_3/(OH)_2/Si_6O_{15}].3H_2O$, Cl. VIII, orthorhombic, H: 2.0, D: 2.0. *Occurrence:* hydrothermal, product of weathering. *Uses:* refractory materials, pipes and cigar holders.

VERMICULITE

Clay mineral with a structure intermediate between montmorillonite and that of chlorite, built up of three-layered composite sheets, between which are sandwiched layers of hydrated Mg^{2+}-ions.

$\left\{\begin{array}{l}\text{SiO}_4\text{-tetrahedral layer}\\\text{Al-octahedral layer}\\\text{SiO}_4\text{-tetrahedral layer}\end{array}\right\}$ Three-layered composite sheet, T + O + T

$\{Mg^{2+}$ surrounded by H_2O-molecules$\}$ hydrated Mg^{2+}

$$\left.\begin{array}{l} SiO_4\text{-tetrahedral layer}\\ Al\text{-octahedral layer}\\ SiO_4\text{-tetrahedral layer} \end{array}\right\} \begin{array}{l} \text{Three-layered,}\\ \text{composite sheet, } T + O + T \end{array}$$

At about 100°C, the water surrounding the Mg^{2+} is driven off and the mineral swells up and curves into vermiform shapes. Formula: $\sim11MgO.3Al_2O_3.11SiO_2.20H_2O$, Cl. VIII, monoclinic, H: 1·0–2·0, D: 2·15–2·75. *Occurrence:* hydrothermal, product of weathering. *Uses:* thermal and sound insulation, filler for linoleum, plastics and rubber, aggregate for light-weight concrete.

CLAY MINERALS WITH INTERLAMINATION OF DIFFERING STRUCTURES

Some clay minerals do not possess a homogeneous structure, but are built up of a layer-like superposition of different clay minerals, e.g. alternation of kaolinite and illite, or of montmorillonite and illite. The interlamination may be regular or irregular.

Corundum, emery, garnet, staurolite

Uses: corundum and garnet, like emery and staurolite, are used mainly as abrasives because of their great hardness, as well as for gemstones (q.v.). Corundum used for abrasive purposes is nowadays almost exclusively artificially synthesized.

   Corundum (see Gemstones).

   Emery: metamorphic rock; a fine-grained mixture of corundum and magnetite with subordinate amounts of hematite and quartz.

   Garnet: almandine (see Gemstones) is the most common variety used as an abrasive.

   Staurolite $Al_4[Fe(OH)_2O_2/(SiO_4)_2]$, Cl. VIII, orthorhombic, H: 7·0–7·5, D: 3·7–3·8. *Occurrence:* metamorphic.

Diamond

Uses: abrasive, cutting purposes, drilling bits, jewelled bearings, drawing dies, gramophone industry, gemstone – also artificially synthesized (p. 193).

   Diamond C, Cl. I, cubic, H: 10·0, D: 3·50–3·53, 100% C. *Occurrence:* ultra-basic igneous rocks, breccias, placer deposits.

   Bort: industrial diamonds, carbonado are clinker-like varieties of diamond used for drilling bits.

Felspars and felspathoids (nepheline, leucite)

Uses of felspar: glass, enamels, glazes, coarse and fine ceramics, binding agent for abrasive wheels, dental cement, scouring soap, ornaments.

Uses of felspathoids: nepheline is used as a substitute for felspar in the ceramic industry and in the manufacture of glass and glazes, bricks and glazed tiles. *Leucite* is used for potassium production and in fertilizers.

Felspars are an aluminium silicate mineral group in which the principal cations are K^+, Na^+, Ca^+, Ba^{2+} and Sr^{2+}. The barium and strontium felspars are economically unimportant.

Potash felspars $K[AlSi_3O_8]$: orthoclase (monoclinic), microcline (triclinic);

Soda felspar (albite) $Na[AlSi_3O_8]$, triclinic;

Lime felspar (anorthite) $Ca[Al_2Si_2O_8]$, triclinic.

Soda-lime felspars (plagioclase) are a continuous mixed crystal series between soda and lime felspar. The plagioclase series is subdivided into six types, each of which has a particular name. Mixed crystals between potash felspar and soda felspar also are possible at high temperatures. On rapid cooling these may not unmix and may be preserved in a high-temperature form, e.g. sanidine $(K,Na)[AlSi_3O_8]$ (see Fig. 65, p. 89).

Orthoclase (adularia, transparent variety) $K[AlSi_3O_8]$, Cl. VIII, monoclinic, H: 6·0–6·5, D: 2·5. *Occurrence:* magmatic, pegmatitic (hydrothermal).

Microcline $K[AlSi_3O_8]$, Cl. VIII, triclinic, H: 6·0–6·5, D: 2·54–2·57. *Occurrence:* magmatic, pegmatitic (metamorphic).

Sanidine $(K,Na)[AlSi_3O_8]$, Cl. VIII, monoclinic, H: 6·0–6·5, D: 2·53–2·56. *Occurrence:* volcanic, hydrothermal.

Albite (soda felspar) $Na[AlSi_3O_8]$, Cl. VIII, triclinic, H: 6·0–6·5, D: 2·62. *Occurrence:* alkali magmatic, hydrothermal, metamorphic.

Anorthite (lime felspar) $Ca[Al_2Si_2O_8]$, Cl. VIII, triclinic, H: 6·0–6·5, D: 2·76. *Occurrence:* magmatic, pyroclastic deposits, metamorphic.

Name	Formula	Percentage of the anorthite molecule (An)	D
Albite	$Na(Ca)[AlSi_3O_8]$	0–10 An	2·62
Oligoclase	$Na_{\frac{4}{5}}Ca_{\frac{1}{5}}[AlSi_3O_8]$	10–30 An	2·64
Andesine	$Na_{\frac{3}{5}}Ca_{\frac{2}{5}}[AlSi_3O_8]$	30–50 An	2·68
Labradorite	$Na_{\frac{2}{5}}Ca_{\frac{3}{5}}[AlSi_3O_8]$	50–70 An	2·70
Bytownite	$Na_{\frac{1}{5}}Ca_{\frac{4}{5}}[AlSi_3O_8]$	70–90 An	2·75
Anorthite	$Ca(Na)[Al_2Si_2O_8]$	90–100 An	2·76

Plagioclase series (soda-lime felspars), H: 6·0–6·5, triclinic. *Occurrence:* magmatic, metamorphic.

Felspathoids contain less silica than the alkali felspars.

Nepheline (eleolite) Na[AlSiO$_4$], Cl. VIII, hexagonal, H: 5·5–6·0, D: 2·60–2·65. *Occurrence:* alkali magmatic (nepheline syenite), alkali pegmatitic, pyroclastic deposits.

Leucite K[AlSi$_2$O$_6$], Cl. VIII, tetragonal, H: 5·5–6·0, D: 2·5. *Occurrence:* alkali magmatic.

Fluorspar (fluorite)

Uses: production of hydrofluoric acid, flux for metallurgical processes, glazes, rocket technology, motor fuel, cement industry, separation of uranium isotopes, insecticides, carbon fluoride products, optical lenses.

Fluorspar CaF$_2$, Cl. III, cubic H: 4·0; D: 3·25–3·01. *Occurrence:* hydrothermal, pneumatolytic, pegmatitic, contact metasomatic.

Gems and precious stones

Beryl Al$_3$Be$_3$[Si$_6$O$_{18}$], Cl. VIII, hexagonal, H: 7·5–8·0, D: 2·63. *Occurrence:* pegmatitic, hydrothermal.

Varieties: Aquamarine, transparent, blue to greenish-blue.
Emerald, transparent, pale to medium green.
Pink beryl (morganite), transparent, pink to rose-red.
Heliodor (golden beryl), transparent, yellow to golden-yellow.
Goshenite, transparent, colourless.
Common beryl, transparent, yellow-green.

Chrysoberyl Al$_2$BeO$_4$, Cl. IV, orthorhombic, H: 8·5, D: 3·75. *Occurrence:* pegmatitic, metamorphic.

Varieties: Alexandrite, transparent, green in daylight, red by artificial light.
Cat's-eye chrysoberyl, translucent to opaque, green schiller.

Corundum α-Al$_2$O$_3$, Cl. IV, trigonal, H: 9·0, D: 3·9–4·1. *Occurrence:* magmatic, pegmatitic, contact metamorphic, regional metamorphic.

Varieties: Ruby, transparent, crimson.
Star ruby, translucent, pale crimson, exhibits asterism (the phenomenon of showing a star-shaped figure, due to the diffraction of light by inclusions of small rutile needles).
Sapphire, transparent, blue to pale violet.
Star sapphire, translucent, blue, exhibits asterism (due to twin lamellae).
Leukosaphir, transparent, colourless.
Padmaragaya, transparent, yellowish-pink.

Felspar (see also Felspar and Felspathoids).

Varieties: Amazonstone (microcline) $KAlSi_3O_8$, Cl. VIII, triclinic, H: 6·0–6·5, D: 2·54–2·57. *Occurrence:* pegmatitic, metamorphic, translucent, green.

Sunstone (aventurine felspar) (oligoclase), Cl. VIII, triclinic, H: 6·0–6·5, D: 2·64. *Occurrence:* magmatic, metamorphic, translucent, white or grey with plate-like inclusions of golden-red hematite.

Labradorite (plagioclase), Cl. VIII, triclinic, H: 6·0–6·5, D: 2·70. *Occurrence:* magmatic, metamorphic, translucent, blue-green schiller.

Moonstone (K–Na felspar or acid plagioclase), translucent, light grey with a pale bluish tinge.

Garnet: crystallographically homogeneous group of minerals with variable chemical composition. General formula of the group is $R_3^{2+}R_2^{3+}[SiO_4]_3$, in which R^{2+} may be represented by Ca, Fe, Mg and Mn, and R^{3+} by Fe, Al, Ti and Cr. Cl. VIII, cubic.

Varieties: Almandine (iron-alumina garnet, 'common' garnet) $Fe_3Al_2[SiO_4]_3$, H: 7·0—7·5, D: 4·2. *Occurrence:* metamorphic, transparent to translucent, brownish-red, often with tinge of purple.

Pyrope (magnesian-alumina garnet) $Mg_3Al_2[SiO_4]_3$, H: 7·5, D: 3·5. *Occurrence:* metamorphic, transparent to translucent, blood-red to brownish-red.

Demantoid (andradite, calcium-iron garnet) $Ca_3Fe_2[SiO_4]_3$, H: 6·5–7·0, D: 3·7. *Occurrence:* contact metamorphic, ore veins, metasomatic, metamorphic, transparent, yellowish-green to deep green.

Grossular (lime-alumina garnet, hessonite, cinnamonstone) $Ca_3Al_2[SiO_4]_3$, H: 6·5–7·0, D: 3·5. *Occurrence:* contact metamorphic, transparent to translucent, orange-yellow to orange-green.

Jadeite (member of the pyroxene group) $NaAlSi_2O_6$, Cl. VIII, monoclinic, H: 6·5–7·0, D: 3·2–3·3. *Occurrence:* metamorphic, translucent to opaque, green, whitish-green.

Lapis-lazuli (lazurite) $3NaAlSiO_4.Na_2S$, Cl. VIII, cubic, H: 6·0, D: 2·38–2·42. *Occurrence:* contact metamorphic, pyroclastic deposits, opaque, dark blue (often with small crystals of pyrites scattered throughout the mass).

Nephrite (member of the amphibole group). Fine felt of minute, interlocking actinolite needles (see actinolite-asbestos). Opaque, yellowish-green.

Olivine $(Mg,Fe)_2SiO_4$, Cl. VIII, orthorhombic, H:6·5–7·0, D: 3·3.
Occurrence: magmatic, contact metamorphic.
Variety: Chrysolite (peridot), transparent, greenish-yellow to yellowish-green.

Opal $SiO_2.11H_2O$, Cl. IV, largely amorphous, H: 5·5–6·0, D: 1·9–2·2.
Occurrence: product of weathering, hydrothermal.
Varieties: Precious opal, translucent, milky to bluish, exhibiting opalescence with a brilliant play of colours.

Fire opal, transparent, yellowish-red to orange.

Quartz SiO_2, Cl. IV, trigonal, H: 7·0, D: 2·65. *Occurrence:* magmatic, hydrothermal, sedimentary.
Varieties: Rock crystal, transparent, colourless.

Amethyst, transparent, violet.

Smoky quartz, transparent, smoky-yellow to smoky-grey (morion).

Citrine, transparent, golden-yellow (false-topaz, gold topaz).

Rose quartz, transparent to translucent, pale pink.

Cat's-eye, opaque, shimmering effect caused by the presence of inclusions of grey-green asbestos needles.

Hawk's eye, opaque, shimmering effect caused by inclusions of blue crocidolite needles.

Tiger eye, opaque, shimmering effect caused by inclusions of brown crocidolite needles.

Chalcedony [minutely crystalline (cryptocrystalline) quartz], translucent to opaque. Varieties of chalcedony include chrysoprase (apple-green), carnelian (yellowish-brown to red), agate (coloured banding), onyx (alternate black and white banding), sardonyx (alternate brown and white banding), jasper (strongly coloured, opaque type of chalcedony), heliotrope (greenish-red variety of jasper.)

Spinels: crystallographically-homogeneous group of minerals with varying chemical composition. General formula of the group: R_3O_4 or $R^{2+}O.R_2^{3+}O_3$, in which R^{2+} may be Mg, Zn, Fe, Mn, Ni and R^{3+} may be Al, Fe, Cr. *Occurrence:* regional and thermal metamorphic.
Varieties: Precious spinel $MgAl_2O_4$, Cl. IV, cubic, H: 8·0, D: 3·5, transparent, various shades of red.

Blue spinel $(Mg,Fe)Al_2O_4$, Cl. IV, cubic, H: 8·0, D: 3·5, transparent, blue.

Green spinel (chlorospinel) $(Mg,Cu)(Al,Fe)_2O_4$, Cl. IV, cubic, H: 8·0, D: 3·5, transparent, grass-green.

Spodumene (triphane) $LiAl(Si_2O_6)$, Cl. VIII, monoclinic, H: 6·5–7·0, D: 3·1–3·2. *Occurrence:* pegmatitic.

Varieties: Kunzite, transparent, pink to lilac.

Hiddenite, transparent, green to yellow.

Topaz $(Al_2[F_2/SiO_4]$, Cl. VIII, orthorhombic, H: 8·0, D: 3·5–3·6. *Occurrence:* pegmatitic, pneumatolytic. Transparent, colourless, yellow, red, brown, green, blue.

Tourmaline $NaMg_3Al_6[(OH)_4/(BO_3)_3Si_6O_{18}]$, Cl. VIII, trigonal, H: 7·0–7·5, D: 3·0–3·25. *Occurrence:* pegmatitic, pneumatolytic, contact metamorphic. Transparent, green (elbaite), red (rubellite), schorl (black), blue, yellow.

Turquoise (kallaite) $CuAl_6[(OH)_2/PO_4]_4.4H_2O$, Cl. VIII, triclinic. *Occurrence:* hydrothermal. Opaque, blue, bluish-green (imitations made from coloured ivory).

Zircon $ZrSiO_4$, Cl. VIII, tetragonal, H: 6·5, D: 3·9–4·8. *Occurrence:* pegmatitic, placer deposits, metamorphic, transparent, yellowish-red (hyacinth), colourless (jargoon), violet, brown, green, blue (through heating).

The following minerals, among others, are also used as precious stones.

Apatite $Ca_5[(F,Cl,OH)/(PO_4)_3]$, colourless, white, green, H: 5·0.

Chrysocolla $CuSiO_3.11H_2O$, green, blue, H: 2·0–4·0.

Cordierite $Mg_2Al_3[AlSi_5O_{18}]$, blue, grey-blue, H: 7·0–7·5.

Epidote (pistacite) $Ca_2(Al,Fe)_3[OH/(SiO_4)_3]$, green, yellow, red, H: 6·0–7·0.

Fluorite (fluorspar) CaF_2, green blue, violet, red, H: 4·0.

Hematite (iron glance, specular iron), α-Fe_2O_3, black, red, H: 5·0–6·5.

Pyrites (iron pyrites) and Marcasite FeS_2, yellow-metallic, H: 6·0–6·5.

Rhodonite $(Mn,Fe,Ca)[SiO_3]$, pink, red, H: 5·5–6·5.

Idocrase (vesuvianite) $Ca_{10}(Mg,Fe)_2Al_4[(OH)_4/(SiO_4)_5/Si_2O_7]$, green, yellow, brown, H: 6·5.

Graphite

Uses: electrodes, buffing brushes, lubricants, reactor material, crucibles, pencils, polish, iron and steel industry, pigment, galvano-plastics, munitions. Also obtained artificially from petroleum coke.

Graphite C, Cl. I, hexagonal, H: 1·0–2·0, D: 2·09–2·23. *Occurrence:* metamorphic, pegmatitic?

Gypsum and anhydrite

Uses: cement manufacture, binding agent, modelling, sheets and boards, moulds, ceramics, fertilizers, sulphuric acid and ammonium sulphate manufacture, filler for textiles, paper, paint and insecticides.

Gypsum $CaSO_4.2H_2O$, Cl. VI, monoclinic, H: 1·5–2·0, D: 2·3–2·4. *Occurrence:* chemical-sedimentary, veins. **Alabaster** is a fine-grained, translucent variety.

Anhydrite $CaSO_4$, Cl. VI, orthorhombic, H: 3·0–3·5, D: 2·9–3·0. *Occurrence:* chemical-sedimentary, veins, product of volcanic exhalation.

Mica minerals

The micas are a group of minerals with a sheet-like aluminium silicate structure and which can be cleaved into thin flakes which are usually transparent.

Apart from the lithium-bearing micas, lepidolite and zinnwaldite (see lithium), and the vanadium-bearing mica, roscoelite, the economically most important micas are muscovite and phlogopite. *Uses of muscovite and phlogopite:* electrical insulators, filler for paper, rubber, plastics, paints and wallpapers, windscreens: *Use of biotite:* finely powdered, as a lubricant.

Muscovite (potash alumina mica) $KAl_2[(OH,F)_2/AlSi_3O_{10}]$, Cl. VIII, monoclinic, H: 2·0–2·5, D: 2·78–2·88. *Occurrence:* pegmatitic, magmatic, pneumatolytic, metamorphic, contact metamorphic. **Sericite** is a variety occurring as fine scales in rocks and clays.

Phlogopite (magnesian mica) $KMg_3[(OH,F)_2/AlSi_3O_{10}]$, Cl. VIII, monoclinic, H: 2·5–3·0, D: 2·75–2·97. *Occurrence:* pneumatolytic, metamorphic, contact metamorphic.

Biotite (magnesian iron mica) $K(Mg,Fe)_3[(OH,F)_2/AlSi_3O_{10}]$, Cl. VIII, monoclinic, H: 2·5–3·0, D: 2·8–3·2. *Occurrence:* magmatic, contact metamorphic, metamorphic, hydrothermal.

Natural stones

A number of types of stone are used either as large pieces or in a crushed form as building material. See the chapter on 'Petrology' for their mineralogical composition and also the chapter on 'Engineering Geology'.

(A) IGNEOUS ROCKS

Granite: very hard and high resistance to abrasion, easily split into large or small blocks with even surfaces, takes a good polish and occurs in many colours. *Uses:* sills, slabs, blocks, paving, monuments, road metal, gravestones.

Granite porphyry: aggregate.

Quartz porphyry: paving, aggregate, chips, columnar blocks.

Pitchstone, obsidian, pumice stone: predominantly glassy volcanic rocks. *Uses:* pitchstone is granulated, briefly heated until it fuses (whereupon it expands) and cooled. The resulting porous material is used as an aggregate in the manufacture of light-weight building materials ('perlite'), and also as an auxiliary filtering agent. Pumice stone: cleansing agent, aggregate for light-weight building materials.

Syenite: splits less well and along fewer planes than granite, high resistance to abrasion. *Uses:* aggregate, road metal, chips, tombstones.

Gabbro and norite: crystallized under high load. *Uses:* in polished blocks and thin slabs for interior architecture, and wall-facing etc., of buildings on account of the bronze schiller of the ortho-pyroxene constituent. As labradorite-rock for the facing of monumental structures. Very difficult to work because of its tenacity.

Dolerite: very tough, wear-resistant rock, with, in many cases, a higher strength than granite. *Uses:* road metal, gravestones, ornamental stones (uniform green colour).

Basalt: harder than granite, extremely high crushing strength and resistance to wear, mechanically difficult to work. *Uses:* road ballast, kerbstones, paving, columnar basalts for canal and road construction. **Cast basalt** is basalt fused in an oil-furnace and used for the manufacture of slabs and stones extremely resistant to abrasion and acids. 'Sonnenbrand' (sun-burn) basalts are types decidedly unsuitable for building purposes. This is because the action of atmospheric substances causes the formation of grey spots, between which star-shaped hair-cracks form later. These eventually cause disintegration of the rock. Sonnenbrand basalts may be recognized because after heating for 10 minutes in hydrochloric acid, white spots appear on the surface of the stone.

Phonolite: used as roofing tiles.

(B) SEDIMENTARY ROCKS

Limestone: easily workable, soft. *Uses:* as polished slabs for wall-facing and staircases. Also as road metal, in the manufacture of sand-lime bricks and as a flux in high-temperature furnaces.

Sandstone: good workability, easily split. *Uses:* important building material. Quartz sandstone (quartz grains with a siliceous cement) is especially suitable for building stone (e.g. the outer court of Dresden and the cathedrals of Strassburg, Basle and Freiburg). Calcareous sandstone (quartz grains with a calcareous cement) is less suitable, because of its attack by sulphur oxides in the atmosphere (Cologne cathedral).

Tuffs: trachyte, andesite, phonolite, and basaltic tuffs are used as building material with a relatively low crushing strength. Trachytic tuffs ('Trass') are used as cement additives.

Gypsum in the form of **alabaster,** easily workable, used for art objects.

(C) METAMORPHIC ROCKS

Marble: easily workable, takes a good polish, manifold colours. *Uses:* for decoration and ornaments, sculpture.

Serpentine (serpentinite): peridotites and augite rocks, which have been extensively altered to serpentine (see Chrysotile-asbestos), dark green colour. *Uses:* ornamental stone and for applied art objects. Serpentine-marble (ophicalcite) is used for the same purposes and for railway ballast.

Amphibolites: rocks composed predominantly of hornblende. Tough and shock-resistant. *Uses:* railway track ballast and road aggregate.

Slates: thinly foliated, hard, weather-resistant (i.e. pyrites-free) and blue-grey types are used as roofing slates. Manufacture of slate boards and slate pencils.

Nitrogen and iodine raw materials

Uses: alkaline nitrates principally as fertilizer, manufacture of nitric acid, glass industry, ceramics, explosives, penicillin, rust-prevention agents. Iodine: pharmacy, pigments, electrical appliances, titanium and zircon extraction, photography, fire extinguishers. Iodine is not obtained from its own rare minerals, but by the dressing of caliche (q.v.), in which it occurs in small quantities as $Ca(IO_3)_2$. The salts are almost invariably associated with terrestrial salt deposits.

Caliche: sedimentary rock composed partly of soda-nitre (5–30%) with NaCl, Na_2SO_4 and salts of potassium, magnesium, calcium and iodine.

Soda-nitre (nitratine, Chile saltpetre) $NaNO_3$, Cl. V, trigonal, H: 1·5–2·0, D: 2·2–2·3. *Occurrence:* chemical-sedimentary.

Nitre (saltpetre, nitrate of potash) KNO_3, Cl. V, orthorhombic, H: 2·0, D: 1·9–2·1. *Occurrence:* chemical-sedimentary.

Lautarite $Ca(IO_3)_2$, Cl. IV, monoclinic, H: 3·0–4·0, D: 4·6. *Occurrence:* chemical-sedimentary.

Quartz, quartz sand, quartzite, kieselguhr

(A) QUARTZ AND QUARTZ SAND

Uses: very clear, inclusion-free quartz crystals are used for oscillators and optical instruments. Pure vein quartz is used in the glass and porcelain industries and in the manufacture of ferrosilicon and silicon carbide. Quartz sands: glass sands in glass manufacture, moulding sands for iron and steel casting, building and spreading sands, sand blasting.

Quartz SiO_2, Cl. IV, trigonal, H: 7·0, D: 2·65. *Occurrence:* magmatic, pegmatitic, hydrothermal, sedimentary.

Chalcedony: mineral composed of fine quartz fibres. **Flint:** variety of chalcedony. Biochemical-sedimentary origin (e.g. in the Chalk of Rügen, England and France). Chalcedony: H: 6·0, D: 2·55–2·63.

Opal $SiO_2.11H_2O$. Consists predominantly of aged, amorphous silica gel: H: 5·5–6·0, D: 2·0–2·2. *Occurrence:* product of weathering, hydrothermal.

At high temperatures, quartz forms several modifications: β-quartz, tridymite and cristobalite (see Figs. 71 and 72). On cooling, tridymite and cristobalite invert to their low-temperature forms, not to quartz again. β-quartz (high quartz) inverts to low quartz (normal, α-quartz) on cooling. Quartz transformation, particularly, is associated with a large expansion (residual quartz content in silica bricks).

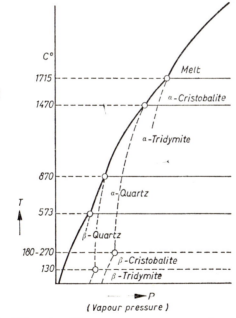

Figure 71   The SiO_2-system. The vapour pressure curves of various SiO_2 modifications are shown schematically. At any given temperature, the stable modification is the one with the lower vapour pressure (P) (i.e. the curve lies nearer to the ordinate).

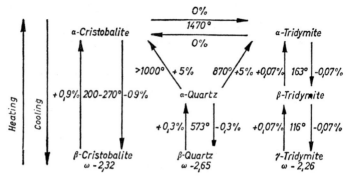

Figure 72 The linear expansion, at the various transformation temperatures, of silica (SiO_2) in silica bricks.

(B) QUARTZITE

For commercial purposes, two types of quartzite are recognized. These are silica rock (quartzite) and ganister. Silica rock may be any of several kinds: metamorphic |quartzité formed by the recrystallization of sandstones, other silica-rich rocks, or sandstones with a siliceous cement. Ganister is composed of quartz grains, cemented by chalcedony with pure opal. *Uses:* ganister and, in part, silica rock used for highly-refractory silica bricks (Fig. 68).

(C) DIATOMACEOUS EARTH (KIESELGUHR)

Earthy material with 70–90% SiO_2, formed of the minute porous shells of siliceous algae. *Uses:* filtering agent, filler for paper, synthetic materials (plastics), rubber, manufacture of water glass, glazes, enamels, abrasives and polishing materials, for light-weight building bricks and light-weight concrete, base for insecticides, chemicals (e.g. nitroglycerine in the manufacture of dynamite) and catalysts.

Salt minerals of marine deposits

Salt minerals do not normally occur singly but are usually associated with other salts. The salts of marine deposits are mostly chlorides and sulphides in contrast with terrestrial deposits which are predominantly nitrates and carbonates.

   Rock salt (halite) NaCl, Cl. III, cubic, H: 2·0, D: 2·1–2·2. *Occurrence:* chemical-sedimentary. *Uses:* raw material for hydrochloric acid, chlorine, soda, caustic soda and other sodium compounds, condiment, preservative, Na-extraction.

   Glauberite $CaNa_2(SO_4)_2$, Cl. VI, monoclinic, H: 2·5–3·0, D: 2·7–2·8.

Occurrence: chemical-sedimentary. *Uses:* glass, textile dyestuffs and paper industry.

Mirabilite (Glauber salt) $Na_2SO_4.10H_2O$, Cl. VI, monoclinic. *Occurrence:* chemical sedimentary. *Uses:* as for glauberite, laxative.

Thenardite Na_2SO_4, Cl. VI, orthorhombic, H: 2·0–3·0, D: 2·65. *Occurrence:* chemical-sedimentary, product of volcanic exhalation. *Uses:* as for glauberite.

Sylvine KCl, Cl. III, cubic H: 2·0, D: 1·9–2·0. *Occurrence:* chemical-sedimentary. *Uses:* the most important potassium salt (63% K_2O), artificial fertilizer, glass, ceramics, scouring soaps, explosives, matches, rocket fuels, pharmacy, photography, textile dyes, K-extraction.

Carnallite $KMgCl_3.6H_2O$, Cl. III, orthorhombic, H: 1·0–2·0, D: 1·60. *Occurrence:* chemical-sedimentary. *Uses:* as for sylvine contains 17% K_2O in addition to recoverable quantities of caesium, rubidium and bromine.

Kainite $KMg[Cl/SO_4].3H_2O$, Cl. VI, monoclinic, H: 2·5–3·0, D: 2·1. *Occurrence:* chemical-sedimentary. *Uses:* artificial fertilizer (19% K_2O).

Polyhalite $K_2Ca_2Mg(SO_4)_4.2H_2O$, Cl. VI, triclinic, H: 2·5–3·5, D: 2·77. *Occurrence:* chemical-sedimentary. *Uses:* not usually worked because of its low K_2O-content (about 14%).

Kieserite $MgSO_4.H_2O$, Cl. VI, monoclinic, H: 3·0–3·5, D: 2·57. *Occurrence:* chemical-sedimentary. *Uses:* pharmacy, tanning, dyeing, manufacture of finishing materials, production of cellulose, sorel cement.

Epsomite (Epsom salts, reichardtite) $MgSO_4.7H_2O$, Cl. VI, orthorhombic, H: 2·0–2·5, D: 1·68. *Occurrence:* chemical-sedimentary, weathering product. *Uses:* as for kieserite.

Sillimanite, andalusite, kyanite, dumortierite

Uses: manufacture of highly-refractory materials. The minerals are transformed to (refractory) mullite ($3Al_2O_3.2SiO_2$) on firing.

Sillimanite $Al[AlSiO_5]$, Cl. VIII, orthorhombic, H: 6·0–7·0, D: 3·2. *Occurrence:* contact metamorphic, regional metamorphic.

Andalusite $AlAl[O/SiO_4]$, Cl. VIII, orthorhombic, H: 7·5, D: 3·1–3·2. *Occurrence:* contact metamorphic, regional metamorphic, pegmatitic.

Kyanite (cyanite, disthene) $Al_2[O/SiO_4]$, Cl. VIII, triclinic, H in the longest direction of the crystal is 4·0–4·5, in the transverse direction is 6·0–7·0, D: 3·6–3·7. *Occurrence:* regional metamorphic.

Dumortierite $(Al,Fe)_7BSi_3O_{18}$, Cl. VIII, orthorhombic, H: 7·0, D: 3·3–3·4. *Occurrence:* pegmatitic, pneumatolytic. *Uses:* limited use in refractory materials.

I

Strontianite and celestine

Uses: firework manufacture, glass industry, brick glazing, as a flux for welding wire, extraction of sugar from molasses, dyes, clarification of soda solutions, as stabilizers for PVC-plastics.

Strontianite $SrCO_3$, Cl. V, orthorhombic, H: 3·5–4·0, D: 3·2. *Occurrence:* veins, chemical-sedimentary.

Celestine $SrSO_4$, Cl. VI, orthorhombic, H: 3·0–3·5, D: 3·9–4·0. *Occurrence:* chemical-sedimentary, veins, volcanic.

Sulphur and pyrites

Uses: manufacture of sulphuric acid, black (blasting) powder, fireworks, disinfectants, insecticides, matches, pharmacy, bleaching of textiles.

Sulphur S, Cl. I, orthorhombic up to, and monoclinic above 95°C, H: 1·0–2·5, D: 2·07 (monoclinic 1·96). *Occurrence:* volcanic, secondary.

Pyrites (iron pyrites) FeS_2, Cl. II, cubic, H: 6·0–6·5, D: 4·8–5·0. *Occurrence:* veins, magmatic, pneumatolytic, hydrothermal, biochemical-sedimentary.

Marcasite FeS_2, Cl. II, orthorhombic, H: 6·0, D: 4·8–4·9. *Occurrence:* veins, metasomatic, chemical-sedimentary.

Talc and pyrophyllite

Uses: talc is used in refractory materials and electrical insulators because of its easy workability and the fact that it possesses a high dimensional stability and strength after firing. Talcum powder is used for cosmetics, fillers for paper, soap, rubber, glass industry, textile dressing, additive for biscuit porcelain, base for insecticides (white talc is much more valuable than the grey variety).

Pyrophyllite, uses as for talc, principally as a refractory material.

Talc (steatite, soapstone, agalmatolite) $Mg_3(OH)_2[Si_4O_{10}]$, Cl. VIII, monoclinic, H: 1·0–1·5, D: 2·7–2·8. *Occurrence:* hydrothermal, metasomatic, regional metamorphic.

Pyrophyllite $Al_2[(OH)_2/Si_4O_{10}]$, Cl. VIII, monoclinic, H: 1·0–2·0, D: 2·8. *Occurrence:* hydrothermal, veins.

7

APPLIED MINERALOGY

7.1. Ceramics, including refractory materials

A ceramic may be defined as any inorganic material other than a metal which undergoes a high-temperature heat treatment as an essential part of its manufacture. This definition includes glasses, enamels, cements, etc., which are dealt with in sections 7.2–7.4.

Subdivision:

Coarse ceramics (7.1.3.)
- (a) Structural ceramics
- (b) Earthenware (coarse earthenware, always coloured)
- (c) Refractory ceramics
    - (i) Silicate refractories
    - (ii) Non-silicate refractories
- (d) Insulating bricks

Fine ceramics (7.1.4.)
- (a) Industrial ceramics
    - (i) Silicate ceramics
    - (ii) Non-silicate ceramics
- (b) Porcelain
- (c) Refractory oxide bodies (including cermets)
- (d) Material for use under extreme conditions

Glazes (7.2.5.)

7.1.1. Raw materials

Most important: clays, quartz, felspar.

Others: quartzites, limestone, sulphite waste liquor for silica bricks; magnesite, dolomite, chromite for refractory bricks and bodies; sillimanite, andalusite, kyanite, steatite, zircon, beryl, bauxite, diaspore, corundum, pyrophyllite, topaz, kieselguhr, perlite, asbestos, vermiculite, coal and carbon-(silicon carbide), boron-, and nitrogen compounds.

7.1.2. Behaviour of clays in ceramic processes

Clays represent the most important ceramic raw material. The industrial terms for ceramic clays are as follows.

China clay (porcelain earth): unconsolidated, composed principally of kaolinite with some quartz-bearing material. Alteration product of felspar-bearing rocks.

Fine china clay: fine-grained product obtained from china clay by washing out, air separation, flotation and electrophoresis.

Refractory clay: all types of clay with a melting point of at least 1,650°C (Seger cone 26).

White ware clay: plastic, refractory clay with white or yellowish fired colour. Composed predominantly of kaolinite with some illite and quartz.

Stoneware clay: plastic, refractory or non-refractory clay (felspar-free); sinters below pyrometric cone 10 (1,330°C); melting point is at least 5 pyrometric cones above the sintering temperature.

Ball clay: highly plastic clays of sedimentary origin which range from refractory to non-refractory. Colour varies from white to black depending on organic content. Clay mineral, livesite or poorly crystallized kaolinite with hydrous mica and quartz, finer-grained than china clay. Silica and alkali contents usually higher than in china clay.

Blue clay: highly plastic, refractory clay with a blue colour in the unburned state.

Saggar clay: plastic, refractory clay; used, on account of its thermal stability, as bonding clay in the manufacture of saggars.

Glass-pot clay: highly plastic, refractory clay with good binding properties and high dry-strength, which fires to a compact mass without appreciable fusion.

Shale: non-refractory argillaceous rock composed of kaolin, illite, sericite and variable amounts of quartz; used partly in brick manufacture. Washed dirt, refuse from coal washery plant; material consisting of shale and sandstone.

Red (glazing) clay: easily fusible, iron-bearing clay, used, without addition of other material, as a glaze for stoneware, etc.

Slip-clay: very fine-grained clay of varying fired colours, used for the unfused, white or coloured coating of ceramics.

Brick clays: non-refractory clays which fuse between 1,000 and 1,200°C, as a result of their high flux content (alkalis, lime, iron compounds). They are mainly composed of varying amounts of illite, kaolinite and montmorillonite. Other constituents: quartz, muscovite, felspar, biotite, hornblende, glauconite, pyrites, marcasite, iron oxides, organic substances.

Loams: mixtures of clay and sand with low fusion temperatures, due to a high iron and lime content [pyrometric (Seger) cone $4 = 1,020°C$]. Commonly used as a glaze for pottery and earthenware pipes. Often washed before processing.

BEHAVIOUR OF CLAY MINERALS IN RELATION TO WATER

Dry clays or clay minerals readily take up water on wetting. The absorbed water is driven off by heating to 100–200°C. Water absorption occurs in the following ways (Fig. 73):

(a) water is taken up in the spaces (pores) between single crystals or crystal aggregates (*pore water, planar water*);

(b) water flowing into the pores also becomes adsorbed on to the surfaces of the clay minerals (*adsorbed water*). The water molecules which occur at or very close to the mineral surfaces do not constitute a fluid phase, in the physical meaning of the term. This film differs, e.g. in density and viscosity, from normal water.

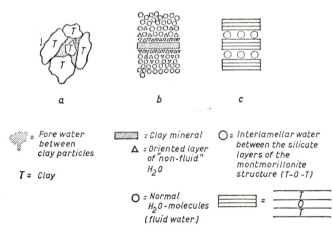

Figure 73 Types of water bound up in clays: (a) pore water, (b) adsorbed water ('non-fluid' water), (c) intra-crystalline swelling (interlamellar water).

As a result of the dipole nature of water molecules, the thin 'non-fluid' layers (~30 Å thick) are bonded to the negatively-charged surfaces of clay minerals in such a way that a kind of 'oriented overgrowth' of the molecules on clay minerals results. It is a state which cannot be termed fluid, but which shows a crystalline tendency, with a specific lattice arrangement. This ordered state exists, however, only in the immediate vicinity of the clay-mineral surface. The thicker the aqueous film surrounding the clay mineral, the less ordered it becomes towards the outside. With increasing distance from the clay-mineral surface, the 'non-fluid' water becomes increasingly like 'normal' water. The 'non-fluid' water layers have considerable technical importance; for example they are the reason for the plasticity of clays and they partly determine the consistency limits (plastic limit, yield point), shearing strength, permeability, drying, thixotropy, compressibility, suitability as additives in drilling fluids, green strength and dry strength of ceramic bodies, etc.

(c) Water penetrates between the composite sheets of the crystal structure and causes an expansion of these sheets. A large one-dimensional swelling of the lattice is thus produced (Fig. 72). Montmorillonoid minerals, in particular, are able to absorb interlamellar water. The quantity of interlamellar water is a function of the ambient water-vapour pressure and adjusts continuously to an equilibrium state. Minerals of the kaolin, illite and chlorite groups show only slight interlamellar expansion. This is structurally determined. The lower the degree of structural order of the minerals, the greater the ability to absorb interlamellar water.

THIXOTROPY

When some clay-mineral powders or clays are mixed with much water, they may, if the particle size is small enough, form suspensions, which, after standing for a while, set to gels (e.g. a suspension of 3% montmorillonite in water). The resultant masses are so rigid that they will not flow out on tilting the container. If, however, the container is shaken, the gel is re-converted into a fluid suspension. This conversion from a fluid to a solid state can be repeated indefinitely. The property of setting of a clay-mineral paste is known as thixotropy. The phenomenon may be explained by the hypothesis that suspended clay particles gradually take up positions of rest, which roughly correspond to a framework like that of a house of cards. The water molecules are enclosed within the interstices of this continuous framework so that they are no longer freely mobile. Any powerful shock will break down the framework and the moisture is free to move again (Fig. 74). Important in bore-hole drilling using muds, in geotechnics, and in filtration and sedimentation processes.

BEHAVIOUR OF CLAY MINERALS IN RELATION TO FOREIGN
IONS IN AQUEOUS SOLUTION (IONIC-EXCHANGE,
ERRONEOUSLY TERMED 'BASE-EXCHANGE')

Clay minerals are able to take up certain cations (e.g. Na^+, K^+, NH_4^+, H^+, Ca^{2+}, Mg^{2+} etc.) and anions (e.g. SO_4^{2-}, Cl^-, PO_4^{3-}, NO_3^-, etc.), and retain them in an exchangeable state, i.e. these ions may be exchanged for other anions or cations, if the clay minerals are treated with an aqueous solution of these ions (ionic-exchange is also possible occasionally under non-aqueous conditions). The exchangeable ions are attached to the surfaces of the clay particles and do not normally penetrate the structure. The ionic-exchange capacity is measured in milliequivalents/g or /100 g of clay mineral. Measurement is made at pH 7. (For example, 1 equivalent of Na^+, expressed as Na_2O, would have a combining weight of 31, since the molecular weight of Na_2O is 62. Thus 1 milliequivalent related to 100 g clay mineral is 0.031% Na_2O). The most common cations exchanged in this way are: Ca^{2+}, Mg^{2+}, H^+, K^+, NH_4^+, Na^+.

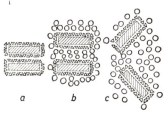

\ = Clay mineral

△ = Oriented, non-fluid layer of H_2O-molecules

○ = Normal, fluid H_2O-molecules

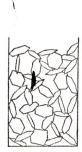

Figure 74 Framework of a thixotropically-set clay-mineral suspension. [Schematic].

Figure 75 (a) Clay particles strongly bonded together by oriented layers of water. (b) Clay particles in a plastic condition. (c) Clay particles in a clay–water suspension. [Schematic]

The phenomenon of ionic-exchange has a particular bearing on the plasticity of clays. Those with Na^+ as the exchangeable cation have, for example, different plastic properties to those with Ca^{2+} as the exchangeable cation.

Cation-exchange capacities:

Kaolinite   3–15   milliequivalents/100 g
Halloysite (2H$_2$O) 5–10   milliequivalents/100 g

Halloysite ($4H_2O$) 10–40 milliequivalents/100 g
Montmorillonite   80–150 milliequivalents/100 g
Illite   10–40 milliequivalents/100 g
Vermiculite   100–150 milliequivalents/100 g
Chlorite   10–40 milliequivalents/100 g

(Not only clay minerals, but all minerals in a state of extremely fine subdivision possess a certain cation-exchange capacity, as a result of the broken bonds at corners and edges of the particles). The rate of cation-exchange varies with the type of clay mineral, cation concentration and type and concentration of the anions:

Kaolinite: very rapid;
Montmorillonite and vermiculite: slow;
Illite and chlorite: very slow.

The nature of the exchangeable cations may often be determined approximately by measurement of the pH.

pH 9: Na^+;   pH 7.5: Ca^{2+};   pH 7: H^+;

Determinations of the anion-exchange capacities of three minerals are:

Montmorillonite 20–30 milliequivalents/100 g
Vermiculite   4 milliequivalents/100 g
Kaolinite   6–20 milliequivalents/100 g

Order of exchangeability of some cations and variation of properties:

$$H > Al > Ba > Sr > Ca > Mg > NH_4 > K > Na > Si$$

decreasing plasticity

decreasing viscosity

PLASTICITY

Clays become plastic, after standing for a short time, if they are mixed with liquids composed of polar molecules (e.g. water). (With non-polar liquids such as CCl_4, the mass does not become plastic.) The plasticity of clays is dependent upon the addition of a certain amount of water; three stages may be observed in the hydration of dry clay-mineral powders (Fig. 75):

(a) The water is bonded completely to the surfaces of the clay minerals in the form of an oriented film ('non-fluid water'). If the non-fluid water layers of two clay-mineral particles are immediately superposed, strong, fixed bonding between the particles results. This is a state which is very resistant to drying [Fig. 75(a)].

(ii) Non-silicate refractories
   1. Basic and neutral bricks.
   (1) Magnesite bricks. Raw materials: crystalline magnesite which
is dead-burned and then ground before being made into bricks. Composition: predominantly periclase, some forsterite and magnesio-
ferrite.
   (2) Chrome-magnesite bricks. Raw materials: 20–70% finely-
ground chromite and 80–30% calcined magnesite. Composition: periclase, chromite, some forsterite and monticellite ($CaO.MgO.SiO_2$).
Chrome-magnesite mixes: plastic masses composed of ~60% chromite, 30% calcined magnesite, 5–15% caustic magnesite and 1–5%
refractory clay or 1% water glass.
   (3) Chromite bricks. Raw materials: chromite with a binding agent
(gypsum, lime, calcined magnesite, bauxite, diaspore). Composition:
chromite grains set in a sintered cement. Chromite mixes: plastic masses
composed of ~80% chromite grains and binding clay (15% kaolin,
5% bentonite or others).
   (4) Dolomite bricks. Raw materials: dolomite is first dead-burned,
the clinker is then ground and made into bricks. SiO_2 is used as the
cementing agent. Composition: periclase, $3CaO.SiO_2$, $2CaO.SiO_2$, free
CaO in some cases. Tarred dolomite bricks and mixes: specially-
prepared tars are added to the burned dolomite.
   (5) Corundum (alumina) bricks. Raw materials: bauxite for the
manufacture of corundum (fusion-cast alumina) from a melt; calcined
alumina in the manufacture of corundum by sintering. The bricks are
manufactured from (a), corundum with refractory clay or kaolin as
the bonding agent or (b), corundum and pre-fired alumina as the bonding agent. Composition: corundum and possibly some glassy material.
   (6) Diaspore bricks. Raw materials: diaspore (with silica as an
impurity). Composition: mullite, glass phase.
   (7) Bauxite bricks. Raw materials: bauxite with kaolin and possibly CaO or MgO as bonding agents. Composition: corundum, spinel
($MgO.Al_2O_3$).

   2. Carbon-bearing bricks.
   (1) Silicon carbide bricks. Raw materials: quartz and carbon form
silicon carbide when heated to 2,000 °C in an electric arc furnace. SiC
bricks are bonded by 5–10% clay and also chamotte in some cases.
Composition: SiC grains, sintered clay (chamotte in some cases) cristobalite. Silicon carbide mixes: plastic masses composed of about 80–90%
SiC and 10–20% bonding clay.

(2) Carbon bricks and mixes. Raw materials: foundry coke or petroleum coke with a maximum ash content of 8%. As a bonding agent, tar used for steel-making purposes. Composition: coke grains bonded by a porous tar-coke framework.

(3) Graphite-bearing products. Raw materials: graphite, fireclay, highly-plastic, low-sintering clay. Composition: graphite, chamotte, sintered clay.

(D) INSULATING BRICKS

Raw materials: kieselguhr, vermiculite, perlite or asbestos as porous constituents, usually bonding clay and pore-forming materials which are burned off. Composition: fragments of porous materials (vermiculite, kieselguhr, perlite, asbestos, etc.) bonded by sintered clay.

7.1.4. Fine ceramics

(A) INDUSTRIAL CERAMICS

(i) Silicate ceramics

1. Fine earthenware (coloured and uncoloured). Raw materials: clays which sinter over a wide range of temperature and sufficient flux to ensure complete sintering. In some cases quartz and felspar. Raw materials for Berlin tiles: 50% marly clay, 30% sandy clay, 20% fine sand. Composition: sub-microscopic mullite and cristobalite crystals, limited glass phase, quartz.

2. Steatite bodies, steatite bricks. Raw materials: about 50% talc and clay, quartz, felspar, possibly corundum. Composition: predominantly small crystals of clino-enstatite and a small amount of glass.

$$\text{(Steatite} \xrightarrow{1,300°} \text{clino-enstatite} \xleftrightarrow{1,190°} \text{enstatite)}$$

3. Cordierite bodies, cordierite bricks. Raw materials: talc, clay, Al_2O_3 or clay, magnesite and chalcedony. Possibly also felspar and syenite (raw materials form cordierite on firing). Composition of the finished product: α-cordierite (α-2[Mg,Fe]0·2Al_2O_3.5SiO_2) with inclusions of corundum, a glass phase and β-cordierite. Zircon is added to some cordierite ceramics as a filler phase.

4. Felspar ceramics. See Dental porcelain.

(ii) Non-silicate ceramics

1. Titania materials. Raw materials: TiO_2 extracted from ilmenite, titanomagnetite or rutile; MgO or BaO as additives in some cases. Composition: rutile, barium titanate, magnesium titanate, strontium titanate, beryllium titanate, calcium titanate. $BeTiO_3$, $SrTiO_3$ and $CaTiO_3$ possess very high dielectric constants ($\varepsilon > 10,000$). Rutile: (parallel to the c-axis) $\varepsilon = 173$, (perpendicular to the c-axis) $\varepsilon = 89$.

2. Various structural materials formed of magnetite, manganoferrite, nickel ferrite, zinc ferrite and niobates and tantalates. Raw materials: corresponding ores (see the summary of important ores).

(B) PORCELAIN

1. Hard porcelain. Raw materials: 50% kaolin, 25% felspar, 25% quartz.

2. Soft porcelain. Raw materials: 20–40% kaolin, felspar, quartz, ball clay (Fig. 77); may contain glass frit as the flux requires lower temperature than hard porcelain.

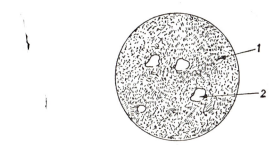

Figure 77 Soft porcelain (thin section): 1 = groundmass composed of fine needles of mullite and glass, 2 = quartz. [Schematic, × 100]

3. Bone china. Raw materials: 45% clay, 40% bone ash (calcium phosphate), 10% quartz, 5% felspar.

4. Dental porcelain (porcelain teeth). Raw materials: 70–80% felspar, 0–4% kaolin, 15–25% quartz, 0–2% marble.

5. Electrical porcelain. Raw materials: 10–30% china clay, 10–30% ball clay, 10–40% quartz and 10–40% felspar. Composition of the finished product: fine mullite derived from the clays, coarser mullite needles from the felspar and partially-dissolved quartz grains, set in glass, which is the dominant phase. Zircon or calcined bauxite may replace part or all of the quartz.

(C) REFRACTORY BODIES WITH AN OXIDE BASE

(i) Oxide ceramics

1. Alumina ceramics. Raw materials: purified calcined bauxite, MgO, CaO and in some cases refractory clay. Composition of the finished product: small crystals of corundum sintered together with spinel or glass phase.

2. Beryllia ceramics. Raw materials: calcined $Be(OH)_2$ extracted from beryl. Composition of the finished product: crystals of bromellite sintered together. Sintered BeO is the main form in which beryllia is used.

(ii) Cermets (ceramic–metal)

Cermets are compound bodies (see p. 133) made of ceramics (metal oxide, carbide, nitride, boride, silicide, etc.), and metals (tungsten, chromium, titanium, zircon, thorium, molybedenum, iron, etc.). Raw materials: corresponding ores (see the summary of important ores). Composition and microstructure (there are four possibilities): 1. metal particles are dispersed in the oxide phase; 2. oxide particles are dispersed in the metal phase; 3. oxide and metallic particles are homogeneously intermixed; 4. oxide and metallic phases form a solid solution.

(D) MATERIALS FOR USE UNDER EXTREME CONDITIONS

Aircraft and space-vehicles, military rockets, magnetohydrodynamic power generation, etc., demand ceramic and metallic materials with extremely high resistance to thermal, mechanical and chemical influences.

The following temperature ranges are encountered.

Aircraft	$-120°$ to $+1,100°C$
Manned space-vehicles	$-180°$ to $+2,000°C$
Intermediate ballistic missiles	$-230°$ to $+3,300°C$
Intercontinental ballistic missiles	$-270°$ to $+5,000°C$
Magnetohydrodynamic (MHD) generators	$1,000°$ to $3,000°C$

The groups of compounds shown in the table opposite are important (after Gugel).

	Melting temperature °C	Density g/cm³	Maximum service temperature (°C) Atmosphere	
			Oxidizing	Neutral and reducing
Borides				
TaB₂	3,150	12·6	1,200–1,400	
NbB₂	3,000	6·6	1,100–1,400	
ZrB₂	2,990	6·1	1,400	
TiB₂	2,900	4·5	1,100–1,700	
Carbides				
TaC	3,780	14·5	1,100–1,400	
ZrC	3,530	6·5	1,100	>2,200
TiC	3,160	4·9	1,100–1,400	3,000
WC	2,600	15·5	500	
B₄C	2,470	2·52	500	2,300
SiC	2,300 (subl.)	3·21	1,650	2,300
Cr₃C₂	1,890	6·7	1,100–1,400	
Nitrides				
BN (hex)	3,000 (subl.)	2·27	800	1,650
ZrN	2,980	7·3	1,100–1,400	
TiN	2,950	5·4	800–1,400	
AlN	2,230	3·25	800	
Si₃N₄	1,900 (subl.)	3·2	1,600	
Silicides				
TaSi₂	2,200	9·1	1,100–1,400	
WSi₂	2,160	9·3	1,400–1,700	
MoSi₂	2,050	6·2	1,700	
Cermets				
70Al₂O₃/30Cr		4·65	1,500	
80TiC/20Ni		5·8	1,200	
80SiC/2C/18Si		3·1	1,400	
Oxides				
ThO₂	3,300	9·7	2,700	good
MgO	2,800	3·5	2,400	2,000
ZrO₂	2,690	5·8	2,500	2,200
CaO	2,560		2,400	>1,400
BeO	2,530	3·0	2,400	very good

κ

7.2. Glasses and enamels

7.2.1. The glassy state

THE STRUCTURE OF GLASS

Glasses: compact, physically-homogeneous and amorphous materials. They represent frozen liquids (non-crystalline) with a corresponding atomic structure, normally formed of a network of SiO_4 tetrahedra which are bonded together by shared oxygen atoms (Figs. 78, 79). Oxides, such as SiO_2 which are essential for glass formation are termed *glass-formers or network-formers*. Oxides which possess no glass-forming properties may also occur in glasses. By their inclusion in the glass network these may produce a greater or lesser degree of modification of the properties of the glass and are called *network-modifiers* or *modifiers* (Fig. 80). A further group of oxides may act both as glass-formers and as modifiers. These elements cannot form glasses on their own but are able in part to replace Si^{4+} isomorphously and are known as *intermediate ions*.

Network-formers: Si^{4+}, Ge^{4+}, Sb^{4+}, As^{3+}, B^{3+}, P^{5+}.

Network-modifiers: Ca^{2+}, S^{2+}, Ba^{2+}, Li^+, Na^+, K^+, Rb^+, Cs^+.

Intermediate ions: predominantly network-formers if they partially replace Si^{4+}: Ti^{4+}, S^{4+}, Al^{3+}, Zr^{4+}.

Partly glass-formers, partly modifiers: Fe^{3+}, Be^{2+}, Mg^{2+}, Ni^{2+}, Zn^{2+}, C^{4+}, Fe^{2+}.

Predominantly modifier: Pb^{2+}.

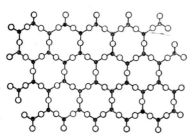

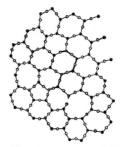

Figure 78   The arrangement of SiO_4 tetrahedra in quartz crystals.

Figure 79   Arrangement of SiO_4 tetrahedra in an SiO_2 glass.

The consequences of the structurally-disordered state of glasses, in contrast to crystals, are: (i) isotropy; (ii) reversible softening and hardening, i.e. on freezing, no crystals separate out as a distinct phase;

Figure 80 Arrangement of SiO_4 tetrahedra and Na^+-ions (shaded circles) in a soda-silicate glass.

no definite melting point, but softening and hardening occur gradually over a range of temperatures (the viscosity of glass melts is temperature-dependent); (iii) the existence of a transformation range (**transformation temperature, transformation point**). In this temperature range (extending over about 50–100 °C) the properties of glass, which becomes plastic, change greatly. It is then in a supercooled liquid state, which, in its equilibrium condition, lags behind the temperature.

Change of the properties of glass on heating

State of the glass	Consistency	Change of properties	
Normal glass	Elastic and brittle	Gradual	increasing temperature
Transformation range	Plastic	Sudden	
Melt	Viscous	Gradual	

DEVITRIFICATION

Almost all glasses may, in a certain time and on the appropriate thermal treatment, be converted to a crystalline state (the state of lowest free-energy). The tendency of glasses to crystallize occurs exclusively above the transformation point, in which condition the elements of the network have a certain mobility. The critical range for devitrification of an undercooled melt occurs at a viscosity of 10^4 poises. Both the tendency to crystallize and the crystal growth velocity are a function of, among other factors, the chemical composition of the glass. Crystallization is more likely and occurs earlier the closer the composition of the glass corresponds to that of a specific compound, which on eventual crystallization can separate out as a single crystalline phase. The tendency of a glass to devitrify or for crystallization of a melt is dependent on the development of nuclei, which may form in places of relatively high order in the glassy network because the nucleation energy is lowest in these regions. The nucleation capacity reaches a maximum (i.e. maximum number of nuclei are formed) within a certain temperature range; a range of maximum linear growth velocity (the fastest growth of the already-formed nuclei) also occurs. In most cases the temperature of maximum nucleation capacity is lower than that of the maximum growth velocity (Fig. 81).

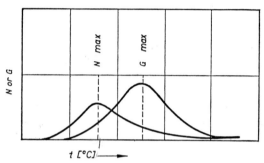

Figure 81 The formation of nuclei (N) and linear growth velocity (G) as a function of temperature.

SURFACE TENSION

The valence forces of molecules or atoms occurring at surfaces are satisfied, predominantly, only in the direction of the interior of the substance. In the interior of the substance (liquid) the valence forces are satisfied on all sides. The surface tension of silicate melts in contact with air is of the same order of magnitude as that of molten metals. It is 3 or 4 times the value for water and is greater than that of molten salts. With increasing temperature the surface tension decreases. It is also strongly influenced by the contiguous medium. If the surface tension of a material against the contiguous medium is small, it can be easily wetted by this medium. If the surface tension against the medium is high, the wettability is poor. Corrosion of refractory material by glass melts is accelerated by good wettability.

The surface tension of silicate melts is modified greatly by additions of: As_2O_3, V_2O_5, WO_3, MoO_3, Cr_2O_3, SO_3.

The surface tension is only slightly modified by: SiO_2, TiO_2, ZrO_2, SnO_2, Al_2O_3, BeO, MgO, CaO, SrO, BaO, ZnO, CdO, MnO, Mn_2O_3, Fe_2O_3, FeO, CoO, NiO, Li_2O, Na_2O, CaF_2.

The following oxides have an intermediate character: K_2O, PbO, B_2O_3, Sb_2O_3, P_2O_5.

Compounds which reduce the surface tension are concentrated in the surface layer and the composition of the surface, therefore, deviates from that of the main body of the glass melt.

7.2.2. Raw materials for glass manufacture

NETWORK-FORMING RAW MATERIALS

SiO_2 in the form of quartz sand, rock crystal, quartzite, felspar sand. A grain size of 0·1–0·4 mm is preferred. The highest possible purity is usually necessary. No iron.

Boric acid: kernite, colemanite, ulexite, pandermite, borax, boracite, sassolite, tincalonite.

Phosphoric acid, As_2O_3 and Sb_2O_3 are manufactured from the corresponding raw materials.

NETWORK-MODIFYING RAW MATERIALS

Na_2O and K_2O: mostly as carbonates (K_2O also as KNO_3), which are manufactured from the corresponding raw materials. Li_2O: as Li_2CO_3, obtained from spodumene or lithium mica.

CaO: limestone, dolomite, anorthite.

BaO: witherite, barytes.

SrO: strontianite, celestite.

MnO: psilomelane, pyrolusite, hausmannite, manganite.

RAW MATERIALS WITH NETWORK-FORMING AND MODIFYING PROPERTIES (INTERMEDIATE COMPONENTS)

Al_2O_3: extracted from bauxite or as additions of albite, anorthite, orthoclase. For poor-quality glasses: porphyrite, nepheline syenite and other materials.

Zirconium: zircon.

MgO: dolomite.

7.2.3. Faults in glass (inhomogeneities)

STRAINING OF GLASS LEADS TO OPTICAL ANISOTROPY

The glass becomes doubly refracting (detected with polarized light).

GASEOUS INCLUSIONS

Air bubbles or gas formed by the dissociation of carbonates, sulphates or hydrates.

STRIAE (FINE CORDS) AND KNOTS (GLASSY INHOMOGENEITIES)

These are recognizable by the fact that they possess a different refractive index to the rest of the glass body. This is caused by local variation of the chemical composition or variable quenching temperature.

STONES (CRYSTALLINE INHOMOGENEITIES)

Cause: incomplete solution of the frit constituents, partial solution of the tank refractories, local de-vitrification. Constituents of stones: small, incompletely-dissolved quartz grains (consisting partly of cristobalite and tridymite), clay particles (partly altered to mullite), corundum and β-Al_2O_3 (mostly from refractory material), nepheline (reaction between glass and refractory), tridymite, cristobalite, devitrite ($Na_2O.3CaO.6SiO_2$), wollastonite, diopside, Cr_2O_3, mullite, etc.; also free iron and lead in some cases.

7.2.4. Enamels

Materials formed from melts or frits (partially-fused mixtures), predominantly glassy with an inorganic, mainly oxidic composition, which, in one or more layers (partly with additives), are fused *on to metallic surfaces*.

RAW MATERIALS

The basic materials for glass formation (the most important constituent of enamels): quartz sand, borax, soda, potash, saltpetre, alkaline earth carbonates, felspar.

Mill addition (to form a slip which can easily be applied to the body): clays and water.

Colouring agents: cobalt oxide, iron oxide, cadmium sulphide, chromium oxide, titanium oxide, tin oxide and various mixtures of these oxides. Manufactured from the corresponding ores.

Main opacifying agents: tin oxide, antimony oxide, arsenic oxide, cerium oxide, zinc oxide, titanium oxide. Opacifying agents already melted in the frit: fluorides of Na, K and Al.

Adhesives: cobalt oxide, nickel oxide, manganese oxide, molybdenum oxide.

FAULTS IN ENAMELS

Crazing, peeling, bubbles (through the formation of gases, foams, dissociation of cementite in cast-iron), discoloration (e.g. by iron impurities).

7.2.5. Glazes

Thin, glassy, coatings applied to the surfaces of ceramic bodies in order, for example, to facilitate cleaning, increase mechanical strength, make a porous ceramic impervious. The glass-forming oxide is essentially SiO_2, maybe with BaO_3 and P_2O_5. Usually applied by spraying or by dipping the ceramic into a suspension of the glass-forming oxides in water. Subsequent firing produces a viscous glass. Salt glazing is an example of vapour glazing, where the glaze is formed by reaction of vapour (from sodium chloride and water) with the ceramic during firing. Raw materials include: flint, quartz, borax, china clay, chalk. Common oxides include SiO_2, B_2O_3, P_2O_5, Al_2O_3, CaO, MgO, BaO, ZnO, PbO, Na_2O, K_2O.

Compositions of glazes. They are extremely varied depending on the individual requirements such as type of glaze, composition of the ceramic body, firing temperature and the use to which the ceramic is to be put. Glaze applied to unfired (green) ceramic must mature under the same conditions as the ceramic; glaze applied to fired (biscuit) ceramic can be matured at a temperature lower than that at which the ceramic has already been fired. The glaze should 'fit' the ceramic as the whole cools down after firing. The thermal expansion of the glaze should be close to but less than that of the ceramic; if it is too low the glaze will 'peel'; if too high, crazing will result. A certain amount of reaction between the ceramic body and the glaze is essential.

TYPES OF GLAZES

Clear and opaque glazes have a characteristic high gloss; a matt glaze, in addition to being more or less opaque, has a matt finish. Colouring agents may be introduced; the colour may be in the glass or the crystal phase.

Clear glaze

The ceramic body may be seen through it.

Opaque glaze

Produced by the presence of a fine-grained opacifier such as cassiterite or zircon (high refractive index) so that light is scattered by each crystal fragment in the glaze.

Matt glaze

Fine-grained devitrification, due to an increase in the proportions of MgO, CaO, Al_2O_3, ZnO, etc., or to the addition of a nucleating agent such as ground rutile, forms on slower cooling.

Crystalline glaze

Requires very slow cooling to allow coarser crystal growth, for decorative purposes.

Specialized glazes

Glazes on electrical porcelain may be made electrically insulating or semi-conducting by use of the appropriate oxides. These are a type of opaque glaze or a combination of an opaque and a matt glaze.

7.3. Raw and constructional materials for nuclear reactors

7.3.1. Raw materials

(A) FISSIONABLE AND BREEDER FUELS FOR NUCLEAR REACTORS

Uranium ores

Natural uranium is a mixture of the isotopes: U^{234} 0·0058%, U^{235} 0·71% (*fissionable*) and U^{238} 99·28%.

Pitchblende (varieties are named ultrichite and uraninite). Formula is approximately UO_2 (46–88% uranium). Usually 0·2% Th-content (may vary up to 45%).

Autunite (lime uranite, calcium uranium mica): $CaO.2UO_3.P_2O_5.10–12H_2O$ (58–63% UO_3).

Torbernite (copper uranite, copper uranium mica): $CuO.2UO_3.P_2O_5.8–12H_2O$ (57–61% UO_3).

Carnotite: $K_2O.2UO_3.2V_2O_5.3H_2O$ (50–65% UO_3).

Additional uranium ores: gummite ($UO_2.nH_2O$), coffinite $[U(SiO_4)_{1-x}(OH_x)]$, tujamunite ($CaO.2UO_3.V_2O_5.H_2O$), zippeite ($2UO_3.SO_3.nH_2O$), uranophane ($CaO.2UO_3.2SiO_2.6H_2O$), beta-uranotile ($CaO.2UO_3.2SiO_2.6H_2O$), sklodowskite ($MgO.2UO_3.2SiO_2.6H_2O$), complex urano-organic compounds (e.g. thucholite).

Thorium ores (no naturally-occurring fissionable isotope. Breeder fuel)

Monazite: $(Ce,Th)PO_4.ThO_2$-content up to 28%.

Thorite: $ThSiO_4$. 49–79% ThO_2.

Thorianite: $(Th,U)O_2$. Forms continuous series of mixed crystals with pitchblende (UO_2).

(B) FUEL-ELEMENT CASING

Aluminium: bauxite.

Magnesium: magnesite, dolomite, magnesium salts from sea water, salt deposits and salt lakes.

Zirconium: zircon; invariably contains HfO_2.
Beryllium: beryl; 11–13% BeO.
Niobium: columbite.

(C) MODERATING AND REFLECTING MATERIALS

Graphite with less than 0·002% ash and a boron content $<1.10^{-5}\%$.
Beryllium: beryl.

(D) CONTROLLING AND REGULATING DEVICES

Boron: kernite, ulexite, colemanite, pandermite.
Cadmium: zincblende, wurtzite, smithsonite (contain small amounts of Cd).
Hafnium: zircon (invariably contains Hf).
Rare earths (europium, gadolinium, scandium): monazite, the basic material for thorium extraction, always contains small proportions of these elements.

(E) COOLING MATERIALS

Sodium: salts of Na (common salt).
Potassium: potassium salts.
Bismuth: from ores of Pb, Zn, Au, W and Sn, in which it occurs in small quantities.

(F) STRUCTURAL MATERIALS

Beryllium: beryl.
Zirconium: zircon.
Molybdenum, magnesium, aluminium, nickel, titanium, vanadium, chronium, iron and copper: see the summary of important ores.

(G) RADIATION SCREENING MATERIALS

Heavy concrete: raw-materials for cement (q.v.) with addition of magnetite, hematite, colemanite and borocalcite; in some cases barytes or lead.

7.3.2. Crystallographic data for reactor metals

FUEL AND BREEDER MATERIALS

Uranium shows three modifications:

α-phase: orthorhombic, stable up to 660 °C;
β-phase: tetragonal, stable from 660–760 °C;
γ-phase: cubic, stable from 760–1,133 °C (melting point).

The transformation from the $\alpha \rightarrow \beta$ phase is associated with a volume increase.

Thorium shows two modifications:

Low-temperature form: cubic, stable up to 1,400°C.
High-temperature form: cubic, stable from 1,400°C to 1,842°C (melting point).

Plutonium shows six modifications:

α-phase: monoclinic, stable up to 122°C, D: 19·82;
β-phase: stable between 122°C and 206°C;
γ-phase: orthorhombic, stable from 206°C to 319°C, D: 17·14;
δ-phase: cubic, stable from 319°C to 451°C, D: 15·92;
δ'-phase: tetragonal, stable from 451°C to 478°C, D: 16·00;
ε-phase: cubic, stable from 478°C to 670°C (melting point), D: 16·51.

The α-phase is the densest. On heating, the metal contracts between 450°C and 670°C.

OTHER IMPORTANT REACTOR METALS

Aluminium: cubic.

Magnesium: hexagonal.

Zirconium: two modifications: α-zirconium, hexagonal, stable up to 863°C; β-zirconium, cubic, stable between 863°C and 1,853°C (melting point).

Beryllium: hexagonal.

Niobium: cubic [capable of absorbing a large gas volume ('getter')].

Graphite: hexagonal; can be converted to a trigonal form by mechanical working.

Boron: two co-existing phases, tetragonal and hexagonal.

Cadmium: hexagonal.

Hafnium: two modifications. Low-temperature phase: hexagonal, stable up to 1,980°C. High-temperature phase: cubic, stable between 1,980°C and 2,130°C (melting point).

Titanium: two modifications. α-Titanium: hexagonal, stable up to 882°C. β-Titanium: cubic, stable between 882°C and 1,690°C (melting point).

Vanadium: cubic.

Molybdenum: cubic.

7.4. Bonding materials

7.4.1. Materials which harden spontaneously in air

(A) LOAM

Unconsolidated rock, which, in addition to clay minerals, contains subsidiary amounts of fine quartz grains. The characteristics of the material vary according to the proportion and type of clay present.

Types of clay-minerals in loam	Behaviour in relation to water	
Montmorillonite	} Absorption of water + interlamellar swelling	} Ionic-exchange
Kaolinite Illite	} Absorption of water	

Highly-plastic loams with high clay-mineral contents are termed 'fat' or 'strong' clays.

Low-plasticity loams with only small proportions of clay minerals are termed 'short' or 'lean' clays.

The hardening of loam on drying is a process connected with the cohesion of the clay-mineral particles and colloidal shrinkage phenomena. The process is reversible by re-wetting the loam. Shortening materials: sand, crushed bricks, straw, wood shavings, etc. (see Fig. 75).

(B) PLASTERS

Burned and unburned products made from gypsum and anhydrite.

Differentiated according to the degree of dehydration.

Gypsum $CaSO_4.2H_2O$

Crystal system: monoclinic; water content 20·92%.

Converted at 100–115°C to the β-hemi-hydrate, and, under pressure, to the α-hemi-hydrate.

α-Hemi-hydrate $CaSO_4.0·5H_2O$

Crystal system: monoclinic. Converted at 110°C to α-anhydrite III.

α-Hemi-hydrate, on hardening, possesses a significantly higher strength than β-hemi-hydrate.

β-Hemi-hydrate $CaSO_4.0.5H_2O$

Changes to *β*-anhydrite III between 140°C and 200°C.

(*Soluble*) *α-anhydrite III* $CaSO_4$

Crystal system: hexagonal. Changes at 250°C to anhydrite II (insoluble, naturally-occurring anhydrite).

(*Soluble*) *β-anhydrite III* $CaSO_4$

Crystal system: hexagonal. Changes at 250°C to anhydrite II (*α*-anhydrite III and *β*-anhydrite III are very similar to one another).

Anhydrite II (*insoluble, naturally-occurring*) $CaSO_4$

Crystal system: orthorhombic. Changes at 1,193°C to high-temperature anhydrite I. $CaSO_4$ dissociates to CaO and SO_3 above about 1,200°C and above 800°C, if impurities are present.

Anhydrite I (*high-temperature*) $CaSO_4$, melts at 1,450°C

The water solubilities of the various modifications and the degrees of dehydration are of the greatest importance for the commercial use of plaster. The setting at low temperatures is connected with the low solubility of pure gypsum as compared with hemi-hydrate and anhydrite III. *α*-Hemi-hydrate is less soluble than *β*-hemi-hydrate. Anhydrite III has the same effective solubility as hemi-hydrate, because anhydrite III hydrates immediately it comes into contact with water.

7.4.2. Lime mortars

Made by burning natural carbonate rocks below the fusion temperature.

Definitions: lime = CaO, limestone = $CaCO_3$, quicklime = $CaO + H_2O$.

Raw materials: limestone, dolomite, marl.

Thermal behaviour:

$$\text{Limestone } CaCO_3 \xrightarrow{880°C} CaO + CO_2$$
$$\text{Dolomite } CaMg(CO_3)_2 \xrightarrow{780-880°C} MgO + CaO + 2CO_2$$

Marl: the carbonate components each dissociate according to their compositions. The clay minerals dissociate into SiO_2, Al_2O_3 and iron oxides between 500°C and 900°C. Reactions occur in the solid state between CaO and iron oxides, Al_2O_3 and SiO_2.

After moderate burning, marl itself reacts only slowly with water.

Lime mortars may harden in air (air-setting lime) or with water (hydraulic).

Air-setting lime hardens in air but not in water. White lime and dolomitic lime belong to this latter type (see Fig. 82).

7.4.3. Bonding materials which do not harden spontaneously in air

(A) HYDRAULIC BONDING MATERIALS (HYDRAULIC MORTARS)

(i) Raw materials
Most hydraulic mortars consist of a non-hydraulic basic component
(lime and magnesia) and an acid hydraulic component (clays, marls,
siliceous limestones, sand, pozzolanas) (see Fig. 83).

1. Marl. The most suitable raw material for cements, since it contains
both the acid and basic components (see Fig. 82).

2. Dolomitic marls. Contain dolomite instead of calcium carbonate.

3. Siliceous limestones (cherty limestones). Very suitable for the
manufacture of hydraulic lime mortars.

4. Clays as hydraulic agents. The following are important: montmorillonite, kaolinites and illites, which contain only a small amount of
sulphides and magnesium (for Portland cement). A further requirement
is that only moderate alkali-contents should occur.

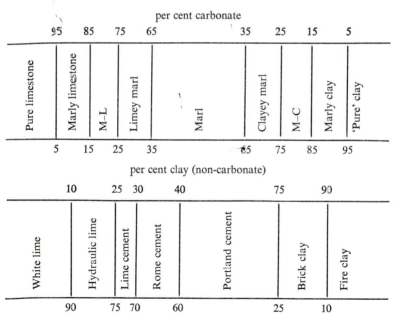

Figure 82 Composition of marls and clays and their use as raw materials for
cements or ceramics (after Correns).

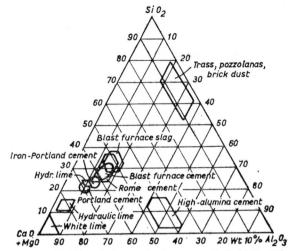

Figure 83 Position of cements in the system CaO–Al₂O₃–SiO₂.

5. Supplementary raw materials for hydraulic-deficient agents: sand, siliceous sinter, bauxite (also the principal raw materials for high-alumina cements), iron ores such as hematite, limonite, siderite, calcined pyrites (roasted pyrites).

6. Pozzolanas. These materials have no cementing properties on their own but when mixed with hydraulic bonding materials they improve the setting properties of the latter.

Natural pozzolanas: trachytic tuffs, dacite, tuffs, kieselguhr, diatomaceous earths, gaize (weathered siliceous rock occurring in limestone deposits).

Artificial pozzolanas: blast furnace slag, Si-material (siliceous residue in the production of aluminium), lignite flue-dust, coal flue-dust.

(ii) Cements

In the manufacturing process the raw materials are ground to a fine powder or slurry and sintered at 1,400°C–1,500°C. The resultant cement clinker, in which crystalline phases (clinker phases) have formed, is finely ground to the cement powder.

1. *Clinker phases.* In the cement industry, the chemical formulae of the oxides are usually abbreviated as follows:

$CaO = C$, $MgO = M$, $Al_2O_3 = A$, $SiO_2 = S$, $K_2O = K$,
$Na_2O = N$, $Fe_2O_3 = F$, $P_2O_5 = P$, $H_2O = H$, $TiO_2 = T$;
e.g. $CA = CaO.Al_2O_3$, $CS = CaO.SiO_2$,
$C_4AF = 4CaO.Al_2O_3.Fe_2O_3$

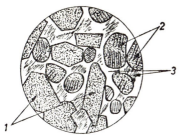

Figure 84 Portland cement clinker (section): 1 = C₃S, 2 = C₂S, 3 = interstitial material comprised of light-coloured constituents of C₄AF and dark constituents of C₄AF. [Schematic, × 500]

Figure 85 Melilite crystals (1) in a smelting slag. (Thin section, schematic, × 30

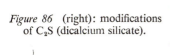

Figure 86 (right): modifications of C₂S (dicalcium silicate).

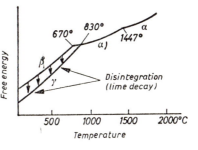

(1) Processes occurring in the firing of cement raw materials to cement clinker. Dehydration: evaporation of adsorbed water at 100–200°C. Clay minerals lose their OH-groups between 400°C and 900°C. Deoxidation: decomposition of dolomite above 700°C, decomposition of calcium carbonate above 900°C. Commencement of reactions in the solid state above 700°C: half the limestone of the raw material for Portland cement enters into newly-formed compounds before the last CO_2 molecules are evolved. The order of formation of the new phases (from left to right) is:

(CA), (CF), (CS), (C₅A₃), β-C₂S, C₃A, C₄AF. The bracketed compounds undergo still further change. Sintering and solid/liquid reactions above about 1,350°C: above 1,400°C melting occurs with the formation of C₂S and C₃S. The method and rate of cooling after firing strongly influence the formation and type of the clinker phases.

(2) Crystal phases in clinker (Fig. 84). Alite: most important constituent. Predominantly composed of C₃S (tricalcium silicate = 3CaO.SiO₂), 58.3% CaO + 41·7% SiO₂. C₃S takes up between 4% and 7% C₃A (tricalcium aluminate) in solid solution and also some MgO.

Properties of C_3S important to its use as cement: rapid setting, high heat of hydration, C_3S exhibits four modifications, which depend on temperature (α, β γ, δ).

Belite: most important constituent is C_2S (dicalcium silicate = $2CaO.SiO_2$), $65 \cdot 1\%$ CaO + $34 \cdot 9\%$ SiO_2. C_2S exhibits four modifications:

α-C_2S stable between 2,130°C (melts) and 1,447°C, trigonal;

α'-C_2S (bredigite) stable between 1,447°C and 830°C, orthorhombic;

γ-C_2S (calc-olivine) stable below 830°C, orthorhombic;

β-C_2S (larnite) metastable phase, monoclinic, from which γ-C_2S forms irreversibly below 670°C. Causes crumbling (see section 7.5.1(d) and Fig. 86).

Small quantities of aluminates, ferrites, etc. also occur in belite as solid solutions. Properties of C_2S: slow, gradual setting, low heat of hydration.

Celite: predominantly composed of C_4AF (brownmillerite is tetra-calcium aluminoferrite, $4CaO.Al_2O_3,Fe_2O_3$, $46 \cdot 1\%$ CaO + $21 \cdot 9\%$ Al_2O_3 + $32 \cdot 0\%$ Fe_2O_3). Additional constituents are especially C_3A (tricalcium aluminate, $3CaO.Al_2O_3$, cubic, $62 \cdot 3\%$ CaO + $37 \cdot 7\%$ Al_2O_3) and C_2F (dicalcium ferrite, $2CaO.Fe_2O_3$ = $31 \cdot 3\%$ CaO + $58 \cdot 7\%$ Fe_2O_3) and 2–3% MgO. Properties important to their use in cements: C_4AF causes slow setting and high resistance to sulphate solutions; C_3A; rapid initial setting, limited resistance to sulphate solutions, in large quantities it causes rapid setting.

Glass: consists of several phases, among which C_3A especially occurs, in part in the form of crystals. Fills the interstices between the crystalline clinker phases. Properties important to its use in cements; rapid initial setting, limited resistance to attack by sulphate solutions, in large quantities causes rapid setting.

The following constituents, among others, also occur:

Lime, CaO: always contained in small amounts in clinker. Important characteristics: harmless in small quantities; in large quantities it causes the blowing of mortar due to slaking and the consequent volume expansion and this greatly reduces the strength.

Periclase, MgO: small quantities often occur in solid solution in C_4AF and in glass. Important properties relevant to cements: under certain conditions larger quantities, as free MgO, cause magnesia-blowing after some years. This may have a catastrophic effect on the strength. Only free MgO is dangerous.

Mean composition of cement:

$C_3S = 45\%$; $C_3A = 12\%$; $C_2S = 25\%$; $C_4AF = 9\%$

Remainder: C, M, $CaSO_4$, Alkalis, H_2O.

2. *Cement setting.* Controlled by complicated reactions involving the hydration and hydrolysis of the clinker phases in the presence of water. The principal constituents of Portland cement (C_3S and C_2S) react with water to form a calcium silicate hydrate (tobermorite gel) and $Ca(OH)_2$. If free CaO occurs, hydration accompanied by expansion may lead to 'lime-blowing'. Reaction of the hydrated C_3A with gypsum produces calcium monosulphoaluminate (cement bacillus) which causes retardation of the setting process and 'gypsum-blowing' in set cement, through the formation of ettringite ($3CaO.Al_2O_3.3CaSO_4.31H_2O$). Free MgO in the form of periclase needs a long time for hydration and leads to 'magnesia-blowing' in set cement. The hydration products of cement are crystallites or amorphous gels. In the hydration process, water first of all reacts very rapidly with the surface zones of the cement grains and then advances slowly into the interior of the clinker-phase grains. C_3A forms crystalline hydroaluminates such as e.g. $3CaO-Al_2O_3-H_2O$.

3. *Concrete and mortar.* Manufactured from bonding agents (cement) and aggregates. Concrete: large, coarse particles occur in the aggregate. Mortar: fine-grained aggregate.

(1) Heavy concrete (cement and dense aggregate).

Natural dense aggregates: sand, gravel, grit, particles of natural stone (granite, diorite, gabbro, basalt, dolerite, quartz porphyry, porphyry, quartzite, limestone, greywacke, sandstone, etc.).

Synthetic heavy aggregates: blast furnace slag, clinker fragments, syntholite, iron and steel scrap, corundum, silicon carbide.

(2) Light-weight concrete (cement and light aggregates).

Natural light-weight aggregates: pumice, scoriaceous lava, tuffaceous rocks, wood wool, etc.

Synthetic light-weight aggregates: granulated blast furnace slag, porous blast furnace slag, granules made from coal flue-dust, refuse slag, fired clays and shales, sintered pumice, hollow clay spheres, synthoporrite, etc.

(3) Concrete for nuclear reactors. Magnetite and hematite, principally, are used as the heavy aggregate. Boron minerals such as colemanite ($Ca_2B_6O_{11}.5H_2O$) and borocalcite ($CaB_4O_7.4H_2O$) are also used.

4. *High-alumina cements.* In contrast to the normal cement (Portland cement), these are alumina-bearing cements, which are manufactured by fusing or sintering a mixture of bauxite and limestone and grinding the resultant clinker. Chemical composition: 35–55% Al_2O_3, 35–45% CaO, 5–10% SiO_2, 1–15% Fe_2O_3.

The most important clinker phase is calcium aluminate ($CaO.Al_2O_3$),

L

which sets very rapidly. Additional phases are dicalcium silicate, gehlenite and pentacalcium trialuminate ($5CaO.3Al_2O_3$).

5. *Sorel cement.* Consists of dead-burned magnesite (predominantly MgO, therefore), which, on addition of $MgCl_2$-solution, sets to a rock-hard mass.

7.5. Smelting industry

7.5.1. Smelting slags (blast furnace slags) and steel slags

Smelting slags are formed in metallurgical processes by complete melting of the non-metallic compounds of ores in the smelting furnaces. *Ferrous smelting slags* are distinguished from *non-ferrous smelting slags*. In *steel slags*, the impurities of the scrap and pig iron exist in a molten state. They occur in much smaller amounts than those of blast furnace slags.

(A) BLAST FURNACE SLAGS

Iron ores ⟨ Pig iron
⟨ Iron blast furnace slag (lime-silicate slag)

SiO_2 28–38%, Al_2O_3 6–17%, FeO up to 3%, Fe_2O_3 —, MnO 0–10%, CaO 35–48%, MgO 2–11%, P_2O_5 up to 1%, alkalis 3–5%.

Copper ores ⟨ Copper matte
⟨ Copper slag (lime-silicate slag)

SiO_2 44–50%, Al_2O_3 15–19%, FeO 3–50%, Fe_2O_3 —, MnO up to 0·3%, CaO 16–22%, MgO 6–9%, alkalis 3–5%, CuO up to 15%, ZnO 5%, S up to 5%, Pb up to 4%, Sn up to 10%.

Lead ores ⟨ Crude lead
⟨ Lead slag (iron-silicate slag)

SiO_2 17–35%, Al_2O_3 0–10%, FeO 21–50%, Fe_2O_3 —, MnO up to 2·4%, CaO 2–22%, MgO 1%, ZnO often up to 30%, PbO up to 3%, CuO up to 2·5%, BaO up to 9%, S up to 12%.

(B) DIRECT-PROCESS SLAGS

Cupola furnace slags, formed when pig iron is remelted with scrap, can also be considered to be a type of blast furnace slag.

Iron ores ⟨ Ball iron
⟨ Direct-process slag (aluminium-silicate slag)

SiO_2 50–62%, Al_2O_3 17–22%, FeO 1–6%, MnO 0·2–1·3%, CaO 7–15%, MgO 1–7%.

(C) STEEL-MAKING SLAGS

Pig iron ⟨ Basic converter steel (Thomas steel)
         ⟨ Basic slag (lime-phosphate slag)

SiO_2 6–8%, Al_2O_3 1–3%, FeO 7–10%, Fe_2O_3 5–6%,
MnO 4–6%, CaO 45–50%, MgO 1–4%, P_2O_5 15–20%.

Pig iron
+   ⟨ Open-hearth steel (Siemens–Martin steel)
scrap   ⟨ Basic or acid open-hearth slag (iron-silicate slags)

Basic open-hearth slag: SiO_2 10–25%, Al_2O_3 up to 3%,
FeO 6–21%, Fe_2O_3 1–10%,
MnO 6–15%, CaO + MgO 35–50%, P_2O_5 up to 30%.

(D) MINERALOGICAL PROPERTIES AND CHARACTERIZATION OF FERROUS AND NON-FERROUS SLAGS

(i) *Ferrous blast-furnace slags*

Such slags become glassy when cooled quickly and largely crystalline if cooled slowly. They possess a low thermal conductivity and have a strong corrosive effect on refractory materials and iron.

Glassy slags: Smelting sand (*slag sand*) is composed of small grains of glassy slag, which may be either colourless or yellow, light brown, dark brown, light grey, dark grey, greenish, pink or bluish. The colour is determined by the nature of the impurities, e.g. 0·5–1% FeO: greenish; about 2% FeO: distinctly greenish; high MnO-content: green; FeS-content: grey or opaque; thiocyanogen-content: reddish to dark brown. The higher the SiO_2-content, the more completely is the material in the glassy state. Refractive index $n = 1·63–1·66$. For manganese and iron-rich slag $n =$ up to $1·70$; n increases with increasing CaO-content. Slag sands with $n < 1·65$ are less suitable for cement manufacture since their hydraulic properties are more limited. The good grindability often required of slag sands is promoted by cracking and porosity of the glass. On storing, glassy slags absorb water (up to 15%) and carbonic acid (up to 8%), thereby reducing the refractive index is to less than 1·60. The hydraulic setting capacity (use as cement) is dependent on the chemical composition, the temperature of formation, proportion of glass, grain-size and the type and amount of the accelerator used. Used for bonding materials (cement) and granulated-slag bricks.

Foamed slag is a porous material produced by frothing of the liquid blast furnace slag. The foaming promotes the fluidity and ductility of the slag ('hot, long slags') as also does a suitable chemical composition

(SiO_2 32–60%, Al_2O_3 0–35%, CaO + MgO + MnO + FeO 35–53%; slags which are particularly readily foamed are SiO_2 40–55%, Al_2O_3 10–25%. CaO + MgO + FeO 35–50%). Colours: yellow, red, blue, brown, green. Sintering commences at 1,200°C, melting point is 1,270°C. Grain-porosity: light-weight foamed slag 80–90%, medium 60–70%; dense ~50%. Uses: filler, light-weight concrete, thermal and sound insulation.

Slag-wool is a mass of intertwined, glassy, slag fibres drawn from small beads of molten slag. The smaller the proportion of beads contained in the wool and the smaller the fibre thickness, the better is the quality of the wool. High-quality slag-wool has a mean fibre thickness of 3–4 μ and contains less than 15% of the small spherical beads. Use: sound-insulating materials.

Predominantly crystalline slag (*lump slag*). The characteristics of slags are dependent on the crystal types occurring, the proportion of glass and the texture of the components. The following crystalline phases occur.

Melilite, which is a mixed crystal series between gehlenite and åkermanite (Fig. 85 on p. 147).

Gehlenite, $2CaO.Al_2O_3.SiO_2$, tetragonal, H: 5–6, melting point, 1,590°C.

Åkermanite, $2CaO.MgO.2SiO_2$, tetragonal, H: 5–6, melting point 1,458°C.

A continuous mixed crystal series exists between gehlenite and åkermanite. Fe and Mn can also be accommodated in the crystal lattice.

Melilite crystals are the most common constituents of crystallized ferrous blast furnace slag.

Lime-olivine (dicalcium silicate), $2CaO.SiO_2$. Occurs as four modifications:

    α-dicalcium silicate: trigonal (stable between 1,447°C and 2,130°C)
    α-dicalcium silicate (bredigite): orthorhombic (stable between 830°C and 1,447°C)
    β-dicalcium silicate (larnite): monoclinic (unstable below 670°C)
    γ-dicalcium silicate: orthorhombic (stable up to 830°C) (see Fig. 86 and section 7.4.3(a) (ii) 1.

The α-, α'- and γ-modifications are stable, whereas the β-modification is unstable and changes to the γ-modification. This transformation ('lime disintegration') is of great importance to the utilization of slags. The start of the transformation is first noticeable by the appearance of white spots in the slag; if the phenomenon is extensive, a white powder forms and the slag crumbles completely. The transformation is accompanied by volume increase. Slags containing β-2CaO.SiO$_2$ are unusable as cement aggregate.

Metal sulphides and oxides occur as extremely minute grains, but often in a dendritic form also (stars, crosses, plates). They are the first phases to separate from the melt and are often opaque: Fe$_3$O$_4$ (magnetite), cubic; MnS, cubic; FeS, cubic. CaS (oldhamite), cubic, D: 2·58, greenish, colourless. Forms rounded grains possessing a very high refractive index.

Merwinite, 3CaO.MgO.2SiO$_2$, monoclinic, D: 3·15, melting point 1,575°C. Occurs as grains and prisms, colourless.

Glass is present in most crystalline slags. Variation of the pozzolanic characteristics of slags is dependent on the glass content. Refractive index $n = 1\cdot55-1\cdot67$.

The following minerals are also found occasionally:

Rankinite, 3CaO.2SiO$_2$, orthorhombic;
Monticellite, CaO.MgO.SiO$_2$, orthorhombic.

The following occur predominantly in acid slags:

Anorthite, CaO.Al$_2$O$_3$.2SiO$_2$, triclinic (see Felspar);
Clinoenstatite, MgO.SiO$_2$, monoclinic;
Diopside, CaO.MgO.SiO$_2$, monoclinic;
Wollastonite, CaO.SiO$_2$, triclinic;
Leucite, (K$_2$O,Na$_2$O),Al$_2$O$_3$.4SiO$_2$, cubic.

Sulphide sulphur in ferrous blast furnace slags is derived principally from the coke used in smelting of the ores and only to a limited extent from the ore itself. The more lime a slag contains, the more sulphur may be bound up in it, since sulphur is extensively converted to CaS in slags.

Iron decay. Slags with a low lime and sulphur content disintegrate on exposure to damp conditions (especially reddish or black slags). Slags with more than 3% FeO invariably decay if the sulphide sulphur content of the slag is 1% or over. The cause is that the mixed crystals of iron and manganese sulphides react with water to release sulphur and form iron hydroxide.

Use: ballast, chippings, paving stones, road making, hydraulic structures, track construction, mortar and concrete aggregate, fertilizer, packing material in mining, glass manufacture.

(ii) *Copper slags*

Solidify in a largely glassy state on rapid cooling, especially if the SiO$_2$-content is high. In addition to glass, the following crystals of elements, sulphides, oxides and silicates may also occur. Free copper mostly occurs in rounded droplets; olivine, crystals of a continuous mixed crystal series between forsterite and fayalite, $2(Fe,Mg)O.SiO_2$; fayalite, $2FeO.SiO_2$, orthorhombic, D: 4·3; forsterite, $2MgO.SiO_2$, orthorhombic, D: 3·2. Fayalite, in particular, is common in copper slags; pyroxenes of the diopside–hedenbergite series: diopside, $CaO.MgO.SiO_2$, monoclinic, D: 3·25; hedenbergite, $CaO.FeO.SiO_2$, monoclinic, D: 3·62; hypersthene, $(Mg,Fe)O.SiO_2$, orthorhombic, D: 3·6; magnetite, Fe_3O_4, cubic, as also other spinels, åkermanite (iron-bearing), $2CaO.(Mg,Fe)O.2SiO_2$, tetragonal; zincblende, ZnS, cubic; chalcocite, Cu_2S, orthorhombic when formed below 103°C, hexagonal above 103°C; copper pyrites, $CuFeS_2$, tetragonal; delafossite, $CuFeO_2$, trigonal; cuprite, Cu_2O, cubic; cassiterite, SnO_2, tetragonal.

(iii) Lead slags

The principal crystalline phases in this material are sulphides, oxides and silicates. With respect to heavy metals, zinc, iron, copper, lead and manganese are always present. The following crystals occur: zincblende, $(Zn,Fe)S$, cubic, always Fe- and often Mn-bearing also; wurtzite, $(Zn,Fe)S$, hexagonal, always Fe-bearing; magnetite, Fe_3O_4, cubic, often Zn- and Mn-bearing (common crystal type); fayalite (see olivine) often as zinc-fayalite, $2(Fe,Zn,Mn)O.2SiO_2$, often Mn-bearing as well as Zn-bearing (common crystal type); Fe-monticellite, $(Fe,Mg,Mn)O.CaO.SiO_2$, orthorhombic; pyroxene (hedenbergite), $(Fe,Zn,Mg,Mn)O.CaO.2SiO_2$; Fe-åkermanite (see melilite), monoclinic, $2CaO(Fe,Mg,Zn,Mn)O.2SiO_2$, tetragonal; galena, PbS, cubic (very rare); pyrrhotite, FeS, hexagonal; chalcocite, Cu_2S, cubic; bornite, Cu_5FeS_4, cubic; cubanite, $CuFe_2S_3$, orthorhombic; willemite, $Zn_2(SiO_4)$, trigonal (common); α-celsian (barium felspar), $BaAl_2Si_2O_8$, monoclinic.

Sulphur first of all forms sulphides preferentially with zinc, and then with Mn, Cu and Fe in the given order. Silicates normally predominate in lead slags, followed by sulphides and magnetite.

(iv) Direct-process slags

These contain olivine, dicalcium silicate, magnetite and large amounts of glass.

(v) Steel slags (basic slag and open-hearth slag)

These can be distinguished from iron blast furnace slags mainly by their dark colour, due to a high iron and manganese content. For this reason the slags are subjected to a second dressing; only basic slag is used further.

Basic slag. Basic converter slag contains a number of crystalline phases, except when it is too silica-rich, when it readily solidifies to a glass:

S-phase (formerly called 'Silicocarnotite') represents mixed crystals of $Ca_3(PO_4)_2$ and $CaSiO_4$, which also contain vanadium, iron and manganese. Colour: blue, D: 3·04, orthorhombic. Changes to a hexagonal R-phase at approximately 1,300°C. Melting point: 1,700–1,800°C.

Tetracalcium phosphate (hilgenstockite), $4CaO.P_2O_5$, orthorhombic, D: 3·06. Melting point: 1,650°C. Occurs most frequently in basic converter slag with a low silica content. Forms light-brown plates.

Apatite (q.v.). Brown hexagonal needles, particularly in shrinkage cavities, presumably hydroxylapatite.

Dicalcium ferrite (lime ferrite), $2CaO.Fe_2O_3$, orthorhombic.

Oxide phase, which forms pine-tree-shaped skeletal or botryoidal crystals. Represents mixed crystals of CaO, FeO and MnO. Lime-rich and iron-rich members occur. Iron-rich member: D: 4, colour: medium brown.

Use: fertilizer (ground basic slag), as over 90% of the phosphoric acid contained in it is present in a soil-soluble form.

Open-hearth slags. Iron or manganese monticellite is often formed as a result of the high iron and manganese content. In addition, the oxides wüstite and magnetite as well as ferrite are important crystalline phases.

Iron-monticellite, $CaO.FeO.SiO_2$, orthorhombic, D: 3·33. Melting point 1,208°C. Related to olivine.

Glaucochroite, $CaO.MnO.SiO_2$, orthorhombic, D: 3·4.

Tricalcium silicate, $3CaO.SiO_2$, trigonal.

Wüstite, FeO, cubic ⎫
Manganosite, MnO, cubic ⎬ form continuous mixed crystal series
Periclase, MgO, cubic ⎪
Oldhamite, CaS, cubic ⎭

Dicalcium ferrite, $2CaO.Fe_2O_3$, orthorhombic.

7.5.2. Foundry sands

Used in the manufacture of moulds (moulding sands) for liquid metals. Where the casting should possess hollow places, sand cores are incorporated in the construction of the mould. These cores are manufactured previously from certain types of moulding material and shaped to the form of the required hollow. Foundry sands consist of quartz sands and a bonding material (predominantly clays), both of which satisfy specific requirements; water is usually added also. In special cases, olivine, granulated chamotte (dead-burned fireclay), periclase and zircon are used instead of quartz sand.

QUARTZ MOULDING SANDS

Quartz sands usually contain impurities of felspar, mica, hornblende, magnetite and, in part, calcite. All these minerals are undesirable. For cast iron, sintering temperatures of 1,300°C are adequate. These requirements are already satisfied by quartz sands containing about 15–20% felspar. Steel moulding demands a higher refractoriness, with no minerals, such as mica, felspar, etc., which lower the melting temperature. Mica is also undesirable because of its laminar or tabular cleavage, which tends to create cleavage surfaces in the moulds. Core sands should, as far as possible, be free from slam materials (mineral fractions <0·02 mm). The texture of the quartz grains should be neither porous nor cracked, nor should the grains be composed of several single crystals.

The *particle shape* should, as far as possible, be well rounded, particularly for core sands. Sands for iron and steel casting must be lime-free (at elevated temperatures, the CO_2 released gives rise to gas bubbles, i.e. flaws in the casting).

7.5.3. Bonding materials for moulding sands

These are clays in most cases. Sands which already contain a suitable clay admixture in the natural deposit are the most suitable. Proportion and quality of the bonding material largely determine the quality of the moulding material. In many cases clays (bonding clays) have to be added to the sands. Bentonites (weathered volcanic rocks, consisting predominantly of montmorillonite) are particularly suitable as bonding clays. Plastic clays composed of kaolinite with small proportions of illite and montmorillonite are also suitable. The kaolinite should consist of poorly-crystallized particles so that it possesses a high plasticity. Occasionally illitic clays are used; readily dispersible in water, they possess a very small particle size and have a high plasticity. The bonding action of clay minerals is due to the adherence of the clay particles to individual quartz grains and to each other because of the absorbed water layer which surrounds each clay particle. Clays with a high ionic-exchange capacity (such as montmorillonite) are particularly suitable for this purpose because of the strong 'non-fluid' water layer which can surround each particle (Figs. 75 and 87). In some cases moulding sands consisting of a quartz sand–bonding agent–oil mixture are used (oil reduces the volume of steam developed on pouring the liquid metal into the mould).

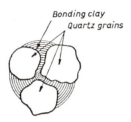

Figure 87   Bonding action of clay between quartz grains of moulding sands.

7.5.4. Fluxes in the smelting industry

In order to lower the melting temperature and produce a good fluid slag in the smelting of iron, the following minerals are used as fluxes: quartz, fluorite, cryolite, apatite, limestone and dolomite. In addition, rock with a low ore content, where smelting alone is not profitable, is often used as flux. For example, ferruginous limestone, metal-bearing quartzites (barren ores), etc.

7.5.5. Slag inclusions in steel

Microscopic slag inclusions in steel may influence the properties and usability. They occur arranged in bands, in shapeless aggregates, as oriented precipitates, on the crystallite-grain interfaces in steel, in eutectic microstructures, with dendritic and globular forms without a specific shape and with a typical crystal form. Crystalline phases alone, glass phases alone and crystalline precipitates in glassy matrices of variable composition have been demonstrated.

Corundum (Al_2O_3), hexagonal; aluminium nitride (AlN), hexagonal; aluminium sulphide (Al_2S_3); chromite ($MnO.Cr_2O_3$ or $FeO.Cr_2O_3$), cubic; chromic oxide (Cr_2O_3), hexagonal; chromium sulphide (Cr_2S_3); cristobalite (SiO_2), pseudo-cubic; iron nitride (Fe_2N or Fe_4N), hexagonal; fayalite ($2FeO.SiO_2$), orthorhombic; graphite (C), hexagonal; haematite (Fe_2O_3), hexagonal; hercynite ($FeO.Al_2O_3$), cubic; ilmenite ($FeO.TiO_2$), hexagonal; magnetite (Fe_3O_4), cubic; manganese-iron silicate, as glass and crystalline; manganese silicate ($MnSiO_3$), triclinic; manganese oxide (MnO), cubic; manganese sulphide (MnS), cubic; mullite ($3Al_2O_3.SiO_2$), orthorhombic; quartz (SiO_2), trigonal; rutile (TiO_2), tetragonal; SiO_2-glass (SiO_2), amorphous; spessartine ($3MnO.Al_2O_3. 3SiO_2$), cubic; tephroite ($2MnO.SiO_2$), orthorhombic; tridymite (SiO_2), orthorhombic; troilite (FeS), hexagonal; titanium sulphide (TSi_2); titanium cyanide (TiCN), cubic; zirconium nitride (ZrN), cubic; zirconium sulphide (ZrS_2); wüstite (FeO), cubic.

7.6. Engineering geology, geotechnics and mining

Mineralogy, petrography and the science of mineral deposits have a fundamental importance in all fields of engineering geology, geotechnics and mining.

7.6.1. Definitions

ENGINEERING GEOLOGY

Branch of applied geology and applied mineralogy, which bridges the gap between geology and mineralogy on one side and constructional engineering in the near-surface regions of the earth's crust on the other side. It represents the technologically-oriented side of geology and mineralogy, of importance to engineers in all fields of constructional engineering.

GEOTECHNICS

Represents the science which both engineering geology and constructional engineering science have in common and clarifies their relationship.

MINING

Systematic operations in the exploration for, production, haulage and dressing of minerals and utilizable rocks which occur as deposits in the earth's crust. Rocks, earths and other non-ores obtained by surface working are sometimes considered separately from mining under the term 'quarrying'.

7.6.2. Physical properties of rocks

These are largely determined by the mineral constituents, microstructure, chemical composition and by the geological history of the rocks. They are of great importance in engineering geology and geotechnics as well as in mining (e.g. geophysical methods such as seismology, geoelectric, geothermal, gravimetric and geomagnetic measurements used to prove and exploit deposits, mining techniques, dressing).

In addition to the petrographic classification of rocks (igneous [magmatic] rocks, sedimentary rocks, metamorphic rocks), they can be subdivided on the basis of their strengths into *consolidated rocks* and *unconsolidated rocks*.

Consolidated rocks include all igneous, sedimentary and metamorphic rocks which form large masses bonded by their mineral constituents (e.g. granite, syenite, diorite, gabbro, quartz porphyry, basalt, trachyte, andesite, rhyolite, tuffs, gneisses, mica schists, shales, quartzites, slates, breccias, conglomerates, sandstones, greywacke, limestones, dolomites, marls, etc.). Unconsolidated rocks are loose sediments or consolidated rocks broken up into small fragments: sands, gravels, blocks, clays, earths, etc. Non-cohesive unconsolidated sediments are: gravels, sands composed chiefly of quartz and, in part, felspar, which do not absorb water. Cohesive unconsolidated rocks exhibit absorptive action between the single grains and have a high water-absorption capacity (up to 100 times that of non-cohesive unconsolidated rocks). They always contain larger quantities of clay minerals.

(A) DENSITIES OF ROCKS

Natural density, bulk density, weight per unit volume = mass/total volume.

Mineral density, true density = mass/mineral volume
Total volume = mineral volume + pore volume
Porosity = pore volume/total volume

Rock densities in kg/dm³

Plutonic		Volcanic		Sedimentary	
Granite	2·52–2·81	Trachyte	2·4–2·8	Limestone	2·34–2·58
Syenite	2·63–2·90	Andesite	2·4–2·8	Marl	1·63–2·63
Diorite	2·72–2·96	Basalt	2·8–3·0	Sandstone	1·65–2·19
Gabbro	2·85–3·12	Lava	2·8–3·0	Shale	2·22–2·56
Norite	2·72–3·02	Phonolite	2·5–2·7	Coal	1·2 –1·8
Peridotite	3·15–3·28			Lignite	1·0 –1·5

(B) ROCK STRENGTH

Crushing strength (see also the concept of hardness applied to consolidated rocks). The cube crushing strength is the strength under a uniaxial stress, e.g. pressing between two surfaces.

Cube crushing strength

Granite	1,230–2,000 kp/cm²
Basalt	920–4,570 kp/cm²
Sandstone	300–1,840 kp/cm²
Shale	35–290 kp/cm²
Coal	30–195 kp/cm²

Confined compressive strength is the resistance of a rock to fracturing when held under a confining pressure. The confined compressive strength increases with increasing lateral (confining) pressure.

Transverse strength is approximately one-seventh the cube crushing strength.

Tensile strength is about one-thirtieth the cube crushing strength.

Shearing strength is about one-fourteenth the cube crushing strength.

(C) ROCK MAGNETISM

The strength of the induced magnetization is dependent mainly on the susceptibility of the rock. It is greatly reduced by any magnetite content but this is, however, usually accessory and therefore often of little importance.

Rock susceptibilities in cm³/p (the figures refer to negative powers of 10):

Magnetite	0–1
Other iron ores	1–2
Basic volcanic rocks	2–3
Acid volcanic rocks	3–4
Sediments	4–6

(D) ELASTIC PROPERTIES OF ROCKS

The velocity of elastic waves in rocks is determined by their elastic properties.

Limiting values of the elastic constants of rocks in Mp/cm²

	E	μ	K
Granite	300–800	200–300	300–500
Sandstone	100–1,000	200–400	300–400
Steel	2,000	700	1,600

E = modulus of elasticity, μ = resistance to change of shape, rigidity, shear modulus, K = modulus of compression

Mean values of the group velocities of compressional waves in various rocks in m/s

Soils	300–1,000
Pleistocene and Tertiary sands, marls, clays	1,800–2,400
Mesozoic sandstone, marls, chalk	2,200–3,000
Limestone, slates	3,000–4,000
Volcanic rocks, rock salt	4,000–6,000

In seismology, the distance travelled by elastic waves is calculated from their velocities. From these calculated values the positions of the boundaries of the various layers in the earth, at which waves are reflected or refracted, may be determined.

(E) ELECTRICAL PROPERTIES OF ROCKS

The electrical conductivity is influenced by electrolytic conductivity (ionic transport in the liquid occupying pore spaces in rocks, particularly in sediments) as well as by metallic conductivity.

Electrical properties of rocks

	Specific resistance, Ωm	Dielectric constants
Rock-forming minerals	10^{10}–10^{14}	4–8
Volcanic rocks	10^{3}–10^{7}	7–14
Sedimentary rocks (wet)	10^{1}–10^{4}	7–14
Sedimentary rocks (dry)	10^{3}–10^{9}	7–14
Ores	10^{-5}–10^{0}	—
Petroleum	10^{9}–10^{14}	10–30
Fresh water	10^{1}–10^{3}	80
Salt water	10^{-1}–10^{0}	80

(F) THERMAL CONDUCTIVITY OF ROCKS
(in kcal/m/sec/degree $\times 10^{-3}$):

Igneous and sedimentary rocks	3–8
Rock salt	13
Graphite	10–20
Magnetite	30

(G) GEOTHERMAL GRADIENT

(sometimes called 'geothermal step') is the increase in depth (in metres) corresponding to a temperature increase of approximately 1 °C.

Ruhrgebiet, Oberschlesien	33 m
Siegerland	41–57 m
Copper mines, Lake Superior, U.S.A.	68 m
Ramsbeck mine (Sauerland)	74 m
Gold mines in the Transvaal	120 m
Mean	33 m

(H) POROSITY AND PERMEABILITY OF ROCKS

These factors control the flow of groundwater through rocks and the flow of petroleum in reservoir rocks. The porosity P of a rock sample is defined as the pore volume of the sample expressed as a percentage of the total volume.

Porosity of sedimentary rocks

Limestone	4·6–13·6% (Mean 8·17)
Marl	1·4–30·3% (Mean 17·5)
Sandstone	10·2–34·7% (Mean 29·6)
Shale	4·1–19·6% (Mean 10·4)

Igneous rocks normally possess porosities of 0·5% to several per cent (<1% very compact, 2·5–5% moderately porous, <20% extremely porous).

The laminar flow of liquids in rocks is given by Darcy's Law:

$$Q = \frac{K}{\eta} \cdot \frac{F}{l} \Delta p$$

Q = quantity of liquid flowing through the rock in unit time; F = cross-section of the column; l = length of the column η = viscosity of the liquid; Δp = pressure difference; K = a constant (independent of the flowing medium and the experimental conditions) termed the *permeability*.

The permeability is measured in cm². The unit used here is the Darcy = 10^{-8} cm.² A porous medium possesses a permeability of 1 Darcy if water, with a viscosity of 1 cp (= centipoise) (viscosity of water is $\approx$1 cp), flows through a cross-section of 1 cm² at the rate of 1 cm³ per second under a pressure gradient of 1 atmosphere per centimetre. In calculations using the given formula, all units must be given in the c.g.s. system. Thus 1 cp = 0·01 g/sec cm, 1 atm = 1·033×9·81 ×10^5 g/cm sec².

A semi-empirical equation for the estimation of permeability is:

$$k = D^2 e^2 . 200$$

k = permeability, D = grain size, e = total pore volume (the ratio of the pore volume to the volume of solid matter is the void ratio).

This holds without qualification, however, only for sands with an approximately uniform grain size. Clay minerals (even in small amounts) greatly decrease the permeability. This is particularly true of disturbed soils, which lack structural features (shrinkage cracks, sedimentary layering, shear cracks, etc.).

The permeability of a soil is determined by: mineral composition, grain size distribution, texture, pore volume, ionic-exchange capacity of the clay minerals, type of pore fluid and its degree of saturation. Permeability is considerably reduced by an admixture of sericite (even 10%), greatly reduced by kaolinite and very greatly lowered by montmorillonite.

Porosity and permeability are not normally constant throughout a rock complex.

7.6.3. Engineering geology and geotechnics

(A) PHYSICAL AND MECHANICAL BEHAVIOUR OF FOUNDATION SOIL

(i) *Consistency of unconsolidated rocks*
Their consistency is determined mainly by the water content, but other factors such as size, shape and type of the soil particles, spacing of the particles, magnitude of the attractive forces and the physical state of the water also play a considerable role. In many cases the consistency is determined, above all, by the clay minerals.

Water absorption and swelling. In unconsolidated rock, water absorption is usually greater than in consolidated rock, and is increased especially by the presence of clay minerals (see the chapter on ceramics: clay minerals and water).

In the following clay minerals of identical grain size the water absorptivity increases from left to right:

Illite	Kaolinite	Kaolinite	Illite	Montmorillonite
well crystallized	well crystallized	poorly crystallized	poorly crystallized	

→

increasing water absorptivity

If water absorption is not solely due to filling of the pores, swelling can occur. Swelling of soils is caused by: 1. release of the compressive stresses caused by enlargement of the capillary films; 2. development of interlamellar water in the lattices of minerals of montmorillonite type; 3. as a result of the reorganization of a microstructure, which has not

attained a state of mechanical equilibrium under the prevailing temperature and pressure conditions, as soon as the pressure is released and
water enters the system. (The swelling phenomena associated with country rocks (shales) in coal mining also belong to this category.)

The *Atterberg consistency limits* are used to characterize the consistency of foundation ground (soils) (plastic limit, flow limit, plasticity
number).

Plasticity. The plastic limit specifies the lowest water percentage possessed by an oven-dried soil, at which it can be rolled out directly, on
a base, into threads of about 3–4 mm thick without crumbling. Foundation soil which cannot be rolled out at any value of the water content is
non-plastic. The presence of clay minerals, especially montmorillonite,
promotes plasticity.

Flow limit. The flow limit is the water content, expressed as a percentage, possessed by an oven-dried soil, at which it begins to flow
immediately on light shaking. Influence of clay minerals present:

$$\text{Montmorillonite–Illite–Kaolinite} \longrightarrow$$

decreasing values of the flow limit

Plasticity number = flow limit minus plastic limit.

Examples of the Atterburg consistency limits for pure clay minerals

	Flow limit	Plastic limit	Plasticity number
Montmorillonite	640–150	100–40	580–100
Kaolinite	80–30	40–20	30–7
Illite	100–70	45–30	60–30

Lean (short) and *fat* (strong) soils may be differentiated according to
their plasticity numbers.

Very lean	1–5%
Lean	5–15%
Medium fat	15–25%
Fat	25–40%
Very fat	>40%

Lean foundation soils: quartz sands, felspar grains, mica; fat foundation soils: illite and kaolinite; very fat foundation soils: montmorillonite.

The engineering difficulties presented by the foundation soil normally increase in proportion to the size of the clay-mineral fraction.

Drying. Even the drying of soils by the atmosphere effects a considerable reduction in the plasticity after re-moistening has occurred.

This is controlled by oxidation of the organic constituents, dehydration of iron hydroxide and the associated phenomenon of partial cementing of the particles. Furthermore, as a result of the shrinkage cracks which develop on drying, the single particles are packed closer together so that the mutual attractive forces are increased and only with difficulty can water penetrate.

Compressibility can be determined either when the soil sample is laterally confined or unconfined. It is controlled chiefly by the clay-mineral fraction, by the proportion of other minerals, grain shape, grain size and the arrangement of the particles. In the type of test where the sample is confined laterally, compression occurs by narrowing of the pores and by escape of pore-water. This occurs rapidly in coarse-grained, permeable material (sand, gravel), very slowly in materials with a high proportion of clay minerals, particularly montmorillonite. When lateral extension is permitted also, even small proportions of clay minerals (particularly montmorillonite) greatly increase the compressibility of sand.

Shearing strength is the maximum stress that a material is capable of sustaining under the given conditions. Breakage occurs when the frictional forces and cohesion are exceeded. The shearing strength decreases with decreasing grain size, i.e. it is particularly low if a high proportion of clay minerals or finely-divided organic substances occur. Shearing strength is an important factor in the stability of embankments, dams and slopes and also in the bearing capacity. The shearing strength of a soil in the natural state is normally higher than that of a soil with an identical moisture content, in a disturbed condition. If no variation of the moisture content occurs, the shearing strength of the disturbed soil increases again considerably with time. It is determined, also, by the cohesion and the coefficient of internal friction. The cohesion is a result of the forces which hold the particles together; in pure sands, therefore, it equals zero. The coefficient of internal friction is a function of the movement of one particle over another and increases with increasing confining pressure (e.g. depth). Montmorillonite produces a greater increase in the cohesion than other clays.

Porosity and permeability of unconsolidated sediments – see the chapter on the physical properties of rocks.

Frost heaves develop by the upheaval of the soil surface and are caused by the formation of ice crystals (frost lenses). The extent of the heaving is determined by the capillarity and permeability of the soil, grain size, rate of freezing, groundwater relationships and the load on the soil surface. The quantity of water which is mobile in the frozen zone causes a

M

corresponding amount of heaving. The grain size with the greatest tendency to frost heaving occurs at 0·02 mm grain diameter. Frost heaving is not normally found in soils containing less than 50% of a material whose grain size is <60 μ. Since clays reduce the permeability of soils, more than 40% of a plastic clay prevents heaving. Small amounts of clay, however, increase the danger of frost heaving. The tendency to frost heaving in relation to the clay minerals present decreases as follows:

Extremely-fine quartz sand–Kaolinite–Illite–Montmorillonite
$$\longrightarrow$$
decreasing tendency to frost heaving

Materials not liable to frost heaving are gravels, coarse sands and scree deposits without visible fine constituents.

(ii) *The concept of hardness as applied to consolidated rocks*

No exact definition exists. It can be defined as compressive strength, abrasive resistance or by a combination of the compressive strength and the amount of hard minerals present. Accordingly, a hard rock must possess a high compressive strength and a high content of minerals with hardnesses greater than 5·5.

Classification of rocks into hardness groups (after Moos-de-Quervain)

Average compressive strength in kp/cm^2	Content of minerals with hardness $>5·5$			
	0–25/%	25–50%	50–75%	75–100%
<600	very soft	very soft	soft	soft
600–1,000	soft	soft	soft	moderately hard
1,000–1,400	soft	soft	moderately hard	moderately hard
1,400–1,800	moderately hard	moderately hard	moderately hard	hard
1,800–2,200	moderately hard	moderately hard	hard	hard
>2,200	moderately hard	hard	hard	very hard

Examples of rock hardnesses are as follows:

Very hard: basalt (compressive strength 2,600 kp/cm^2—30% augite, H: 5·5; +25% felspar, H: 6; +20% olivine, H: 6·5; +25% glass, H: 5·5).

Hard: granite (compressive strength 1,760 kp/cm^2 —50–60% felspar, H: 6; +30–40% quartz, H: 7; +10–15% mica, H: 3); quartz porphyry, quartzite, diorite, porphyry, syenite, sandstones with a mainly siliceous cement, etc.

Soft: shelly limestone (compressive strength 710 kp/cm^2 —75% calcite, H: 3; +25% quartz, H: 7); dolomite, shales, tuffs, sandstones with a calcareous and clay cement, coals.

(B) BEHAVIOUR OF ROCKS AS FOUNDATION GROUND

(i) *Foundations in unconsolidated rocks*

For this purpose, it is essential to have knowledge of the bulk density, porosity, consistency, shearing strength, compressibility and permeability of the various layers composing the underlying strata. The position and fluctuation of the water table must also be known. Foundations in non-bonding unconsolidated rocks (gravel, sand, silty sands) lying above the water table present no technical problems caused by rapid settlement. Binding unconsolidated rocks (clays, loams, etc.) often present difficulties due to non-uniform settling. Soils with a high montmorillonite content (swelling) and those containing an organic fraction (sapropel, peat, lacustrine Cretaceous) demand special attention.

Behaviour of the clay-mineral fraction in foundation soil.

A. With increasing soil moisture, a high montmorillonite content causes low permeability, low compressibility and loss of strength. Under certain circumstances, the soil characteristics change greatly even during construction as a result of the high ion-exchange capacity.

B. High halloysite content can cause great differences in plasticity. Halloysites with $2H_2O$ and $4H_2O$ are only slightly plastic, whereas the intermediate stages of hydration exhibit high plasticity. Disturbed halloysite clays have, therefore, quite different properties to those of the normal soil, if variation of the moisture content is involved in the working.

C. High cation-exchange capacity is not only conditioned by montmorillonite but also, under certain conditions, by other poorly-crystallized or extremely fine-grained clay minerals or by the presence of finely-divided organic material. These soils then possess the physical characteristics of montmorillonite-bearing soils.

D. If the chief exchangeable cation in clay minerals is Na^+, the clay particles are mostly very small. As a consequence the permeability is reduced. In this case maximum swelling results if clay minerals capable of swelling are present. Since Na^+ is easily replaced by Ca^{2+}, Na-montmorillonite soils are converted to Ca-montmorillonite by addition of Ca^{2+}-ions. The latter mineral possesses a considerably lower swelling capacity and is thus more stable.

E. A high soluble-salt content may lead to catastrophic results during or after construction, through loss of the salt content.

(ii) *Foundations in consolidated rocks*

It is frequently necessary to establish by petrographic and geological investigation, whether the rock is a large detached block or whether it really is an outcrop of solid rock. The state of weathering, the water table and the jointing are also important.

Permissible bearing capacities of consolidated rocks

Marls, shales, slates, weathered rocks	5–10 kp/cm^2 or less
Molasse sandstones, limestones	10–20 kp/cm^2
Limestones, sandstones, gneisses, mica schists	20–30 kp/cm^2
Granites, porphyries, basalts	30–40 kp/cm^2

(iii) *Road, railway and runway construction*

The rock underlying these structures should be uniformly compressible and homogeneous down to a certain depth and have good drainage and frost-resistance (see the section on 'Consistency of unconsolidated rocks'). Uniformity of the underlying ground can, where necessary, be produced by addition of other materials or by artificial compaction (see also 'Compaction and stabilization of foundation soils'). Well-drained soils are composed of non-bonding rocks such as gravel or coarse sand. Unconsolidated rocks which bond (rocks containing large amounts of clay minerals, such as loam and clay) and also peat and lacustrine Cretaceous undergo severe settlement on dehydration.

(iv) *Compaction and stabilization of foundation soils*

This is carried out to improve the mechanical properties, for the prevention of erosion and water penetration, reduction of settlement, etc.

1. By the addition of quicklime to clay-rich, swelling soils. The effect involves a lowering of the plasticity number and increase of the compressive strength. Causes: flocculation of the extremely fine clay particles, ionic-exchange of Ca^{2+} for H^+, Na^+, K^+; pozzolanic reactions through the formation of Ca-silicates from free SiO_2 and $Ca(OH)_2$; gradual CO_2-adsorption and formation of $CaCO_3$, which cements the clay particles.

2. By the addition of lime and light ash. Cementation of the soil particles occurs since both lime and flue-dust have a pozzolanic action.

Clay minerals react relatively rapidly with lime to form calcium silicates; reaction with light ash occurs slowly.

3. By injection (grouting) or addition of cement, especially to gravels, coarse sands, jointed rocks, etc.

4. By injection of water glass with coagulants, especially for fine sand, porous sandstones, very finely-jointed rocks.

5. By injection of bentonite and other clay suspensions. The large swelling capacity and thixotropic behaviour results in sealing of the pore spaces in sand and of joints.

6. Soil stabilization by organic material. Petroleum and bitumen have been used for centuries to stabilize earthen roads. Attempts are also being made to use organic compounds (e.g. calcium acrylate), which form large structural complexes with clay minerals. Polymeric synthetic resins are used to seal joints and for strengthening.

(v) *Construction of dams from unconsolidated sediments*

With the exception of lacustrine Cretaceous rocks, peat (compressibility is too high) and readily-soluble rocks (gypsum, rock salt, etc.), all types of rock are suitable. Advantageous properties are: low compressibility, high shearing strength, also, in particular cases, low permeability (water storage dams, etc.). When non-binding, permeable rocks (blocks, sands, gravels) are used, sealing can be achieved by building an impermeable loam core (clay minerals are impermeable). Normally- and readily-bonding unconsolidated rocks can also be used. Readily-bonding rocks often present difficulties because of their high clay-mineral content (high compressibility, high plasticity, large settlement, etc.). In certain cases, therefore, they are shortened by gravels or sand.

(vi) *Landslides*

Sliding is caused by water impregnation, weathering, temperature variations, frost, shocks and load.

Unconsolidated rocks. Non-binding rocks (gravel, coarse sand, fine sand) have a natural angle of rest. In a moist, unsaturated condition, these rocks possess a larger angle of rest than in a dry state, due to the action of capillary forces. Gravel, coarse sands and scree behave in a similar way when saturated as in a dry state; under water, however, the angle of rest is smaller. Water-saturated fine sands become unstable when vibrated and give rise to specific, dense, water-sand fluids, which flow and come to rest at a very small angle (quicksands; principal grain-size range 0·02–0·2 mm). The behaviour of unconsolidated rocks which bond (loam, clay) is largely dependent on the type and amount of the clay-mineral content (see 'Clay minerals in soils' [7.9.1(d)]). In the presence of montmorillonite, variation of water content can lead to great instability of the slope. Solifluction (soil creep) is a phenomenon which may occur in the early part of the year and is due to a sudden excess of water caused by the thawing of soils with ice lenses (the soil becomes plastic or semi-liquid).

Consolidated rocks. Landslides and subsidence are almost exclusively conditioned by joints, cracks and zones of weathering in rocks.

(c) WORKABILITY OF ROCK DEPOSITS

The rock type and texture determine the ease with which material can be separated from the rock mass, extracted and hauled.

Methods of winning (after Keil)

1. Soils which can be scooped out: quicksands, muddy sands and soils, gyttja. Equipment: scoops.

2. Soils that can be excavated by shovel or spade: sand, gravel, fine gravel, shingle, loess, peat. Equipment: spades, shovels.

3. Soils that can be worked easily with a pick: loess loam, meadow loam, loamy, argillaceous, readily-caking gravelly sands, loamy rock-debris, weathered scree, root-bearing peat, stony soils. Equipment: mattocks, spades, shovels.

4. Soils which can, with difficulty, be excavated by pick: loam, loess loam, rubbly marl. Equipment: mattocks, pick-axes, shovels.

5. Rocks which can be worked with a pick: intensely disturbed strata, consolidated marls, disturbed limestones, soft argillaceous sandstones, calcareous gravelly sands and shingle. Equipment: pick-axes and chisels.

6. Rocks which can be worked easily by blasting: limestones, slaty marl, marly sandstone, dolomite, gypsum, anhydrite. Equipment: pick-axe, chisel, wedge, crow-bar (pick-hammer).

7. Rocks blasted with difficulty: all igneous rocks, crystalline schists, cemented tuffs, limestones and dolomites.

7.6.4. Mining

(A) EXPLORATION FOR MINERAL DEPOSITS

This involves geological and mineralogical investigation of rocks outcropping on the earth's surface and of the underlying strata. Areas which are likely to be ore-bearing are often associated with acid plutonic rocks (e.g. granites), such as, for example, lead, zinc, silver, uranium, tin and tungsten among others; chromite and nickel pyrrhotite are commonly associated with basic and ultra-basic rocks. Alluvial deposits give an indication of the ore content of the catchment area. Occurrences of coal and lignite as well as of some iron and manganese ore-deposits occur mainly in certain geological formations. Saline springs indicate salt deposits; petroleum often occurs in the vicinity of salt deposits and this may occasionally be indicated by seepage of naphthalene and natural gas.

In *oil-well drilling* the bore-hole is flushed by circulation of a fluid (from the bottom of the bore-hole to the surface and back again). The drilling fluids used are usually clay–water suspensions (drilling mud). The clays used are chiefly Na-bentonites (montmorillonites with Na^+ as the exchangeable cation), because these readily become thixotropic (see Thixotrophy [7.1.2(c)]) and, with water, disintegrate into very thin plates with a large surface area. Clays containing non-clay minerals (e.g. sand) are unsuitable. The function of the drilling mud is to remove loosened material (usually called cuttings) from the bottom of the bore-hole, to prevent contamination of the deposits (the flakey clay minerals coat and seal the wall of the bore-hole), to prevent the cuttings settling to the bottom of the bore-hole (through the thixotropic effects), and to cool the drilling bit. The drilling fluid should have a viscosity of about 15 centipoises. If the pressure of the liquids occurring in the formations being drilled is large, dense materials (barytes, in some cases hematite, celestine) are added to the drilling fluid. To prevent change of the thixotropic behaviour by electrolytes, when drilling through salt- or gypsum-bearing formations, additives (condensed phosphates, humic acids, etc.) are used. The normal drilling fluid contains 65–98% water, 2–30% clay (only 2% in the case of Na-bentonite, which has a high swelling capacity), 0–35% dense materials, 0–10% cuttings. The composition of the drilling fluid is checked continuously.

(B) INVESTIGATION OF MINERAL DEPOSITS

In addition to determination of the structure, depth and form of the deposit, evaluation of the quantities and grade of usable minerals is necessary. The grade of a deposit is the content of commercially-recoverable metals expressed as a percentage, or in the case of semi-precious or precious metals, in grams per ton. Attention must also be paid to the possible presence of constituents which are deleterious in the particular smelting process under consideration and to the gangue type (non-ore content). For dressing, the type of intergrowth of the ore minerals with one another and with the gangue minerals are important.

With coal seams, it is necessary to evaluate the type and quality of the coal with respect to calorific value, volatile constituents, mineral content (especially sulphur-bearing minerals), fusion temperature of the ash and coking capacity, in addition to the type and properties of the country rock. The reserve of the deposit may be calculated by multiplication of the determinable area by the average thickness and density of the occurrence. Estimations of the mining losses and of the dressing and washing losses must also be made.

An important mineralogical problem is the determination of whether any vein or seam is the same as that already worked in another part of the mine or in other mines. In coal mining, a record is plotted; containing the results of all the systematic observations and investigations of the seams carried out; this presents a clear overall picture of the area worked. Sections across the seams are constructed at as many points as possible in the entire area mined. From these sections, the macroscopic structure with respect to seam-types can be determined.

(c) DRIFT, TUNNEL AND SHAFT CONSTRUCTION

This requires determination of the rock succession, stratification, jointing, the existence of zones of faulting, areas of slipping and subsidence and the probable water and gas accumulation. The resistance of rocks to drilling and blasting is dependent on the texture and mineral composition. An important factor is the hardness of the rock (see the hardness characteristics of rocks).

Drillability

Easily-drilled rocks: marly and pelitic slates, shales, gypsum, anhydrite, argillaceous sandstones.
Moderately-difficult rocks: limestones, calcareous sandstones, gneisses, mica schists.
Difficult rocks: siliceous limestones, siliceous sandstones, granites, prophyries, porphyrites.
Rocks very difficult to drill: quartzites, amphibolites, diorites, quartz veins.

The amount and type of explosive used is determined, likewise, by the rock type. The jointing in rocks is a further determining factor.

Bridging or 'Stand-up' capacity of rock with respect to the cavities formed by mining excavation (rock mechanics, rock pressure)

The stability is controlled by: rock type and consistency, attitude of the most important fabric surfaces, overlying strata and the structural setting of the geological unit in question.

The following types are differentiated:

Firm ground (often without support): unjointed, massive granites, gneisses, mica schists, sandstones, limestones, etc.

Teary ground (ruptures rapidly into small fragments in cavities): thinly-bedded strata, most consolidated rocks which are strongly stratified or foliated.

Weak ground: rocks with numerous joints and faults.

Running ground (the rocks have a large pore volume, completely filled with water): scree, gravel, semi-fluid loam and clay.

(D) DRESSING

Dressing is the physical and physico-chemical processing of the raw material won by mining into a marketable form. Mineralogical-petrographic characterization of the extracted material (mineral quantity, intergrowth, fabric, etc.) should precede selection of the method of dressing.

Electromagnetic dressing (magnetic separation)

This is used for the separation of mineral mixtures on the basis of the varying magnetic properties of minerals in an electric field (see 'Crystal Physics – Magnetism' 2.4.2).

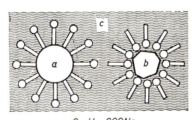

$$C_{17} H_{33} \ COONa$$

Hydrophobic Hydrophilic

Figure 88   Schematic drawing illustrating the adsorption of flotation agents, (after Mayer & Schranz, *Flotation*): (a) air, (b) mineral, (c) pulp.

Electrostatic separation

Separation of mineral mixtures in an electric field can be carried out because of the varying surface conductivities and dielectric constants of the minerals to be separated. Used in the separation of diamonds, wolframite–cassiterite, ilmenite–garnet–quartz, zircon–rutile among others.

Gravity concentration in water

Jigging is the process of stratification, according to density, of a granular mixture by a current of water or air, which is pulsated normal to the plane of stratification. The dense mineral collects in the lower and the lighter minerals in the upper parts of the layer.

Tabling is the separation of fine-grained minerals with a grain size <1 mm (coal <30 mm) on concentration tables (fixed or movable, ribbed surface, on which the minerals are stratified in grooves according to specific gravity and grain size).

Equal-falling classification is the separation of a charge in a medium according to specific gravity on the principle of equal falling-rate.

Flotation (froth flotation)

Flotation methods are used for the separation of mineral mixtures or rocks, finely crushed and dispersed in water. The principle of the method is that mineral particles have a varying capacity for becoming attached to gas bubbles, which carry them to the surface of the pulp where they are skimmed off as a mineralized froth. The mineral constituents of the charge possess varying water wettabilities, which are differentiated further by the addition of flotation agents; i.e. the hydrophilic (good wettability) and hydrophobic (poor wettability) properties of the system are modified.

Hydrophobic or lyophobic (water-hating) materials are: fresh sulphide ores, heavy metals, coals, diamonds and several metal oxides.

Hydrophilic or lyophilic (water-loving) materials are: silicates, phosphates, sulphates, carbonates, halide salts and all minerals with an ionic lattice. Lyophobic minerals are more easily wetted by hydrocarbons than hyophilic minerals, which in this case are non-wettable.

As flotation agents, 'collecting foaming agents' are used preferentially, i.e. chained hydrocarbon molecules, which are hydrophilic at one end and hydrophobic at the other end (Fig. 88).

With respect to mineral particles, the molecules act as collectors, i.e. the hydrophilic end is attached to the mineral, whereas the hydrophobic end is oriented towards the liquid. Mineral grains coated with collector molecules are hydrophobic towards the liquid. Molecules acting as frothing agents attach themselves to an air bubble by their hydrophobic ends with their hydrophilic end projecting into the liquid. The entire air bubble now behaves in a hydrophobic manner. Through mechanical agitation of the pulp, the air and mineral particles approach one another close enough to form bonds and the mineral grains are then carried to the surface by the air bubbles. A mineralized froth is thus formed and extracted.

(E) EXAMINATION OF THE CONCENTRATES (MINERAL-ENRICHED END-PRODUCT OF THE SEPARATION)

Several types of mineral, rock or metal constituents may be enriched in a concentrate. In the separation of a quartz-bearing lead–zinc ore on a concentration-table, for example, galena may occur in the first layer, galena–zincblende intergrowths in the second, zincblende in the third and zincblende–quartz intergrowths in the fourth. Principally by means of ore-microscopic examination, the composition of these concentrates can be checked and classified with respect to their intergrowths.

The same possibilities exist for the treatment of raw and washed coals: by means of reflected-light microscopy, the coal types in a mixture may be determined and graded according to their volatile content, their behaviour as fuels and in relation to their suitabilities as coking coal, and it is possible to select types suitable for the production of the cleanest coals (very low ash-content). The quality of coke can also be assessed microscopically.

7.7. Weathering of natural and artificial stone buildings

7.7.1. Causes and results of weathering

To a greater or lesser degree, stone structures are attacked by atmospheric influences (rain, snow, hail, wind), by surface water, micro-organisms, plants and animals as well as by impurities in the air (flue gases, flue-dust) and water (alkalis, acids, organic substances). Whereas flue gases and dust affect the entire building more or less uniformly, ground dampness affects only the region 1–1·5 m above the ground with the strongest effect at the upper margin of this region. The effect of rain water is also variable: particularly vulnerable are areas that are marginal between parts of the structure which remain dry and parts which get wet; parts of the structure in the open air but which are sheltered from water by trees the whole year round; undersides of projecting parts of the structure (balconies, cornices, etc.) and marginal areas of a stone occurring next to another with low permeability (e.g. sandstone–granite) are liable to excessive decay. Places that are subject to most damage are those which, while not being rained upon directly, remain damp for long periods.

7.7.2. Types of weathering affecting stone

Disintegration by chemical action

Air polluted by flue gases contains sulphur oxides, which can, through the formation of sulphates, lead to damage of limestones and calcareous stones (e.g. sandstones with a calcareous cement) and may also cause damage to silicate stones. This action causes roughening of the surface, disintegration into single grains, e.g. quartz grains and crumbling (disintegration into stone fragments). Discoloration of the stone surface is due to the oxidation of iron-bearing minerals, e.g. pyrites or marcasite and biotite, with the formation of iron oxides. In the case of pyrites and marcasite, sulphuric acid is also formed. Gypsum incrustations occurring on limestones and calcareous sandstones are an indication of the alteration of calcite to calcium sulphate by the sulphuric acid in flue gases. Calcite incrustation results from the leaching of mortar or concrete through reprecipitation of lime dissolved by the action of carbonic acid.

DISINTEGRATION BY PHYSICAL PROCESSES

Stone damage by disintegration into single grains, crumbling, exfoliation and spalling can be caused by temperature variation and frost. These phenomena may also be due to diffusion of material from the interior towards the outer parts of the stone. For example, Na- and Mg-sulphates in the stone which, under certain conditions, are formed initially by the sulphur oxides of flue gases, are dissolved and become concentrated at the surface (salt efflorescence). Since these salts take up differing amounts of water of crystallization (thenardite Na_2SO_4, glauber salt $Na_2SO_4.10H_2O$), surface disintegration of the stone (bursting expansion) may result if the anhydrous form changes to the hydrated form, with a higher volume, inside the stone pores.

STONE DAMAGE BY MICRO-ORGANISMS AND ANIMALS

Bacteria which grow on natural or artificial stones are capable of causing a spotty discoloration of the surface and may also partially decompose the mineral components as well as affecting glass. Acid- and rust-forming micro-organisms exist, amongst others. Pigeons often peck mortar and lime from outer walls; pigeon droppings can also damage stones.

7.8. *Treatment of water, molecular sieves*

7.8.1. Filtering sands

Water, acids, alkalis, etc., can be purified by filtering sands. The sands should possess a uniform grain size, absence of constituents that can be washed out and should be unreactive and not liable to chemical attack.

For moderately turbid water: fine-grained sands (the purity achieved by the process increases with the fineness of the sand grains).

For turbid water: coarse sands. Grain sizes: for rapid filtering 1–2 mm, for slow filtering 0·2–1 mm, according to the turbidity of the water.

For acids and alkalis: the purest possible quartz sands.

For gases and liquids: kieselguhr, quartz.

Filtering sands for storage dams and water wells, designed to remove extremely fine particles, are prepared according to the coarseness of the groundwater-bearing medium. The finer-grained the medium, the finer-grained the filtering beds.

7.8.2. Purification of drinking water

By clays of colloidal grain size: bentonite and attapulgite are dispersed in water and flocculated by a suitable agent. During flocculation the colloidal material accumulates in the flocculated clay particles and is easier to deposit as a sediment and filter.

7.8.3. Deacidification of water (pH correction)

By filtering with granulated marble, porous limestone or porous magnesite. The rocks should be poor in silicic acid and iron. Magno (dolomite roasted at 600 °C, producing a very porous material composed of MgO and $CaCO_3$) is also used.

7.8.4. Softening of hard water

Clays (Na-montmorillonite, bentonite, etc.) with high ionic-exchange capacities are used as filters, which adsorb the Ca^{2+} and Mg^{2+} ions of hard water and exchange the Na^+ ions.

7.8.5. Molecular sieves

Zeolites (faujasite $(Na_2Ca)[Al_2Si_5O_{14}].12H_2O$, cubic; chabazite $(Ca, Na_2K_2)[Al_2Si_4O_{12}].6H_2O$, trigonal; analcite $Na[AlSi_2O_6].H_2O$, cubic; mordenite $(Ca,K_2Na_2)[AlSi_5O_{12}]_2.7H_2O$, orthorhombic; etc.) possess numerous, relatively-large pores, normally filled with H_2O, in their structures (e.g. chabazite, 0·54 cm³ H_2O per cm³, with a pore diameter of 3·7Å). After dehydration in a vacuum at about 350°C, zeolites can be used as molecular sieves because of their properties of sorbing polar and undersaturated molecules, e.g. organic substances and gases.

7.9. Soils – mineral fertilizers

7.9.1. Soils

(A) SOIL FORMATION

Results from the weathering of bedrock [see 'Sedimentary Rocks: Origin', Chapter 2] and by the mixing of the resultant newly-formed minerals and rock fragments with more or less large proportions of organic material. The type of soil formed is dependent on mineralogical, climatic and geological factors.

(B) SOIL CLASSIFICATION

(i) Terrestrial soils (soil formation outside the groundwater regime with a dominant downward movement of soil solutions). The most widely distributed group in Germany.

(ii) Semi-terrestrial soils (soil formation under conditions of a high groundwater level, and, in addition, periodic flooding).

(iii) Sub-aqueous soils (soil formation under water, with permeation by water from all sides).

(iv) Marshy soils (soil formation chiefly by plant remains under partly sub-aqueous and partly semi-terrestrial conditions). All soils can be divided into a sequence of different layers (horizons) from the surface to the bedrock. The whole sequence is termed a soil profile. Each single horizon is labelled with a letter (A, B, C, G, M, D, T, Go, etc.), which on a clearly distinguishable further subdivision (soil type, colour) is given a numerical suffix (A_0, A_{00}, A_1, A_{12}, B_1, etc.).

A = generally, a humous mineral-soil horizon formed on the surface.
A_0 = superficial layer of virgin humus or mould.
A_1 = humous, mineral-soil formed at the surface.
A_2 = impoverished, bleached, light grey (wood ash-coloured) horizon termed podsol (bleached forest soil).
B = subsoil, an enrichment horizon of terrestrial soils (enrichment of clay minerals, hydroxides or humous materials).
G = Gleisoil. Horizon affected by groundwater.

C = substratum, unaltered rock from which the soil is formed.
C_1 = slightly-weathered transition to the fresh rock (C_2).

Examples of terrestrial soils: podsol (bleached forest soil) with an
A–B–C profile in damp (humid) climates.
Soil profile of a podsol:

A_0 = Superficial layer of virgin humus;
A_1 = humous, mineral-soil horizon;
A_2 = bleached, pale-green horizon;
B_1 = enrichment horizon, coloured by residues and humus (hard
      soil);
B_2 = enrichment horizon, rock hard, very rich in ferric hydroxide
      (hard pan);
C = primary rock (parent rock, substratum).

Podsol is widely distributed in north-west Germany.

Black earths (chernozems) with an A–C profile. The dark topsoil (A)
is up to over 1 metre thick and contains up to over 8% humus. Formed
in relatively dry regions with cold winters and hot summers. Widely
distributed in central Germany, Schwarzerdegebiet.

Brown earths with an A–B–C profile are ochreous to dark-brown
soils formed in a moderately-humid climate. Transitions between the
different horizons are gradual, without sharp boundaries. Relatively
low humus formation; iron hydroxides are uniformly distributed in the
soil. Silicates are extensively weathered to clay minerals (illite, montmorillonite).

Examples of semi-terrestrial soils: meadow soils are formed in broad
valleys (meadows) with a strongly fluctuating and, in summer, low
groundwater level. Gleisoils are soils with a fluctuating, high water
table.

(c) ADDITIONAL PROPERTIES FOR CHARACTERIZATION OF
SOILS

Soil colour, humus content (slightly humous $<2\%$ humus content,
moderately humous 2–4%, richly humous 4–10%, very richly humous
10–15%, semi-marshy 10–30%, marshy soils $>30\%$), soil type (defined
by the proportions of three grain size groups): clay <0.002 mm, silt
0.002–0.02 mm, sand 0.02–2 mm; texture (single grained texture, crumb
structure, tubulate structure, spongy structure, friable structure, platy
structure, lumpy structure, etc.), pH of the soil-water suspension, ionic-
exchange capacity, nutrient-content, (Ca, K, P), content of organic
substances, carbonate content, grain size analysis.

(D) CLAY MINERALS IN SOILS

Are one of the most important and widely-distributed soil constituents. They possess, among others, the following characteristics:

They control the flow of water through and in the soil. Extensive influence on the supply of water to plants; the capacity of soils to hold water is approximately proportional to the clay-mineral content.

Important influence on the soil fertility through its ionic-exchange capacity; K, Ca and Mg are adsorbed in an exchangeable form by the clay minerals (e.g. on fertilizing) and gradually released to plants, since plant growth, weathering of organic material and micro-organisms result in the formation of H^+-ions, which are exchanged for the metal ions (particularly montmorillonite). Kaolinite and halloysite are also effective through anion exchangeability in which their OH-ions can exchange for PO_4-ions; the minerals thus act as a phosphate reservoir.

Influence on the physical properties of soil particles, since organic substances and clay minerals are mutually bonded by ionic-exchange reaction.

Na-rich soils in dry regions can be made fertile by treatment with water-soluble Ca-salts, since the sodium occurring in clay minerals in exchangeable form is exchanged for calcium.

7.9.2. Mineral fertilizers

Used chiefly as sources of K, P and N. Potassium salts are extremely important as potash fertilizers, especially sylvine (63% K_2O), carnallite and cainite, also illite under certain circumstances. Phosphorous fertilizers are manufactured chiefly from phosphorite (as a deposit of animal excrement in the form of guano) and, in small amounts, from apatite.

Ground basic slag [see 'Smelting slags' (7.5.1.)] are obtained by the basic Bessemer process, in which steel is produced from phosphorus-rich iron ore. Basic slags contain phosphorus in a soil-soluble form. Chile saltpetre (nitrate of soda, nitratine, soda-nitre) is still an important mineral fertilizer today, in spite of the recovery of nitrogen from air.

7.10. Asbestos

Commercially-important properties and distinguishing features. *Difference* between serpentine asbestos (chrysotile) and hornblende (amphibole) asbestos (anthophyllite, amosite, actinolite, tremolite, crocidolite):

the refractive index of serpentine asbestos is *lower* than 1·58, that of hornblende asbestos always *higher* than 1·58.

SERPENTINE ASBESTOS (CHRYSOTILE ASBESTOS): $Mg_6(OH)_8Si_4O_{10}$
The most suitable type for spinning. Not acid and alkali resistant, very good fibrous characteristics, thin bundles of fibres without transverse cracking. Electrical charge +. Melting point 1,550°C.

HORNBLENDE ASBESTOS (AMPHIBOLE ASBESTOS)
Anthophyllite: $(Mg,Fe)_7(OH)_2Si_8O_{22}$ (iron-free to iron-poor). Poor spinning properties, only slightly flexible, very high resistance to acids and alkalis. Electrical charge −. Fibres, in part cracked transversely. Melting point approximately 1,470°C.

Amosite: $(Mg,Fe)_7(OH)_2Si_8O_{22}$ (iron-rich anthophyllite). Moderately easily spun, good flexibility, good acid and alkali resistance. Electrical charge −. Fibres, in part, transversely cracked. Melting point approximately 1,400°C.

Tremolite (grammatite): $Ca_4Mg_{4-10}Fe_{0-6}(OH)_4Si_{16}O_{44}$. Long, acicular prisms and fibrous aggregates, transverse cracks in some cases, poor spinning qualities, slightly flexible, good acid and alkali resistance. Electrical charge −. Melting point 1,370°C.

Actinolite (Strahlstein): $Ca_2(Mg,Fe)_5(OH)_2Si_8O_{22}$. Needles and fibres. Transversely cracked in some cases, poor spinning properties, only slightly flexible, good acid and alkali resistance. Electrical charge −. Melting point 1,360°C.

Crocidolite (blue asbestos): $Na_2Fe_4(OH)_2Si_8O_{22}$. Fibrous to felt-like, moderate spinning properties, good flexibility, transverse cracks rare, good acid and alkali resistance. Electrical charge −. Melting point 1,190°C.

All types of asbestos may be distinguished, under the polarizing microscope, by their differing optical properties.

7.11. Mineral pigments

Used as colouring matter for paint pigments, stucco, plaster, mortar, cement, linoleum, rubber and other materials.

7.11.1. The following are used in the natural form

(a) *Pigments consisting chiefly of iron oxides and iron hydroxides*
Hematite, e.g. as red ochre; limonite, magnetite.

N

(*b*) *Coloured earths containing a large clay fraction or other non-colouring admixture in addition to iron oxides and iron hydroxides*

Bole is the collective term for brown to yellow mixtures of clay minerals (especially montmorillonite) which also includes ochre, hypoxanthite, and, in part, umber.

Ochre (colour: yellow to yellowish-brown, burned-red, reddish-brown, salmon shade): Fe_2O_3 16–60%, SiO_2 35–50%, Al_2O_3 10–40%, loss on ignition 10–12%. Dominantly composed of clay minerals and iron hydroxides. Yellow ochre, yellow earth (melinite).

Hypoxanthite (Terra di Sienna) (colour yellowish-brown to brown, burnt Sienna: a dark reddish-brown): Fe_2O_3 25–75%, small amounts of MnO_2, SiO_2 10–35%, Al_2O_3 10–20%, loss on ignition: 15–20%.

Cyprian or Turkish umber (colour buff to dark brown): Fe_2O_3 37–60%, MnO_2 11–23%, SiO_2 16–35%, Al_2O_3 3–13%, loss on ignition 10–15%.

Shales stained by ferric hydroxide.

(*c*) *Coloured earths not stained by iron compounds*

Cologne umber (Van Dyke brown) (dark brown to black): mixture of lignite and clay minerals.

Green earths (Tyrolean green): composed of glauconite (a micaceous mineral with composition approximately $K_{2-3}(Mg,Fe,Ca)_{1-3}(Fe,Al)_{3-6}(OH)_8(Al,Si)_{16}O_{40}$) or of the very similar celadonite and clay.

Graphite (black).

Shales, stained by carbonaceous material (black).

Molybdenite (black), used as a pigment for plastics.

7.11.2. Artificial pigments manufactured from mineral raw materials

(*a*) *Pigments composed chiefly of iron oxides or iron hydroxides*
(colour: red, yellow, black, venetian red)

(*b*) *Pigments composed of other colouring matter*

Lithopone: non-poisonous, white pigment composed of zinc sulphide and barium sulphate, zinc white, titanium white, white lead, red lead (minium), cadmium sulphide (yellow), cobalt pigments, ultramarine (synthetic product with the structure of the hauyne group), uranium pigments, chromium pigments, etc.

7.12. Meteorites

Meteorites represent material (rocks) from astronomical bodies belonging to the solar system. Up to the present time about 1,500 meteorites, which have fallen on the earth, have been scientifically studied. They provide data on the composition of extra-terrestrial bodies, on specific problems occurring in iron-nickel metallurgy, information about radiation in interstellar space, the composition of the upper atmosphere and the behaviour of solid bodies travelling with high velocity in space and on entry into the earth's atmosphere. Their importance to space research and space-flight is considerable. Classification: stony meteorites (predominant group), iron meteorites (siderites, smaller group), stone-iron meteorites (mesosiderites, very restricted group). Glassy meteorites and cosmic dust which fall on the earth must also be included here.

7.12.1 Iron meteorites

Mainly composed of nickel-iron (4–20% Ni) with small contents of Co and Cu as well as elements of the Pt- and Pd-group. Additional constituents are troilite (pyrrhotite), schreibersite $(Fe,Ni,CO)_3P$, cohenite (cementite, Fe_3C), graphite, diamond (rarely), moissanite (SiC), and lawrencite $(FeCl_2)$. Polished surfaces of iron meteorites usually show lamellar structures (Widmanstätten structures), usually recognizable with the naked eye. The lamellae intersect in two, three or four directions and are formed of kamacite (nickel-poor, α-iron with a body-centred cubic lattice). The outside of the kamacite lamellae is always coated with a thin layer of taenite (nickel-rich, γ-iron with a face-centred cubic lattice). The interstitial material between the lamellae is composed of an intimate mixture of kamacite and taenite [plessite (Fig. 89)]. The Widmannstätten structures are an indication of an extremely slow cooling lasting millions of years. Iron meteorites with a limited nickel

Figure 89   Widmannstätten structures in a polished iron meteorite
(after P. Ramdohr).

content often contain single crystals of α-iron. Iron meteorites with numerous inclusions of olivine grains are called pallasite.

7.12.2. Stony meteorites

Composed mainly of silicates and, in small quantity, other minerals which also occur in terrestrial rocks: olivine, orthorhombic pyroxene; plagioclase, troilite, chromite, graphite, copper pyrites, ilmenite, native copper. Minerals not occurring terrestrially are schreibersite and daubréelite ($FeCr_2S_4$) in addition to kamacite, taenite and plessite.

Chondrites are stony meteorites, formed of small spheres (up to the size of a pea). These are the commonest stony meteorites. Carbonaceous chondrites are those containing up to 5% carbon. The small spheres consist chiefly of olivine and/or pyroxene.

Achondrites: stony meteorites not formed of small spheres.

Chondrites contain, in part, small amounts of organic substances (e.g. colouring matter similar to porphyrins).

7.12.3. Stone-iron meteorites (mesosiderites)

Approximately 50% composed of silicates and 50% of nickel-iron.

7.12.4. Glassy meteorites (tektites)

Named after the main locality where they are found: moldavite, australite, billitonite, etc. Greenish, crystal-free glass with up to 97% SiO_2-content in addition to Al_2O_3, K, Na, Ca and very small amounts of Fe and Mg. Their extra-terrestrial origin seems to establish that they may perhaps be parts of the moon's craters.

7.12.5. Cosmic dust

Falls continuously on to the earth's surface and has become mixed, in considerable quantities, with the rocks of the earth's surface.

7.13. Abrasives

Materials used for sharpening, cutting, polishing, grinding, cleansing. Essential physical characteristics: suitable hardness, tenacity, grain shape, grain size, cleavage and fracture properties, purity or homogeneity, in some cases heat resistance and capacity to form a strong bond with the surface of the support. Hardness values are generally given according to the Mohs' Scale (q.v.).

Natural abrasives

High hardness (>7)	Diamond	Hardness 10
	Corundum	Hardness 9
	Emery	Hardness 7–9
	Garnet	Hardness 6·5–7·5
	Staurolite	Hardness 7·0–7·5

Medium hardness (5·5–7)	Quartz	Quartzite
	Chalcedony	Basalt
	Flint	Felspar
	Sandstone	Granite

Low hardness (<5·5)	Apatite	Magnetite
	Calcite	Hematite
	Diatomaceous earth	Pumice
	Clay	Talc
	Dolomite	Gypsum

Most important natural abrasives:

7.13.1. Industrial diamonds

Bort: colourless diamond fragments, which are of no value as gem-stones.

Carbonado: coke-like in appearance, very hard, diamond aggregates.

Ballas: hard and tenacious, radiating, diamond aggregates.

Diamonds are combustible in an oxidizing atmosphere at about 900°C. Diamonds have recently been synthesized from carbon (graphite, soot, carbon obtained from sugar) by using chromium, manganese and other metals as catalysts at 55,000–120,000 atm and 1,200–2,400°C; see 'Diamond synthesis' (p. 193). Diamonds break into fragments with sharp edges (cleavage parallel to the octahedral face).

7.13.2. Corundum and emery

Natural corundum is hardly ever used nowadays, the corundum being produced artificially by fusing bauxite in an electric arc or by calcining alumina.

Emery is a metamorphic rock composed of 60–75% corundum and 10–35% magnetite. In some cases, hematite, spinal or plagioclase also occur. Corundum possesses the conchoidal fracture suitable for abrasives.

7.13.3. Garnet

The two types chiefly used are:

Almandine, $Fe_3Al_2[SiO_4]_3$;
Spessartine, $Mn_3Al_2[SiO_4]_3$ (in few cases only).

Garnets possess no perfect cleavage and have a conchoidal fracture. The lamellar partings which occasionally occur in single crystals are detrimental, since they cause disintegration into tabular fragments under pressure. Exceptionally suitable for abrasive papers and cloths.

7.13.4. Quartz sand

Used for sand blasting and ground quartz for sandpaper (danger of silicosis!).

7.13.5. The most important synthetic abrasives

Silicon carbide (SiC), electrocorundum (Al_2O_3), sintered corundum (Al_2O_3), boron carbide (B_4C_3) cubic boron nitride (BN, hardness approximately the same as that of diamond), tungsten carbide, synthetic diamonds, chromic oxide. All synthetic abrasives are manufactured from mineral raw materials.

7.13.6. Lubricants and polishing agents

Graphite, molybdenite, tungstite (WS_2), talc and pyrophyllite are used for the above purposes.

7.14. Power generation by high-pressure steam power plants

Coal, lignite and fuel-oil [see also 'Raw and construction materials for nuclear reactors' (7.3.)] are burned in the boiler furnaces to produce the high-pressure steam driving the generator turbines.

7.14.1. Pollution and corrosion caused by furnaces and flue gases

(A) FUELS AND THEIR ASH-FORMING CONSTITUENTS
All fuels used in power stations contain a proportion of incombustible mineral material, which leads to corrosion and pollution.

The mineral material in coal consists mainly of clay minerals (over 50%, usually over 70%) in addition to iron sulphides, carbonates, quartz, etc.).

Clay minerals: sericite, kaolinite, illite.
Iron sulphides: pyrites, marcasite (usually with As).
Carbonates: calcite, siderite, dolomite, ankerite, chalybite.
SiO_2-minerals: quartz, chalcedony.
Phosphorous minerals: phosphorite, apatite.
Salts: rock salt, gypsum.
Iron hydroxides.

Chemical composition of the total ash is typically:

approx. 40–50% SiO_2
approx. 20–30% Al_2O_3
approx. 5–15% Fe_2O_3
approx. 2–6% CaO
approx. 0–3% MgO
approx. 3–5% K_2O
approx.   1% Na_2O

Plus small amounts (usually $<1\%$) of P_2O_5, Zn, Ti, Pb, Cu, Cl, As, B, Ge, etc.

Lignites contain quartz, pyrites, marcasite, carbonates, clay minerals (kaolinite, illite), rock salt, thenardite, gypsum, phosphorite, ferric hydroxide. Sodium, calcium and sulphur occur also in organic compounds. The chemical composition of total ash is typically:

approx. 5–25% SiO_2
approx. 2–15% Al_2O_3
approx. 5–20% Fe_2O_3
approx. 15–35% CaO
approx. 0–5% MgO
approx. 0–2% K_2O
approx. 3–10% Na_2O
approx. 0–8% P_2O_5
approx. 0–3% Cl

In 'saline coals' the Na_2O content of the ash may be as high as 40%. Heavy fuel-oil contains chiefly sulphur, sodium and vanadium (see table overleaf).

(B) DEPOSITS AND CORROSION IN FURNACES

Coal-fired crucible furnaces

Mineral substances in the coal melt to form a fluid slag which becomes deposited on the cylindrical walls of the furnaces, where it subsequently solidifies. Crystalline phases [mainly mullite and magnetite, often corundum, also, iron-aluminium-spinels (hercynite), anorthite, etc.] are thus formed in the solidified slag (Fig. 90).

Element	Source	Solubility in oil	Mode of occurrence in oil
Sodium	inorganic	insoluble	as salts dissolved in an aqueous emulsion or as a suspension of micro-crystalline particles in oil
Sulphur	organic	soluble	in organic compounds, as sulphuric acid and as the element
		insoluble	as dissolved sulphate in a water emulsion
Iron	organic	soluble	organic compound (porphyrin)
	organic	insoluble	suspension of iron oxides
Nickel	organic	soluble	organic compound (porphyrin?)
Calcium	organic	soluble	organic compound
	inorganic	insoluble	suspension of Ca-minerals or dissolved in water emulsion
Silicon	inorganic	insoluble	suspension of clay minerals and quartz
Aluminium	inorganic	insoluble	suspension of clay minerals
Vanadium	organic	soluble	as porphyrin complex

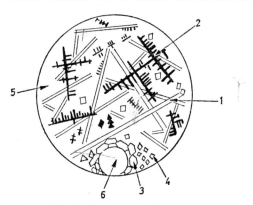

Figure 90 Crystallized coal clinker: 1 = mullite, 2 = magnetite as dendritic crystals, 3 = corundum, 4 = hercynite (FeO.Al$_2$O$_3$), 5 = groundmass formed of aluminium silicate glass, 6 = bubble-shaped cavity. [Thin section, schematic, ×100]

In the fluid state the slag also contains sulphur oxides and water vapour. A thin coating of corrosive, mixed sulphates and mixed pyrosulphates of Fe, Na, Al, Ca and Mg is often formed between the layer of slag and the furnace wall. In a reducing atmosphere, a relatively thick scale of iron monosulphide (troilite) may also be formed on the wall. The ramming material used to line the furnace may become corroded. Depending on the conditions, chromite of the chromite bodies decomposes to form aluminate spinels, aegirine-augite [(CaO.[Mg,Fe]0.2SiO$_2$)(Na$_2$O.Fe$_2$O$_3$.4SiO$_2$)] and α-Fe$_2$O$_3$-silicon carbide bodies are converted, by reaction with iron droplets in the molten slag, to ferrosilicon and graphite. SiC is partly oxidized to SiO$_2$ and CO$_2$.

In coal-fired boilers with a discharge of dry ash, furnace corrosion occurs only to a limited extent and is mostly of no practical importance.

Dry-firing with lignite

No fusion of the ash to a slag occurs here, but the ash products are, however, frequently deposited very firmly on the walls of the furnace. These deposits consist dominantly of hematite, maghemite (γ-Fe$_2$O$_3$, cubic), magnetite and considerable amounts of anhydrite and occasionally CaO and Mg-ferrite.

When, in exceptional cases, lignite is used to fire a crucible furnace, a strongly-corrosive coating of alkali sulphate is formed on the furnace walls underneath the layer of slag. The crystalline fraction of the slag layer consists of melilite [mixed crystals of gehlenite (2CaO.Al$_2$O$_3$.SiO$_2$) and åkermanite (2CaO.MgO.2SiO$_2$, tetragonal)].

Oil-fired boilers

Highly-corrosive deposits of sodium vanadyl vanadates are formed in addition to sodium sulphate, nickel-iron spinels, nickel-iron olivine [(Ni,Fe)$_2$SiO$_4$] and, in some cases, nickel sulphide. Iron sulphate and hematite occur as corrosion products (Fig. 91).

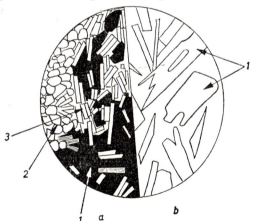

Figure 91 (a) oil clinker (thin section): 1 = sodium vanadyl vanadate (dark brown), 2 = nickel-iron olivine (green), 3 = sodium sulphate (white); (b) polished section: 1 = sodium vanadyl vanadate needles. [Schematic, ×100]

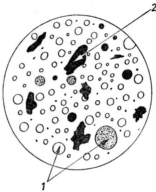

Figure 92 Coal flue-dust: 1 = glassy clinker – spherical cavities, 2 = coke dust.

(C) DEPOSITION OF MATERIAL ON, AND CORROSION OF HEATING SURFACES

Deposition of material from flue gases, thus restricting heat transfer.

Coal-fired boilers

The deposit consists of minute, hollow spheres of glassy slag (Fig. 92), which are bonded by mixed sulphates (in rare cases by mixed phosphates) of Na, K, Li, Ca, Mg, Fe, Al, etc., and by sintering. A thin layer of mixed sulphates occurs directly on the surface of the flue. Under certain conditions this can be strongly corrosive at a wall temperature of over 550°C. Arsenic and chlorine compounds, also, may possibly cause corrosion.

Lignite-fired boilers

The compounds consist of iron oxide and anhydrite.

Oil-fired boilers

Strongly corrosive deposits of sodium vanadyl vanadates and sodium sulphates are deposited on the heating surfaces. Ferric sulphate and ferric oxide occur as corrosion products. The lampblack formed may contain free sulphuric acid.

(D) AIR POLLUTION

Waste gases from power stations can pollute the air with gases, which are injurious to health (especially SO_2 and SO_3), and also with flue-dust. The amount of sulphur oxides is dependent on the amount of sulphur in the fuel; this occurs in coals mainly as pyrites and marcasite and in lignite and fuel-oils chiefly in organic compounds. It is possible to remove part of the sulphur oxides as sulphates of the alkaline earths by spraying the stream of flue gas with dolomite, limestone, lime milk, etc. (Fig. 92).

(E) CORROSION BY FLUE GASES

The sulphur oxide content of gases, which also contain water vapour and, under certain conditions, chlorine, leads to the formation of sulphurous, sulphuric and, in some cases, hydrochloric acid, when the temperature falls below the condensation point. At temperatures below 200°C, these acids have a strongly corrosive effect on boiler linings, insulating sheets and the metal of the air-preheater as well as on the flue. On reaching the atmosphere they attack the metals and stone of buildings and damage plant growth.

(F) GAS TURBINES

Deposition and corrosion phenomena in gas turbines fired by coal or oil are very similar to those in high-pressure steam power plants.

7.14.2. Deposition and corrosion caused by water and steam

DEPOSITION OF SOLID PHASES ON THE INSIDE OF THE TUBE WALLS

The insides of new steel tubes become coated with a protective layer of magnetite in about 50 hours according to the equation

$$3Fe + 4H_2O \rightarrow Fe_3O_4 + 2H_2 + 2H_2O$$

Deposition of solid phases, particularly in the presence of alkalis, can lead to corrosion of this protective coating, e.g. deposition of phosphates [wolfeite $(Fe,Mn)_2(OH/PO_4)$ and poorly-crystallized hydroxl-apatite $Ca_5(OH/[PO_4]_3)$]. Sulphate deposits (gypsum, etc.) can also be corrosive.

In exceptional cases, silicates are deposited.

Hide-out effect: intermediate precipitation of salts (probably phosphates and sulphates) on the inside of the tube during operation of the boiler; the salts pass into solution again on turning off the boiler. The residues of these deposits cause corrosion in some cases.

DEPOSITION OF MAGNETITE

In structural elements through which rapid flow occurs (ventilators, nozzles, etc.); this is mainly the deposition of fine-grained magnetite from superheated water with a pH <9.3, and is not formed from the metal of the part concerned. The cause of magnetite formation is presumably the decrease of pressure in confined places (hydromechanical paradox).

DEPOSITS ON TURBINE BLADES

With a well-treated water supply, these should consist only of silica gel and iron oxides. In addition, the following minerals occur: quartz (usually if the Na_2O content of the deposit is 1%), aegirine ($Na_2O.Fe_2O_3.4SiO_2$), nepheline ($Na_2O.Al_2O_3.2SiO_2$), minerals of the sodalite group (sodalite $2NaCl.3Na_2O.3Al_2O_3.6SiO_2$, nosean $2Na_2SO_4.Na_2O \cdot Al_2O_3.6SiO_2$, hauyne $2CaSO_4.3Na_2O.Al_2O_3.6SiO_2$), sodium silicates, minerals of the diopside series [$8CaO.8(Mg,Fe)O.16SiO_2$], thenardite (Na_2SO_4), thermonatrite ($Na_2CO_3.H_2O$), common salt, wolfeite ($(Fe,Mn)_2(OH/PO_4)$), cuprite (Cu_2O), tenorite (CuO), delafossite ($CuFeO_2$) among others.

7.14.3. Deposits (fur) in decarbonation plants

The bicarbonate content of untreated water is usually removed by funnel-shaped or cylindrical 'fast reactors', into which the water is passed. Calcium hydroxide solution is added through the tip of the funnel or the bottom of the cylinder, in which small quartz or slag grains, etc., are placed to act as nuclei for crystallization. In this way, according to the solution relationships, the bicarbonate is precipitated as calcite, which is deposited around the nuclei provided. After growing to a certain size, deposition stops and the nuclei-forming material must be renewed (formation of artificial ooliths).

7.15. Single crystals and the artificial preparation of crystals (crystal growth)

Single crystals are used extensively for optical elements (prisms, polarizers, windows, filters, lenses), X-ray monochromators, energy counters (scintillation counters, neutron counters, pulsation counters), piezoelectric crystals, semi-conducting crystals, crystals for microwave amplification (masers) and as synthetic gemstones. Their commercial preparation is therefore of great importance.

7.15.1. Methods for the artificial preparation of crystals (crystal growth)

CRYSTAL GROWTH FROM SOLUTION

Crystals are prepared by precipitation from supersaturated solutions under normal pressure. Used for the preparation of ethylene diamine tartrate (EDT), ammonium dihydrogen phosphate, lithium sulphate, sodium chlorate, lead chromate, potassium sodium tartrate, anthracene (from ether solution), alums, lead chloride, lead nitrate, cadmium iodide, beryllium sulphate, guanidine aluminium sulphate hexahydrate, iodic acid, copper sulphate, sodium chloride, potassium chloride, saccharose, sulphur, zinc sulphate, potassium ferrocyanide, ammonium bromide, ammonium chloride, ammonium orthoarsenate, ammonium ortho-phosphate, gadolinium chloride, potassium nitrate, potassium ortho-phosphate, magnesium sulphate, rubidium orthophosphate, sorbitol hexa-acetate, etc.

HYDROTHERMAL SYNTHESIS

Crystal growth from solution in a closed system (autoclave) at elevated temperatures and pressures. Crystal precipitation results from cooling, which produces a decrease of the solubility. The method is used for the preparation of: quartz, aluminium orthophosphate (berlinite), alumi-nium arsenate, emerald (green variety of beryl), calcite, corundum, zinc oxide, zinc silicate, chrysotile asbestos, felspar (orthoclase), topaz, cryolite, tourmaline, tremolite asbestos.

DIAMOND SYNTHESIS

Graphite, lampblack or charcoal obtained from sugar are mixed with catalysts (Cr, Mn, Fe, Co, Ni, Pt, Os, Zn, Rh, Pd and Ta) and heated in a small tube to a temperature sufficiently high to partly melt the carbon-saturated catalyst. Diamonds are formed at temperatures from $1,200\,°C$ to $2,400\,°C$ and under pressures from 55,000 to 120,000 atm. The crystal form is temperature-dependent (low temperatures: cubes; high temperatures: octahedra). Colour: at low temperatures, black; medium temperatures, dark green–pale green–yellow; high temperatures, colour-less. Cubic boron nitride (BN, borazon) is prepared by the same process as for diamond; this possesses the same hardness as diamond but is, however, stable in air up to $1,900\,°C$ (diamond burns at $850\,°C$).

CRYSTAL GROWTH FROM THE MELT

The most extensively-used methods for the preparation of single crystals (metals, inorganic and organic compounds) in which the tem-perature of the melts can vary from $-273\,°C$ to $3,700\,°C$. The crystals separate from the melt on cooling. Used for the preparation of: A, Ag, Al, Au, Be, Bi, Cd, Co, Cu, Fe, Ge, Hg, K, Mg, Na, Ni, Pb, Se, Sb, Sn, Te, Zn, Si; alloys (Ag-Zn, Au-Ag, Au–Sn, Cu–Al, Cu–Mg, Cu–Si, Cu–Sn, Cu–Zn, Ni–Te); inorganic compounds [LiF, NaF, NaCl, NaBr, NaI, KCl, KBr, KI, CsF, CsCl, CsBr, CsI, CaF_2, $NaNO_3$, $NaNO_2$,

AsI_2, MgF_3, Fe_3O_4, $BaTiO_3$, micas (muscovite, phlogopite, biotite), ice, PbS, PbSe, PbTe, CdS, CdTe, SnSe, ZnF_2, ZnS, ZnSe, Zn_2Te, As_2Te_3, Sb_2T_3, Bi_2Te_3, Cu_3Au, Mg_2Sn, $HgBr_2$, $CaWO_4$, MnF_2, RbCl, RbBr, RbI, ZnSb, GaSb, AlAs, GaAs, ZnAs, AlSb, corundum, spinel, mullite, chrysoberyll, nepheline, perovskite, scheelite, pyrites, hausmannite, rutile]; organic compounds (anthracene, acenaphthene, acridine, benzoic acid, pyrocatechol, dibenzothiophene, dibenzyl, p-dibromobenzene, diphenyl, diphenylacetylene, diphenylbutane, diphenylbutadiene, diphenyl oxide, fluorene, flouranthene, hexamethylbenzene, naphthalene, pentamethylbenzene, phenazine, phenanthrene, pyrene, quaterphenyl, resorcinol, stilbene, terphenyl, tetraphenylethylene). A variation of this method is the 'flame fusion' process [Verneuil process, see 'Synthetic gemstones', (7.15.2(F))].

CRYSTAL GROWTH FROM THE VAPOUR PHASE

In this method crystals are prepared either by condensation of the vapour onto a foreign substrate or by reactions in the vapour phase. Used for the preparation of: Ag, As_4O_6, BaO, Cd, CdS, CdSe, C_6H_6, benzophenone, hexamethylenetetramine, Fe, GeO_2, HgS, I_2, Mg, Mo, Nb, P, PbS, S, Se, SiC, SnS, Ta, Ti, UO_3, Zn, ZnS, Zr, Si, W, ZnO, CdTe, Ge, HgSe, HgTe.

CRYSTAL GROWTH BY RECRYSTALLIZATION

By annealing at temperatures of up to near the melting point single crystals of metals and oxides can be prepared from polycrystalline aggregates (recrystallization). Used for the preparation of: Al, BaO, Cu, Fe, Mg, Pb, Se, Sn, TiO_2, Al_2O_3, α-U, Zn, ZnO, MgO.

CRYSTAL GROWTH BY ELECTROLYSIS

Crystalline phases can be precipitated from electrolytes at the cathode. Used for the preparation of Ag, Cu, Cd, Zn. In a similar way, crystallization from melts is also possible. Used for the preparation of Ag, Co, Ni, W.

PREPARATION OF CRYSTAL WHISKERS

Crystal whiskers are single crystals with a cross-sectional diameter of the order of 10^{-4} cm and a length of up to a thousand times the diameter. Whiskers, like normal crystals, can be prepared from the solution, melt, vapour or in the solid state, but mainly, however, from solution. The tensile strength of crystal whiskers is much higher than that of normal crystals; e.g. Ag, Au, Cd, Cu, Fe, Mg, NaCl, Ni, Cr, Fe_3C,

Cr_3O_4, ZnO, NiO, α-Al_2O_3, NH_4Cl, LiF, $CaSO_4.2H_2O$, hydroquinone, resorcinol, KI, KBr, $MgSO_4.7H_2O$, $ZnSO_4.7H_2O$, $NiSO_4.7H_2O$.

7.15.2. Applications and properties of single crystals

(A) OPTICAL ELEMENTS

For this purpose, the following properties of single crystals are important: range of wavelengths transmitted, refraction of light, influence of temperature on the refraction, dispersion, thermal expansion, water-solubility and hardness.

Prisms. In vacuum-path ultraviolet: single crystals of CaF_2 and LiF_2; in air-path ultraviolet: quartz; in near-infrared (up to 2·8 μ): quartz; long-wave ultraviolet: NaCl (up to 16 μ), KCl (up to 25 μ), thallium bromoiodide (up to 40 μ), caesium iodide (up to 50 μ).

Polarizers. Calcite, quartz, polarizing films of small, oriented, herapathite crystals, AgCl plates for infrared.

Windows designed for the transmission of rays from specific regions of the spectrum. For vacuum ultraviolet, the transmission limit for a thickness of 0·1 cm of lithium fluoride is 0·11 μ, calcium fluoride 0·12 μ and sodium fluoride 0·13 μ. Quartz with a thickness of 0·2 mm transmits at 0·145 μ and synthetic mica, 10 μ thick, transmits below 0·2 μ. In infrared, thicknesses of 1–2 mm of the following crystals are used; quartz, up to 4 μ; corundum, up to 6 μ; magnesium oxide, up to 10 μ; thallium bromoiodide, up to 60 μ; and diamond, 11 μ and over.

Filters for the elimination of undesired regions of the spectrum. This may be achieved by absorption, reflection, interference or scattering. Crystals for polarization-interference filters: quartz, ethylene diamine tartrate, ammonium dihydroyen phosphate, $NaNO_3.CaCO_3$.

Lenses for regions of the spectrum in which optical glasses are non-transmitting. In ultraviolet: a combination of CaF_2 or LiF_2 with quartz is used for achromatic lenses between 0·185 and 1·4 μ. In infrared: Ge and Si single crystals.

X-ray monochromators. To obtain a monochromatic beam from a heterogeneous X-ray beam (white radiation). The size of the crystals is about 30 $\times$ 20 $\times$ 0·5 mm. LiF_2, diamond, NaCl, calcite, quartz, pentaerythrite, Al, gypsum, beryl, mica, sugar, fluorite, ureanitrate.

(B) SINGLE CRYSTALS AS ENERGY COUNTERS

Scintillation counters. When γ-rays, X-rays, electrons, protons and α-particles pass through matter, excitation of the electrons, or ionization, occurs. On the return of the electrons to the ground state, light is emitted, which is then converted to electrical impulses by means of a photomultiplier. In order to obtain the most efficient conversion of the light emission, single crystals are used because of their clarity and transmittancy. For this purpose, activating elements (bracketed) must be added to the individual inorganic substances: NaI(Tl), CsI(Tl), ZnS(Ag), KI(Tl), ZnS(Cu), CsI, CsF(Tl), $CaWO_4$, $CdWO_4$, anthracene, dibenzyl, diphenyl acetylene, naphthalene, phenanthrene, quaterphenyl, stilbene, terphenyl. For neutron scintillation counters, only crystals which undergo no nuclear reaction on bombardment with neutrons can be used. For neutron energies <50 keV: LiI with the activators TlI, SnI_2, $EuCl_2$, SmI_3, ZnI or AgI. For neutron energies >100 keV: anthracene (yields only very small impulses).

Current impulse counters (crystal counters) measure the current impulses produced through the mobility of the electrons released when a potential is applied to a crystal. The following crystals are used: AgCl, AgBr, As_2F_3, CdS, CdTe, diamond, Ge, HgS, MgO, NaCl, S, SbS_3, SiC, TlCl, TlBr/TlI, ZnS.

(C) PIEZOELECTRIC CRYSTALS [see 'Crystal physics' (2.4)]

Used for wireless transmitters or receivers, frequency stabilizers, electrical filters and pressure gauges. Electrical polarization is induced by mechanical deformation (tension, compression, shearing) in crystals of 20 of the crystal classes (mechanical energy $\rightarrow$ electrical energy). The

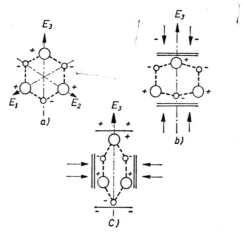

Figure 93   Schematic illustration of the piezoelectric effect: (a) simplified diagram of the quartz lattice, (b) compression in the direction of the electrical axis, (c) compression normal to the electrical and *c*-axis (after W. Kleber).

Zn^{2+} O^{2-} Zn^{2+} O^{2-} Zn^{2+}
    e^- Zn^{2+}
O^{2-} Zn^{2+} O^{2-} Zn^{2+} O^{2-}
  Zn^+ e^- e^-
Zn^{2+} O^{2-} Zn^{2+} O^{2-} Zn^{2+}

Figure 94
Model of the defects in ZnO.

Cu^{2+} Cu^+ Cu^+ Cu^+ Cu^+
   O^{2-} O^{2-} O^{2-} O^{2-}
Cu^+ $\square$ Cu^+ Cu^{2+} Cu^+
   O^{2-} O^{2-} O^{2-} O^{2-}
Cu^+ Cu^+ Cu^+ Cu^+ $\square$

Figure 95
Model of the defects in Cu_2O.

piezoelectric effect is reversible: electrical energy can be reconverted into mechanical energy by such crystals.

The following, among others, are piezoelectric crystals:

cubic: $NaClO_3$, $NaBrO_3$, NH_4Cl, ZnS.

trigonal: dextrose sodium chloride, dextrose sodium bromide, dextrose sodium iodide, tourmaline, lithium potassium chromate, low quartz;

tetragonal: barium titanate, potassium dihydrogen phosphate, ammonium dihydrogen phosphate, ammonium dihydrogen arsenate, potassium hydrogen arsenate, nickel sulphate;

orthorhombic: lithium ammonium tartrate, lithium potassium tartrate, sodium ammonium tartrate, strontium formate, barium formate, iodic acid;

monoclinic: seignette salt (Rochelle salt) ($KNaC_4O_6.4H_2O$), raw sugar, Epsom salt ($MgSO_4.7H_2O$), ammonium tartrate, ammonium oxalate, lithium sulphate, l- and d-tartaric acid, potassium tartrate, ethylene diamine tartrate.

Quartz is the most mechanically-stable material of all piezoelectric crystals. Its piezoelectric constants are small, however. Used as frequency stabilizers and for filtering. Good transmitters or receivers are Rochelle salt (water of crystallization readily evaporates, however) or ammonium dihydrogen phosphate (without the disadvantages of Rochelle salt). For large filters instead of quartz: ethylene diamine tartrate. Tourmaline is used for pressure measurement.

Explanation of the piezoelectric effect of quartz: Fig. 93 (a) shows, in a schematic and simplified way, the negative and positive ions of the low-quartz lattice. The polarity of the axes [see 'Crystal physics' (2.4)] is distinguishable by the fact that positive charges occur at one end of the axes (E_1, E_2, E_3) and negative charges at the other end of the same axes. If this lattice-structure is compressed in the direction of a polar axis [Fig. 93 (b)] deformation of the lattice occurs with a displacement of the charges in such a way that positive charges predominate on one side and negative charges on the opposing side. If the pressure is applied

o

normal to the electrical axis [Fig. 93 (c)] opposing charges again result on opposite sides, with the charges in this case, however, interchanged with those in Fig. 93 (b). If an electrical field is applied parallel to a polar axis, the charges of the lattice are displaced, i.e. the quartz lattice expands or contracts parallel to an E-axis. If the field is reversed, the compressed lattice expands and the expanded lattice contracts. The corresponding lattice deformation occurs on excitation by an electrical field normal to the polar axis and normal to the c-axis.

(D) SEMI-CONDUCTOR CRYSTALS [see also 'Crystal physics', 'Electrical conductivity' (2.4.2)]

At the present time these are the most important of all single crystals. The semi-conducting property is connected with defects in the crystal lattice. For example, a number of ionic compounds depart from the ideal stochiometric composition and have an excess of either cations or anions. In order that electrical neutrality be preserved when an excess of cations occurs, the excess positive charge must be balanced by additional electrons (excited electrons), as in ZnO, for example (Fig. 94). If an excess of anions is present, the charge balance is achieved by the removal of an electron from a cation position. The point from which the electron has been removed is the electron point defect or electron hole, e.g. the Cu^{1+}-ion becomes a Cu^{2+}-ion by removal of an electron (see Fig. 95).

The conduction results from the excited electrons or electron holes, and, in this way, is also possible in elements. For example, the conductivity of pure germanium at room temperature is low; it can, however, be significantly increased by incorporation of foreign atoms (substitution) in the Ge-lattice (P or B partly replace Ge in the Ge-lattice).

The electrical resistance of semi-conductors lies between 10^{-3} and 10^6 ohms. The essential difference between metals and semi-conductors is that the number of charge-carriers in semi-conductors can be varied between wide limits by additions of specific materials or by temperature.

As semi-conducting crystals the following, among others, are used: diamond, Si, Ge, α-Sn, AlAs, AlSb, AlP, GaAs, GaSb, GaP, ZnAs, ZnP, ZnSb, Bi_2Te_3, PbS, PbSe, PbTe, anthracene, naphthalene, pyrene, terphenyl, stilbene, phthalocyanine.

The most important semi-conductors are Si and Ge, which are used mainly in the manufacture of transistors. Compounds of Groups III–V and II–VI of the periodic table are also suitable for this purpose. For rectifiers: Si, Se and CuO; for transistors: Ge, B, U_3O_8; for varistors: SiC; for photocells: PbS, PbSe, PbTe, Se, CdS, Ge; for luminescence:

CdS, ZnO, ZnS. Semi-conductors are used also as infrared detectors, photoconductors and photomagneto-conductors.

(E) CRYSTALS FOR MASERS AND LASERS

For masers, mixed crystals with a low concentration of paramagnetic ions of the rare earths and the transition metals are placed in a magnetic field. The following are used: lanthanum ethyl sulphate + 1% gadolinium ethyl sulphate (or 0·5% Ge^{3+} + 0·2% Ce^{3+}), chromium cyanide, potassium cyanide and ruby (corundum + a small amount of chromic oxide).

Laser crystals (light amplification by stimulated emission of radiation) effect amplification in the region from the ultraviolet to infrared.

As solid lasers, single ruby crystals containing 0·05% Cr_2O_3 are used, for example. Gallium arsenide is used as the active material in semiconductor laser diodes. Laser effects have been demonstrated in 50 different substances up to the present time.

(F) SYNTHETIC GEMSTONES (DIAMOND, see p. 193)

Prepared by means of the flame-fusion process (Verneuil method). Constitutes an intermediate stage between crystal growth from the melt and from the vapour phase. The powdered starting-material is melted into small droplets which are deposited on the surface of the newly-formed crystal. Used for the manufacture of ruby (Al_2O_3 + a maximum of 3% Cr_2O_3), sapphire [Al_2O_3 + 0·12% TiO_2 or 1·5% (Fe_2O_3 + TiO_2)], yellow sapphire [Al_2O_3 + (NiO + V_2O_3)], yellowish-green sapphire [Al_2O_3 + (Fe_2O_3 + TiO_2)], green sapphire [Al_2O_3 + (CaO + MgO + ZnO)], rutile (if required, it may be coloured red by the addition of 0·1% Cr_2O_3), spinel [starting material $Mg(NH_4)_2(SO_4)_2.6H_2O$ + $AlNH_4(SO_4)_2.12H_2O \rightarrow MgO.Al_2O_3$, in some cases also, colouring additives], chrysoberyl.

Prepared by hydrothermal synthesis. Used for the manufacture of corundum, ruby (by the addition of 0·1 g/l.$Na_2Cr_2O_6.3H_2O$), emerald (by solid-state diffusion reactions under hydrothermal conditions).

CRYSTAL WHISKERS

Exhibit an almost ideal lattice-structure and therefore possess bonding forces between the lattice-units which almost equal those calculated theoretically. Their strength may be from 100 to 1,000 times greater than normal single crystals. They are therefore imbedded in metals to increase the strength, e.g. metals which have to satisfy the demands made by space flight.

7.16. Protective coatings on metal surfaces

7.16.1. Structure and composition of oxide layers on metals

(A) GENERAL

The start of metal oxidation results from the penetration of the crystal surface by oxygen molecules. Tarnishing or reaction films, formed by the action of oxygen (and also of sulphur oxides or halogens) are not usually built up on the metal surface in a random way [see 2·1(b)]. The growth of oxide layers probably occurs by diffusion of metal or oxygen ions through the resulting oxide layer separating the metal and oxygen reactants. With multivalent metals such as Fe and Cu, for example, various oxidation stages may occur, depending on the conditions (temperature, oxygen pressure, etc.). The oxide layer protects against corrosion.

(B) OXIDE LAYERS

Iron

The oxide coating on iron is not usually homogeneous but consists of oxides of varying oxygen contents. Under normal conditions of temperature and pressure, the sequence of films forming the oxide layer is:

Air or water	surface of the protective layer
Fe_2O_3 = hematite	
Fe_3O_4 = magnetite	
(FeO) = wüstite	metal surface

The quantitative formation of individual oxides is temperature-dependent. Below 570°C, the oxide coating is dominantly composed of Fe_3O_4; above 570°C FeO is very strongly predominant. FeO is practically non-existent below 570°C.

The chief constituents of iron rust are lepidocrocite (γ-FeOOH) and goethite (α-FeOOH).

The oxide layers formed by water and steam in the steel pipes of high-pressure steam power stations consist exclusively of magnetite (see the chapter on 'Power generation'), as long as they are not overheated, in which case wüstite is formed.

Both magnetite and wüstite can form oriented overgrowths on iron surfaces (Figs. 96, 97 and 98). Oriented intergrowths of magnetite and wüstite and between hematite and magnetite are also possible (Figs 99 and 100).

Zinc

The metal crystallizes with a hexagonal close-packing structure. In air or by anodic oxidation, a coating of hexagonal zinc oxide forms

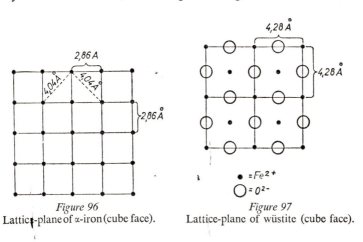

Figure 96	Figure 97
Lattice-plane of α-iron (cube face).	Lattice-plane of wüstite (cube face).

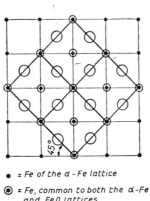

● = Fe of the α-Fe lattice

◉ = Fe, common to both the α-Fe and FeO lattices

○ = O²⁻ of the FeO lattice

Figure 98 Lattice-plane of wüstite showing, on rotation through 45°, oriented overgrowth on the lattice-plane of α-iron.

immediately. This zinc oxide forms an **oriented** overgrowth up to 100 Å thick on the zinc surface. In thicker layers or after heating to 300°C, the zinc oxide occurs in an unoriented polycrystalline state.

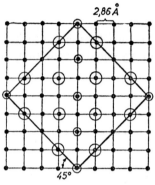

2,86 Å

45°

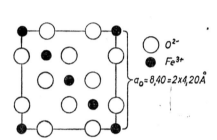

O^{2-}

Fe^{3+}

$a_0 = 8,40 = 2 \times 4,20$ Å

● = Fe of the α-Fe lattice

◉ = Fe belonging to both the α-Fe and Fe O lattice planes

◯ = O^{2-} of the $Fe_3 O_4$ lattice

Figure 99   Lattice-plane of magnetite.

Figure 100   Lattice-plane of magnetite showing, on rotation through 45°, oriented overgrowth on the lattice-plane of α-iron. Both cube faces.

Copper

The metal crystallizes with a cubic close-packing structure. Under the influence of atmospheric oxygen, cubic Cu_2O is formed, which grows parallel to the copper lattice. The $Cu-CuO_2$ intergrowth is essential to the understanding of the $Cu-CuO_2$ rectifying effect, since it is bound up with the transitional bonding at the interface of the copper and Cu_2O lattices. On heating copper in air, a layer of small, randomly-oriented, orthorhombic CuO crystals is formed instead of an oriented overgrowth of Cu_2O.

The oxidation of copper is very strongly dependent on the lattice-plane presented to the oxygen. A cube surface, which is most densely packed with atoms, shows a considerably lower oxidation rate than an octahedral surface with a less dense packing of metal atoms.

Aluminium

In air the metal, which crystallizes in the cubic system, becomes coated with an oxide film about 5 Å thick. The film consists of disordered Al_2O_3, amorphous to X-rays. On heating to above 450°C, this Al_2O_3 layer is converted to cubic γ-Al_2O_3.

Magnesium

Crystallizes in the hexagonal system, and in air, becomes coated with an amorphous MgO-layer. On annealing this layer, recrystallization to cubic MgO results. This may form oriented intergrowths with the metal.

Tin

The oxide layer is similar to those of Al and Mg. Tin oxide is practically amorphous and changes to the crystalline state at 130°C.

Oxide coating of alloys

The oxide layers on alloys often contain different ratios of the metal components to those in the alloys. On heating, pure ZnO films form on brass (30% Zn + 70% Cu) surfaces. Aluminium bronzes composed of Cu and Al have oxidation layers formed of γ-Al$_2$O$_3$. An oxide layer of crystalline γ-Al$_2$O$_3$ forms on Al–Mg alloys between 120°C and 350°C. Above 350°C the γ-Al$_2$O$_3$ layer is overlain by crystalline MgO.

Oxide layers on liquid metals

The oxide skin on liquid Zn, Sn, Pb and Bi consists of oxide crystallites with their cube faces resting on the liquid surface. On cooling, the lesser oxide crystals become absorbed into larger ones and this coarsening process can lead ultimately to the formation of large single-crystal sheets (*Sammelkristallization*).

7.16.2. Phosphate coatings on sheet iron (after Neuhaus)

(A) PROTECTION OF METAL SURFACES FROM CORROSION (COATING THICKNESS ~20 μ)

Phosphate baths are used for the process. Non-coat-forming baths contain only (PO$_4$)$^{3-}$-anions with the metallic component (Fe) of the layer being derived exclusively or mainly from the support. Coat-forming baths are those in which the material composing the coating comes exclusively or mainly from the material used in the bath.

(B) PHASE CONSTITUTION OF THE COATINGS

This is dependent on the type of bath (coat-forming or non-coat-forming) and the type of the coat-forming material (iron, manganese or zinc phosphate coatings).

Iron phosphate coatings from non-coat-forming baths are nearly amorphous to X-rays under normal phosphatizing conditions. Essential constituent of the layer: vivianite, $Fe_3(PO_4)_2.8H_2O$; in part, also iron-hureaulite, $Fe_5H_2(PO_4).4H_2O$.

Iron phosphate coatings from coat-forming baths consist of monoclinic iron-hureaulite, $Fe_5H_4(PO_4).4H_2O$.

Zinc phosphate coatings are composed of orthorhombic hopeite, $Zn_3(PO_4)_2.4H_2O$ and variable amounts of monoclinic phosphophyllite, $Zn_2Fe(PO_4)_2.4H_2O$. The amount of phosphophyllite is dependent on the conditions under which the coating is carried out; in chlorate-accelerated baths it becomes the dominant component. Zn–Ca phosphate solutions produce coatings of $Zn_2Fe(PO_4)_2.H_2O$, scholzite $(Zn_2Ca(PO_4).2H_2O$; orthorhombic) and $Zn_3(PO_4)_2.4H_2O$.

Manganese phosphate coatings are composed of monoclinic hureaulite, $(Mn,Fe)_5H_2(PO_4)_4.4H_2O$, containing only limited amounts of Fe.

Ca-phosphate coatings from Ca-phosphate solutions are composed of brushite $(CaHPO_4.2H_2O$; monoclinic) and monetite $(CaHPO_4$; triclinic).

(C) PHOSPHATE COATINGS FROM AGED BATHS

Contain the same crystalline phases as those from normal baths. In Zn-phosphate coatings a large proportion of phosphorphyllite occurs instead of hopeite.

(D) ADHESION OF PHOSPHATE COATINGS TO THE IRON SURFACE

All known hydrated phosphates show extensive oriented overgrowths on rolled Fe-sheets [see 2.1(b)].

7.17. Biomineralogy

7.17.1. Silicosis

This is a disease of the respiratory organs caused by the inhalation of mineral and rock dust, which leads to hardening of the lung tissue.

(A) TYPES OF SILICOGENIC DUST (AFTER H. JUNG)

The most harmful is quartz dust.

Minerals which are silicogenic to a greater or lesser degree

Quartz	Micas	Serpentinized olivine
Cristobalite	Serpentine asbestos	Leucite (?)
Tridymite	Talc	Nepheline (?)
Chalcedony	Beryl	
Alkali felspars	Sillimanite	

The following intensify the effect of quartz: fluorspar, cryolite, iron pyrites and carbonaceous substances.

Rocks which are, to a greater or lesser degree, silicogenic

Quartzites	Silica bricks	Kieselguhr
Quartz sands	Dinas bricks	Tripoli
Sandstones	Hornstone	Siliceous sinter
Granite	Quartz diorite	Quartz porphyry

Other rocks (in some cases quartz-bearing) include

Kaolin	Diorite	Greywackes
Clays	Arkosic sandstone	Gneiss
Graphite	Conglomerates	Mica schists
Ochre	Breccias	Phyllite
Greisen	Slates	Shale
	(Roofing slates)	Ceramic products (e.g. porcelain)

The more quartz-rich the rock, the greater is the danger of silicosis, if it is inhaled in the form of dust. The more iron- and calcium-rich a rock, the less dangerous is the dust formed from it (e.g. felspar basalts, limestone, dolomite, siderite, gypsum, rock salt, etc.).

Smelting of ores of arsenic, beryllium, lead and uranium can produce dust which leads, however, not to silicosis, but to symptoms of poisoning.

The grain size of silicogenic dusts is $<5\,\mu$ (predominantly $<1\,\mu$) but coarser dusts also have an irritative effect on the respiratory organs.

(B) CAUSES OF SILICOSIS

These have not yet been clearly established. At the end of a normal lifetime lungs contain approximately the following amounts of dust: open-air worker, 0·5 g; ore miner, 5–15 g; coal miner, 150 g.

(i) According to the matrix theory, albuminous substances in the lungs are adsorbed in a specific way, structurally, by the surfaces of dust particles (especially quartz), and they may perhaps be constitutionally changed (epitaxis, q.v.). Reactions leading to silicosis may thus be initiated.

(ii) The solubility theory assumes that SiO_2 gradually dissolves in the lung fluids and in this way induces thickening of the lung tissue.

(iii) A further possibility which must be considered is whether electron emission (outer electrons) from the crystal lattice can have a silicogenic effect. Perhaps the piezoelectric effect [see 'Piezoelectricity' (2.4.2)], produced by the pulsation pressure on crystals in the lungs, may also, to some extent, promote silicogenesis.

The silicogenic action, which leads to hardening of the tissue by the development of tubercles in the connective tissue, is above all caused by quartz dust. Dusts from silicates and other minerals cause no typical silicotic condition but produce divergent types of lung disease, mostly not as serious as silicosis (silicosis is only one specific variety of lung disease caused by dust inhalation).

(c) SUMMARY OF THE FACTORS WHICH CAN CAUSE SILICOSIS

Grain size and mineral composition of the dust, dust concentration, duration of the dust action, climatic conditions, the heaviness of the work performed, physical disposition of the person, proportion of injurious gases in the air breathed.

7.17.2. Bio-crystals and biocrystalline aggregates

These are crystals which have grown in an organic environment (man, animals, plants), and consist mainly of crystalline material with inclusions of non-crystalline organic substances.

BONE

The crystalline part consists of hydroxyl apatite of varying crystal size and texture.

TEETH

The enamel (covering layer) is composed of relatively large apatite crystals and possibly some amorphous $CaCO_3$. Dental cement (thin covering layer on dentine) is also formed of apatite. Dentine consists predominantly of apatite and a certain amount of amorphous $CaCO_3$(?). Tartar: apatite.

GALLSTONES

Crystalline constituents composed of bilirubin urates of Ca and Cu, $CaCO_3$, Ca-phosphate, in addition to albuminous material and often crystalline cholesterol.

RENAL CALCULI

Crystalline constituents, whewellite ($CaC_2O_4.H_2O$, monoclinic) and wedellite ($CaC_2O_4.2H_2O$), also apatite, struvite ($MgNH_4PO_4.6H_2O$), uric acid, brushite ($CaHPO_4.2H_2O$) and whitlockite [β-$Ca_3(PO_4)_2$].

SALIVARY CONCRETIONS

Whitlockite [β-$Ca_3(PO_4)_2$], apatite, calcite.

CALCIFICATION

Of the brain, muscles, lungs, vein stones, eye lenses, in thrombus, in arteriosclerosis, etc.: chiefly apatite.

TOPHI-LIKE DEPOSITS ASSOCIATED WITH GOUT

Crystalline constituents are composed of monosodium urate monohydrate.

ENTEROLITHS IN HORSES AND CATTLE

Struvite $(NH_4)Mg(PO_4).6H_2O$, orthorhombic.

MUSSEL SHELLS, PEARLS, CORALS AND CALCIFICATION OF PLANTS

Mostly calcite or aragonite.

7.18. Silicones

Silicones are a class of synthetic materials, which, on account of their unusual properties, are finding increasing application as industrial and adjuvant substances (silicone oils, silicone rubber, silicone resins, silicone varnishes, silicone films on the surfaces of solids and as hydrophobic and parting compounds, etc.). They possess excellent electrical characteristics at both extremely low and high temperatures and are very resistant to weather and other influences.

From the point of view of structural chemistry they take up an intermediate position between the silicates [see 'Lattices resonating between ionic and homopolar' (2.3)] and the organic polymers. The basic structural unit in the silicones also is the SiO_4 tetrahedron.

Polymeric compounds occur in which silicon atoms are bonded by oxygen atoms (siloxane bonding: Si—O—Si) with the silicon valencies not satisfied by oxygen being saturated by at least one organic group (R). The structure of a simple linear polymeric silicone (organopolysiloxane) is shown below.

$$\begin{array}{cccc}
R & R & R & R \\
| & | & | & | \\
-Si-O-Si-O-Si-O-Si- \\
| & | & | & | \\
R & R & R & R
\end{array}$$

R is an organic group (e.g. CH_3)

In a similar way to the silicates, organo-polysiloxane molecules may also form structures composed of separate groups, two or more groups, chains, rings and frameworks. The following functional groups (siloxane units) are possible (after W. Noll):

$$
\begin{array}{c}
\mid \\
O \\
\mid \\
-O-Si-O- \\
\mid \\
O \\
\mid
\end{array}
\quad
\begin{array}{l}
\text{tetrafunctional} \\
\text{(four-fold bonding)}
\end{array}
$$

$$
\begin{array}{c}
\mid \\
O \\
\mid \\
R-Si-O- \\
\mid \\
O \\
\mid
\end{array}
\quad
\begin{array}{l}
\text{trifunctional} \\
\text{(three-fold bonding)}
\end{array}
$$

$$
\begin{array}{c}
R \\
\mid \\
R-Si-O- \\
\mid \\
O
\end{array}
\quad
\begin{array}{l}
\text{difunctional} \\
\text{(two-fold bonding)}
\end{array}
$$

$$
\begin{array}{c}
R \\
\mid \\
R-Si-O- \\
\mid \\
R
\end{array}
\quad
\begin{array}{l}
\text{monofunctional} \\
\text{(single bonding)}
\end{array}
$$

$$
\begin{array}{c}
R \\
\mid \\
R-Si-R \\
\mid \\
R
\end{array}
\quad
\begin{array}{l}
\text{non-functional} \\
\text{(no bonding is possible)}
\end{array}
$$

By combination of functionally-different siloxane units in one and the same molecule, systematic synthesis of the different polymer types (oils, rubber, resin) is possible, since each of the siloxane units possesses specific properties which depend on its functionality.

The dependence of methyl silicones on the functionality of the siloxane units
$(R = CH_3)$

Siloxane units	$SiO_{4/2}$	$RSiO_{3/2}$	$R_2SiO_{2/2}$	$R_3SiO_{1/2}$
Functionality (number of bonds)	4	3	2	1
State	Silicic acid-like polyester	resin, rubber, oil		low-boiling liquids

It is further possible to modify and substitute, in various ways, the hydrocarbon radicals bonded to the silicon atoms in silicones.

7.19. Application of X-ray structural investigation

Methods of investigation, which depend on the behaviour of crystalline material in an X-ray beam [see 'Crystal physics, Crystals and X-rays' (2.4.2)] are becoming increasingly important in science and technology.

7.19.1. Investigation of crystalline materials and mixtures of materials

(A) DEMONSTRATION OF A CRYSTALLINE STATE

If no diffraction and interference of the X-rays by the material investigated occurs the substance is amorphous to X-rays. In such a case it cannot be decided whether the substance is really amorphous or whether it is composed of extremely fine crystalline particles, which produce insufficient or no interference.

(B) IDENTIFICATION OF ONE OR MORE CRYSTALLINE SUBSTANCES IN A MATERIAL

Since each crystalline substance possesses a specific crystal lattice which diffracts the incident X-rays correspondingly, typical X-ray diffraction patterns result for each crystalline substance. By comparison of the X-ray diffraction data, it is possible to identify a material and also other crystalline and amorphous substances, which may occur.

(C) QUANTITATIVE DETERMINATION OF THE PROPORTION OF CRYSTALLINE MATERIAL IN A SUBSTANCE

In many cases this is possible by interpretation of the intensity of the diffraction produced by the crystal lattices of the various substances (greater amounts of a substance produce more intense diffraction patterns). Here, however, a number of factors must be taken into consideration such as the degree of crystallinity of the individual minerals, grain size, interference by other substances, accidents in preparation of the specimen to be investigated, etc.

(D) DISTINCTION BETWEEN DIFFERENT MODIFICATIONS OF A SUBSTANCE

The modifications of a substance (e.g. SiO_2: quartz-tridymite-cristobalite-quartz glass) cannot be distinguished chemically. Since the crystal modifications always possess differing crystal lattices with varying X-ray diffraction patterns, identification is usually possible without any difficulty.

(E) ESTIMATION OF THE GRAIN SIZE OF POLYCRYSTALLINE MATERIALS

The width of the reflections in the diffraction patterns increases with decreasing grain size. This fact enables estimation of the grain size to be made (Fig. 101).

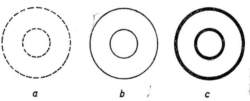

a b c

Figure 101   Grain sizes of polycrystalline materials shown by the diffraction rings in a Debye–Scherrer photograph: (a) coarse-grained, (b) fine-grained, (c) extremely fine-grained.

(F) DETERMINATION OF THE CRYSTALLOGRAPHIC ORIENTATION OF CRYSTALS

The crystallographic orientation, i.e. the attitude of the crystallographic axes, of fragments of single crystals showing no recognizable external form can be determined by means of Laue photographs (Fig. 44).

Investigations of the arrangement of crystallites in materials (texture of tubes, wires, sheet-metal, castings, fibrous material, etc.): crystalline industrial materials (metals, ceramics, etc.) are usually a mixture of a large number of minute single crystals (crystallites). These crystallites can become crystallographically-oriented in certain directions by working; this may be undesirable because the anisotropy of crystals then has an intensified effect (tensile strength, tendency to become corroded, expansion, electrical conductivity, etc.). This preferred orientation of crystals of the same kind leads to the frequent occurrence of specific identical X-ray reflections which can easily be recognized (Fig. 102).

Investigation of the influence of working and heat treatment on crystal orientation and crystallite size: during these processes the crystallites composing polycrystalline materials often take up a preferred

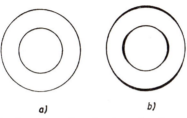

a)   *b)*

Figure 102 Determination of preferred orientation in polycrystalline material (Debye–Scherrer photograph): (a) no preferred orientation, (b) preferred orientation is recognizable by the thickening of the diffraction rings.

orientation or show an increase in crystal size. Coarse-crystallinity can be recognized by the occurrence of dark spots in the diffraction rings of Debye–Scherrer photographs, whereas fine-grained material produces uniformly-black diffraction rings.

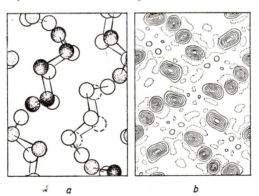

a   *b*

Figure 103 Structure of α-selenium: (a) projection of the structure, (b) corresponding map of the electron density (after W. Kleber).

(G) INVESTIGATION OF THE INFLUENCE OF IMPURITIES ON CRYSTALLINE MATERIALS

The formation of mixed crystals can be recognized by change in the position of lines in the diffraction pattern, since the lattice constants of mixed crystals are changed with respect to those of the pure substance. Particularly applicable to the study of metal alloys.

7.19.2. Determination of crystal structure

In many cases, this is prerequisite for the synthetic preparation, and for the characterization of inorganic and organic crystals. Up to the present time, the structures of not only almost all minerals and metals but of a large number of organic substances also (e.g. haemoglobin, penicillin, amino-acids, etc.) have been determined. A structural analysis comprises determination of the form and size of the unit cell, determination of the lattice-symmetry, calculation of the number of atoms in the unit cell, determination of the type of Bravais-lattice and the space group and evaluation of the atomic positions. The latter are principally determined by Fourier syntheses. It is assumed that electrons are distributed continuously over the unit cell and that the atoms are located in the positions of high electron density. Between these positions the electron density is lower (Fig. 103).

7.20. Application of polarizing microscopy to the testing of materials

The development of microscopic techniques has always been greatly influenced by mineralogy and they have been applied in a wide range of ways [see 'Crystal physics' (2.4)].

7.20.1. Possible information obtained by microscopic examination

Distinction between crystalline and amorphous materials; identification of minerals, rocks and synthetic products; quantitative determination of the components in a mixture or solid; estimation of the chemical composition, especially of mixed crystals, and of the amount of volatile constituents in coals; behaviour on heating or cooling; determination of strain; determination of textures and structures in polycrystalline materials (fabric analysis); identification by microchemical reactions; behaviour of the specimen examined on attack by chemicals and solvents; observation of crystallization from solutions or melts; determination of the fluorescent properties in ultraviolet light; microhardness testing of single grains; recognition of inclusions, impurities and unmixing in single grains or glass; recording of the results by photomicrography.

7.20.2. Methods

POLARIZING MICROSCOPY IN TRANSMITTED LIGHT FOR
MATERIALS WHICH ARE TRANSPARENT UNDER THE MICROSCOPE

Preparation: thin sections (20–30 μ thick slice of the material); powder specimens in the form of ground material or material which already exists as a powder, which are set in synthetic resin or liquids (of known refractive index).

Applicable to:

(a) Examination of grain form and size, cleavage and fracture of individual grains, twinning, inclusions (solid, liquid or gaseous) and intergrowths of individual grains, unmixing in single grains, qualitative and quantitative determination of the separate components, type and amount of the impurities.

(b) Determination of the optical properties of a material for the purpose of identification: optical isotropy and anisotropy; colour and pleochroism; straight/inclined extinction with respect to bounding faces or cleavage cracks; refraction of light, n (single or double refraction); nature of the double refraction (positive or negative); interference colours (polarization colours); distinction between uniaxial and bi-axial minerals, size of the optic axial angle; dispersion; double refraction caused by strain; variation of the optical properties produced by variation in the chemical composition (e.g. mixed crystals).

(c) Testing the behaviour of materials with respect to chemical attack and solvents, carrying out micro-chemical and staining tests for the identification of single grains.

(d) Determinations by means of auxiliary microscopic equipment; fluorescence in ultraviolet light; micro-hardness testing; behaviour on heating or cooling (modification transformation, sintering, melting, solidification, crystallization, thermal decomposition); fabric analysis (only possible in thin section) to determine the orientation of single crystals of polycrystalline materials by means of their optical properties in order to establish: anisotropy in the crystal fabric (determinative for thermal conductivity, electrical conductivity, compressive or tensile strength, solubility, corrosion, permeability, magnetization, resistance to abrasion, thermal expansion, etc.), movement directions in the fabric, types of deformation and their dynamic interpretation.

Materials examined by transmitted-light microscopy: all minerals and rocks that are transparent under the microscope and also coals, glasses, glazes, enamels, synthetic crystalline inorganic and organic substances, ceramics and refractories, plastics, textiles, biological substances (tissues,

P

wood, teeth, bones, renal calculi, etc.), bonding materials, corrosion products, slags, ashes, all types of dust, products of dressing, slurries, filter cake, deposits formed in industrial processes, archaeological objects (evaluation of the possible sources, restoration, etc.).

POLARIZING MICROSCOPY IN INCIDENT LIGHT

Depends on the reflection of light by a polished surface of the material.

Specimens: polished sections, thin sections or grains embedded in synthetic resin. Applicable to:

(a) Determination of optical properties; optical isotrophy or anisotropy; reflectivity (reflection coefficient); colour and reflection pleochroism (bireflection); internal reflection; anisotropic effects.

(b) Determination of grain shape, grain size, cleavage and fracture surfaces of individual grains, twinning, inclusions, unmixing and intergrowths of individual grains, qualitative and quantitative determination of individual components.

(c) Etching to identify individual grains and to reveal the grain structure, micro-chemical reactions, comparative hardness determinations, fabric analysis (to a more limited extent than under transmitted light), determination of the total volatile content of coals.

(d) Determination with auxiliary equipment [see 'Transmitted light microscopy' (7.20.2)]. The possibilities for fabric analysis are, however, limited.

Materials examined by incident-light microscopy: ores, metals, metal alloys, coals, cokes, slags, ashes, cement clinker, ceramics, refractory constructional materials, cermets, glass, glazes, enamel, ore concentrates, products of dressing.

BIBLIOGRAPHY

(suitable for further study)

Allemand, T. E., *Microscopic Identification of Inclusions in Steel*, British Iron and Steel Research Association (London, 1962).

Barth, T. F. W., *Theoretical Petrology*, 2nd ed. Wiley (New York and London, 1962).

Bateman, A. M., *Economic Mineral Deposits*, Wiley (New York and London, 1958).

Bates, R. L., *Geology of the Industrial Rocks and Minerals*, Harper and Row (New York, 1960).

Brewer, R., *Fabric and Mineral Analysis of Soils*, Wiley (New York, 1964).

Buerger, M. J., *Elementary Crystallography*, Wiley (New York and London, 1956).

Bunn, C. W., *Chemical Crystallography*, 2nd ed. Oxford University Press (Oxford, 1961).

Cameron, E. N., *Ore Microscopy*, Wiley (New York, 1959).

Chesters, J. H., *Steelplant Refractories*, United Steel Companies Ltd (Sheffield, 1957).

Dana, J. D., and Hurlbut, C. S., *Manual of Mineralogy*, Wiley (New York, 1959).

Dana, J. D., Palache, C., Berman, H., and Frondel, C., *The System of Mineralogy*, 7th ed. 2 vols. Wiley (New York, 1951).

Deer, W. A., Howie, R. A., and Zussman, J., *Rock Forming Minerals*, Longmans (London, 1962).

Eitel, W., *Silicate Science*, vols. I–V, Academic Press (New York and London, 1964–6).

Garrels, R. M., and Christ, C. L., *Solutions, Minerals and Equilibria*, Harper and Row (New York, 1965).

Gay, R., *Cours de Cristallographie*, vols. I, II, III, Gautier-Villars (Paris, 1958–61).

Grim, R. E., *Applied Clay Mineralogy*, McGraw-Hill (New York, Toronto, and London, 1962).

Gumz, W., Kirsch, H., and Mackowsky, M. Th., *Schlackenkunde*, Springer-Verlag (Berlin and Göttingen, 1958).

Heinrich, E. W., *Mineralogy and Geology of Radioactive Raw Materials*, McGraw-Hill (New York, Toronto, and London, 1958).

Hey, M. H., *Chemical Index of Minerals*, British Museum (Natural History) (London, 1956).

Hömig, H. E., *Physikochemische Grundlagen der Spiesewasserchemie*, 2nd ed. Vulkan-Verlag Dr W. Classen (Essen, 1963).

Insley, H., and Fréchette, Van Derck, *Microscopy of Ceramics and Cements*, Academic Press (New York, 1955).

Int. Comm of Coal Petrology, *Lexique International de Pétrographie des Carbons*, 2nd ed. Centre National de la recherche scientifique (Paris, 1963).

Johnstone, S. J., and Johnstone, M. G., *Minerals for the Chemical and Allied Industries*, Chapman and Hall (London, 1961).

Kerr, P. F., *Optical Mineralogy*, McGraw-Hill (London, 1959)

Kleber, W., *Einführung in die Kristallographie*, 8th ed. VEB Verlag Technik (Berlin, 1963).

Kraus, E. H., and Hunt, W. F., *Mineralogy*, 5th ed. McGraw-Hill (New York, 1951).

Krinov, E. L., *Principles of Meteoritics*, Pergamon (London, 1960).

Mason, B., *Principles of Geochemistry*, Wiley (New York, 1958).

Milner, H. B. *Sedimentary Petrography*, Allen and Unwin (London, 1962).

Moos, A. v., and Quervain, F. de, *Technische Gesteinskunde*, 2nd ed. Birkhäuser Verlag (Basel and Stuttgart, 1967).

Muan, A., and Osborn, E. F., *Phase Equilibria among Oxides in Steel-Making* Addison-Wesley (Reading, Mass., 1965).

Norton, F. H., *Elements of Ceramics*, Addison-Wesley (London, 1952).

Phillips, F. C., *An Introduction to Crystallography*, Longmans (London, 1951).

Ryshewitch, E., *Oxide Ceramics*, Academic Press (New York, 1960).

Seeley, W., *Industrial Minerals and Rocks*, 3rd ed. American Institute of Mining and Metallurgical Engineers (New York, 1960).

Smith, G. F. H., *Gemstones*, Methuen (London, 1958).

Strunz, H., *Mineralogische Tabellen*, 4th ed. Akademische Verlagsgesellschaft (Leipzig, 1966).

Wahlstrom, E. E., *Petrographic Mineralogy*, Wiley (New York and London, 1955).

Winkler, H. G. F., *Petrogenesis of Metamorphic Rocks*, Springer-Verlag (New York, 1966).

Wooster, W. A., *Experimental Crystal Physics*, Oxford University Press, (Oxford, 1957).

INDEX

The structural formulae given with mineral names are after H. Strunz, *Mineralogische Tabellen*, 3rd Edition, 1957. In the text, condensed formulae or oxide formulae are often used.

abrasives, 184–6
acenaphthene, 194
achondrites, 184
acid rocks, 46, 48
actinolite (alkali-bearing amphibole), Na$_2$Ca$_4$(Mg,Fe)$_{10}$[(OH)$_2$O$_2$/Si$_{16}$O$_{44}$], 82, 99, 181
adsorbed water, 121
aegirine, NaFe(Si$_2$O$_6$), 127
aeolian sediments, 57
agate, 110
Agricola, 4
aircraft, materials for, 132
air pollution, 176, 190–1
åkermanite, 152, 154
alabaster, 112, 114
Albertus v. Bollstaedt, called Magnus, 4
albite (soda felspar), NaAlSi$_3$O$_8$, 33, 65, 107
Algonkian, 44
alkali granite, 51
alkaline rocks, 49, 51
alkali syenite, 51
allanite, 95
allochemical recrystallization, 64–5
alloys, 18, 203
alluvial deposits, 76–7
almandine, 109, 186
altered rocks, *see* 'metamorphic rocks'
alumina, 56, 199, 202
    bricks, 128, 129
    ceramics, 132
aluminium, 18, 31, 56, 84, 142, 202
alumogel (kliachite), AlOOH + nH$_2$O, 84
amazonstone, 109
amblygonite, LiAl(F/PO$_4$), 72, 90
amesite, 105
amethyst, 110
amorphous materials, 5, 209
amosite, (Mg,Fe)$_7$(OH)$_2$Si$_8$O$_{22}$, 99, 181
amphiboles (hornblendes, 21, 99

amphibolite, 114
andalusite, 66, 73, 117, 119
andesine (plagioclase), 107
andesite, 51, 54, 113
angle of rest, 169
anglesite, PbSO$_4$, 76, 78, 90
anhedral crystals, 50, 52
anhydrite, CaSO$_4$, 22, 33, 60, 63, 80, 111–112, 144
anisotropy, 5, 25, 137
    and thermal properties, 28–9
ankerite, CaFe(CO$_3$)$_2$, 89
anorthite (lime felspar), CaAl$_2$Si$_2$O$_8$, 33, 64, 107, 126, 153
anthophyllite, (Mg,Fe)$_7$(OH/Si$_4$O$_{11}$)$_2$, 99, 181
anthracite, 61
antimonite (stibnite, antimony glance), Sb$_2$S$_3$, 23, 74, 84
antimony, 25, 74, 84
anti-stress minerals, 66
apatite, Ca$_5$[(F,OH,Cl)(PO$_4$)$_3$], 11, 12, 25, 53, 73, 98, 111, 155, 157, 206
aplite, 51, 53
aquamarine, 108
aragonite, CaCO$_3$, 22, 28, 102
Archaean, 44
arenites, 57
argentite (silver glance), Ag$_2$S, 76, 78, 94
argillites, 57, 60
argyrodite, 4Ag$_2$S.GeS$_2$, 87
Aristotle, 4
arkose, 58, 59
arsenic, 75, 84
arsenopyrite, FeAsS, 82, 84
asbestos, 11, 99, 120, 180–1
asbolite (cobalt-bearing MnO$_2$.nH$_2$O), 86
ash, 58, 186–7
asphalt, 62
Atlantic-type rocks, 49
atmophile elements, 38

atmosphere, 38, 41
atomic bonding, 1
atomic radius, 17
attapulgite (palygorskite), $Mg_{2\cdot5}[(H_2O)_2/OH/Si_4O_{10}]$, 105
Atterberg consistency limits, 164
augite (specific), $Ca_{6\cdot5}Na_{0\cdot5}FeMg_6(Al,Fe,Ti,)_2(Al_{1\cdot5-3\cdot5}Si_{14\cdot5-12\cdot5}O_{48})$, 24, 26, 48, 49, 51, 52, 65, 82
augite gneiss, 67
autometamorphism, 63
autunite (lime uranium mica), $Ca(UO_2/PO_4)_2.12–10H_2O$, 97, 140
Avicenna, 4
axes, crystallographic, 8–10
azurite, $Cu_3(OH/CO_3)_2$, 76, 87

baddeleyite, ZrO_2, 98
ballas, 185
ball clay, 120
ball iron, 150
ballistic missiles, materials for, 132
barium felspar (celsian), 154
Bartolinus, Erasmus, 4
barytes, $BaSO_4$, 22, 74, 75, 99
basalt, 47, 51, 52, 55, 113
    cast, 113
basaltic tuffs, 59, 113
base exchange, 123–4
basic rocks, 46, 48
basic slag, 155
bauxite, 67, 84, 119, 140
    bricks, 129
    deposits, 77
bedding, 59
beidellite, $Al_{2\cdot17}[(OH)_2/Al_{0\cdot83}Si_{3\cdot17}O_{10}]_{0\cdot32}Na_{0\cdot32}(H_2O)_4$, 104
bending strength, 27
bentonite, 59, 77, 104, 156
beryl, $Al_2Be_3(Si_6O_{18})$, 48, 72, 85, 108, 119, 141
beryllia ceramics, 132
beryllium, 18, 85, 142
bilirubin urates, 206
biocrystals, 206–7
biogenic sediments, 59–63
biomineralogy, 204–7
biophile elements, 38
biosphere, 38
biotite, $K(Mg,Fe,Mn)_3[(OH,F)_2AlSi_3O_{10}]$, 24, 47, 49, 51, 112
    gneiss, 67, 69

bismite (bismuth ochre), Bi_2O_3, 85
bismuth, 85, 140
bismuthinite, Bi_2S_3, 85
bismutite, $Bi_2(O_2/CO_3)$, 85
bitumen, 62–3
bituminous limestone, 60
blackband ironstones, 81
black earths, 179
blast furnace slag, 150
blasting, resistance of rocks to, 170
blue clay, 120
boehmite, γ-AlOOH, 57, 84
bog iron ore, 79
boiling points, 15
bole, 104, 182
bonding,
    covalent, 16
    electrovalent, 15–16
    heterodesmic, 17
    heteropolar, 15–16
    homodesmic, 17
    homopolar, 16
    hybrid (mixed), 17
    inter-molecular, 16
    ionic, 15–16
    metallic, 16
    mixed, 17
    polar, 15–16
    Van der Waals, 16–17
bonding materials, 143–50
    air-hardening, 143–5
    for foundry sands, 156–7
    hydraulic, 144, 145–50
bone, 206
    china, 131
boracite, β-$Mg_3(Cl/B_7O_{13})$, 63, 100
borates, 20, 79
borax (tincal), $Na_2B_4O_7.10H_2O$, 100
borazon, BN, 186, 193
borides, 133
bornite (variegated copper ore), 74, 76, 78, 87, 154
boron, 75, 99–100, 141, 142
    carbide, 186
    nitride, see 'borazon'
bort, 106, 185
boulangerite, $5PbS.2Sb_2S_3$, 90
bournonite (wheel-ore), $2PbS.Cu_2S.Sb_2S_3$, 74, 81, 84, 90
Bragg W. H., 4
Bragg equation, 34–5
braggite, $(Pt,Pd,Ni)S$, 93
braunite, 81, 91
Bravais, Auguste, 4

Bravais lattices, 6–7
breccia, 58, 59
bredigite, γ-$Ca_2(SiO_4)$, 152
breeder fuel, 140–2
Breithaupt, 4
breunnerite (mesitite), 65
brick clays, 121
bröggerite (thorium-rich pitchblende), 96
bromargyrite (bromyrite), AgBr, 100
bromine, 100
bronzite, $(Mg,Fe)_2Si_2O_6$, 51
brown earths, 179
brown spar, 74
brushite, 206
bytownite (plagioclase), 107

cadmium, 28, 85, 142
caesium, 85
Cainozoic, 44
calaverite, 88
calc-alkali rocks, 49, 51
calcareous marl, 61
calcareous mica schists, 67, 68
calcareous muds, 59, 60
calcareous sandstones, 59
calcareous sinter, 60
calcareous tufa, 60
calcification, 207
calcite, $CaCO_3$, 22, 23, 59, 65, 67, 74, 100, 102
    coefficient of expansion of, 28
    etch figures, 13
    hardness, 25
    lattice, 22, 23
    magnetism, 31
    refractive index, 33
    thermal conductivity, 29
    twinning, 27–8
calcium, 18
calc-phyllite, 67, 68
calaverite, $(Au,Ag)Te_2$, 88, 94
caliche, 114
calomel, Hg_2Cl_2, 91
Cambrian system, 44
carbides, 133
carbon, 36
carbonado, 185
carbonates, 55, 59, 61
carbon-bearing bricks, 129–30
carbon dioxide, 62
Carboniferous system, 44
carnallite, $KCl.MgCl_2.6H_2O$, 63, 117
carnelian, 110

carnotite, $K_2(UO_2/VO_4).3H_2O$, 78, 97, 140
carrolite (copper-bearing Co_3S_4), 86
cassiterite (tinstone), SnO_2, 74, 154
    placers, 77, 95
cast basalt, 113
cataclasis, 66
cat's eye, 110
CdS, 34
celestine, 118
celsian (barium felspar), $Ba(Al_2Si_2O_8)$, 154
cement(s), 146–50
    bacillus, 149
    clinker, 146–9
    setting, 149
ceramics, 119–33
    coarse, 127–30
    fine, 130–3
    industrial, 130–1
    raw materials of, 119–20
    refractory, 127–30
cerite, $(Ca,Fe)Ce_3H[(OH)_2/SiO_4/Si_2O_7]$, 95
cermets, 132
cerussite, $PbCO_3$, 76, 78, 90
cervantite, 84
chalcedony (finely fibrous quartz), 57, 110, 115
chalcocite (copper glance), CuS, 76, 78, 81, 86, 154
chalcophile elements, 38
chalk, 60
chamosite, 89
chamotte, 128, 156
chemical sediments, 57, 59–63
chemical weathering, 55, 56–7
chemiluminescence, 33
chernozem, 179
Chile saltpetre, 79, 180
China clay, 120
chloanthite, $NiAs_{3-2}$, 92
chlorides, 60
chlorite, 55, 65, 66, 105, 124
    schists, 68
chloritoid, $(Fe,Mg)_2Al_4[(OH)_4/O_2(SiO_4)_2]$, 66
chondrites, 184
chrome-magnesite bricks, 129
chromic oxide, Cr_2O_3, 186
chromite (chrome iron ore), $FeCr_2O_4$, 86, 119
    bricks, 119, 129
chromium, 18, 71, 86

chrysoberyl (alexandrite), Al_2BeO_4, 28
chrysocolla, $CuSiO_3.nH_2O$, 87, 111
chrysolite, 110
chrysoprase, 110
citrine, 110
cinnabar, HgS, 74, 91
clarite, 62
clarodurite, 62
clastic sediments, 57–9
clay(s), 57, 58, 59, 67, 120–6, 145
  behaviour of, in ceramic processes,
    120–6
    with organic compounds, 125
    with water, 121–5
  deposits of, 77
  marl, 61
  minerals, 55, 101–6, 143
    in soils, 180
    with double chain structure, 105
    with variable layering structure, 106
  thermal behaviour of, 125–6
cleavage, 26
cleveite, 97
clinker, 188
  phases, 146–9
clinochlore, 105
clinoenstatite, 130, 153
clunch, 59
coal(s), 42, 60, 80, 120
  formation of, 61–2, 80
  seams, 172
cobalt, 18, 31, 74, 86
cobaltite, CoAsS, 86
coffinite, $U[(Si,H_4)O_4]$, 140
cold-drawing, 27
colemanite, $Ca[B_2BO_4(OH)_3].H_2O$, 100,
  140
cologne umber, 182
columbite, $(Fe,Mn)(Nb,Ta)_2O_6$, 92, 141
compaction, of foundation soils, 168–9
compressibility, 165
  modulus of, 160
compressive strength, 27, 160
concrete, 149
conglomerate, 58, 59
consolidated rocks, 159
  foundations in, 168
  hardness of, 166–7
  landslides in, 170
contact metamorphism, 63, 66, 67
contact metasomatism, 63
contact-pneumatolytic replacement deposits, 73–4
controlling devices (nuclear reactors), 141

cooperite, PtS, 93
copper, 18, 86–7
  dendritic crystals, 12
  deposits, 74
  glance, see 'chalcocite'
  matte, 150
  oxide, 202
  pyrites (chalcopyrites), $CuFeS_2$, 74, 78,
    79, 81, 82, 86, 154
  slag, 150, 153–4
coral limestones, 60
corals, 64, 207
cordierite, α-$Mg_2Al_3(Al,Si_5O_{18})$, 32, 66,
  111, 126, 130
corrosion,
  by flue gases, 190–1
  in furnaces, 186–91
  in high-pressure steam generators, 191
  protection of metal coatings from,
    203–4
corundum, α-Al_2O_3, 25, 29, 33, 106, 108,
  120, 185, 186, 199
  bricks, 129
cosmic dust, 184
covellite, CuS, 87
Cretaceous system, 44
cristobalite, SiO_2, 115, 125, 126, 127,
  128
crocidolite,
  $(Na,K,Ca)_{3-4}Mg_6Fe(Fe,Al)_{3-4}$
  $[(OH)_4/Si_{16}O_{44}]$, 99, 181
cross-beeding, 59
cryolite, β-$Na_3(AlF_6)$, 72, 84, 157
cryptocrystalline rocks, 51
cryptomelane, $K_2Mn_8O_{16}$, 75
crysoberyl, 108
crystal chemistry, 14–24
crystal classes, 9
  and piezoelectricity, 30
crystal etching, 14
crystal faces, 10–11
crystal forms, 11
crystal growth, 13–14, 192–5
  by electrolysis, 194
  from the melt, 13, 193–4
  by recrystallization, 194
  from solution, 13, 192
  from the vapour, 13, 194
  velocity of, 13–14
crystal habit, 11
crystal lattice, 6–7, 17–24
crystalline schists, 67, 81
crystallization nuclei, 13, 14
crystalloblastic structures, 65

crystallographic axes, 8–10
  orientation of, 210–11
crystallography, 5–13
crystalloluminescence, 33
crystal optics, 31–3
crystal phosphors, 33, 34
crystal physics, 24–36
crystals, 192–9
  bond types in, 15–24
  deformation, 26–8, 196–8
  dissolution of, 14
  doubly-refracting, 31–2, 33
  electrical conductivity of, 29–30, 196–9
  ferromagnetic, 31
  ideal, 14
  impurities in, investigation of, 211–12
  investigation of, 209–14
  for lasers and masers, 199
  magnetism of, 31
  paramagnetic, 31
  singly-refracting, 33
  specific heat of, 24–5
  thermal conductivity of, 29
  thermal expansion of, 28–9
  twinning of, 11
crystal structure determination, 212
cubanite, 81, 154
cube-crushing strength, 160
cube face, 10
cuprite, Cu_2O, 87, 154
current impulse counters, 196
Cyprian (Turkish) umber, 182

dacite, 51, 54
dam construction, 169
Darcy's Law, 162
de-acidification of drinking water, 177
decarbonation plants, deposits in, 192
deformation, elastic, 26
  of crystals, 26–8
  plastic, 27–8
delafossite, $CuFeO_2$, 154
demantoid (andradite, lime-iron garnet),
  $Ca_3Fe_2(SiO_4)_3$, 109
dendrites, 11, 12
density,
  bulk, 24
  of rocks, 159
  true, 24
dental ceramics, 131
descendent mineral deposits, 81
descloizite, 97
detrital (placer) deposits, 76–7
devitrification, 135–6

diabase, 55
diagenesis, 58
diamagnetic crystals, 31
diamond, 18, 21, 25, 106, 185
  industrial, 185
  synthesis, 193
diaspore, α-AlOOH, 57, 84, 119
  bricks, 129
diatomaceous earths, 60, 116
dickite, $Al_4[(OH)_8/Si_4O_{10}]$, 103
dilation, 28–9
diopside, $CaMg(Si_2O_6)$, 81, 153
  gneiss, 67
diorite, 46, 47, 51, 54, 67
  porphyry, 51
dioritic magmas, 49, 54–5
direct-process slags, 154
dislocation metamorphism, 63
disthene, see 'kyanite'
dolerite, 51, 113
dolomite, $CaMg(CO_3)_2$, 13, 59, 64, 65,
  74, 100, 102
  bricks, 129
dolomites, 60, 119, 140, 157
dolomitic limestones, 59, 60, 145
dolomitic marl, 59
dolomitic mud, 59
double refraction, 31–2, 33
dressing, of minerals, 173–5
drillability of rock, 172
drilling fluid, 171
drying of soils, 164
dumortierite, $(Al,Fe)_7[O_3/BO_3/(SiO_4)_3]$,
  73, 117
dunite, 47, 51, 55
durite, 62
duroclarite, 62
dust, respiratory diseases caused by,
  204–6
dyke rocks, see 'hypabyssal rocks'
dynamic metamorphism, 63
dyscrystalline rocks, 51

earthenware, coarse, 127
earth's crust,
  average chemical composition of, 37–
    40
  composition of, in atomic and volume
    per cent, 39–40
  geochemical balance, 40–2
effusive rocks, see 'extrusive rocks'
elastic characteristics of rocks, 160–1
elastic deformation, 160
elasticity, modulus of, 160

electrical conductivity, 29–30, 161
electrical porcelain, 131
electrocorundum, 186
electroluminescence, 33
electromagnetic dressing, 173
electron diffraction patterns, 35
electron emission, 34
electronic conduction, 29
electrostatic separation, 173
elements, as rock-forming minerals, 45
eleolite, *see* 'nepheline syenite'
emerald (green beryl), $Al_2Be_3[Si_6O_{18}]$, 108, 199
emery, 67, 106, 185
enamels, 138
 faults in, 138
 raw materials, 138
endellite, *see* 'halloysite'
engineering geology, 158
enteroliths, 207
epidote, $Ca_2(Al,Fe)Al_2$ $[O/OH.SiO_4/Si_2O_7]$, 66, 82, 111
 chlorite schists, 67, 68
 gneiss, 69
epitaxis, 11–13
epizone, 66
epsomite (Epsom salts), 78, 117
eruptive rocks, *see* 'volcanic rocks'
eschynite, 95
essential constituents (of rocks), 43
etch figures, 13, 14
etching, 14
etch pits, 14
ethane, 62
eucrystalline, *see* 'holocrystalline'
evaporites, 60
exhalation deposits, 75
exinite, 62
exploration for mineral deposits, 70, 170–1
extreme conditions, materials for, 132–3
extrusive rocks, 50–1, 53, 54, 55

face-types (crystals), 10–11
fayalite (iron-olivine), $Fe_2[SiO_4]$, 154
FeAl, 18
Fe_3Al, 18
Fedorov, E. von, 4
felsic minerals, 44
felspar ceramics, 130
felspar pegmatites, 48
felsparphyric basalts, 51, 55
felspars, 22, 25, 44, 48, 49, 55, 59, 107–8, 108–9, 119

felspathoids, 44, 107–8
ferric minerals, 44
ferrite, 31
ferromagnetism, 31
fertility of soils, 180
fertilizer industry, 155
filtering sands, 177
filters, optical, 195
fine ceramics, 130–3
fine china clay, 120
fine earthenware, 130
firebricks, 128
firm ground, 173
flame-fusion process, 199
flint (mainly chalcedony), 128
flotation, 174
flow
 limit, 164
 of magmas, 51
flue dust, 190–1
flue gas, 190–1
 dirt and corrosion caused by, 191
fluorite, CaF_2, 28, 33, 74, 75, 108, 111, 157
fluorspar, *see* 'fluorite deposits', 25, 108
fluviatile sediments, 57
fluxes, in the smelting industry, 157
foamed slag, 151–2
foliation of metamorphic rocks, 66
foraminiferal mud, 60
formations (mineral), 74
forsterite (magnesia olivine), $Mg_2(SiO_4)$, 154
 bricks, 128
fossil fuels, 61–2
foundation ground, rocks as, 167–70
foundation soil,
 compaction, 168–9
 physical behaviour, 163–7
 stabilization, 168–9
foundry sands, 155–7
foyaite, *see* 'eleolite syenite'
frankeite, $5PbS.3SnS_2.Sb_2S_3$, 96
Frankenheim, M. L., 4
franklinite, $ZnFe_2O_4$, 82, 98
fresh water limestone, 60
frost,
 action, 56
 heaves, 165–6
 lenses, 165
froth flotation, 174
fuels, 80, 186–91
 nuclear, 140, 141–2

fullers earth, 104
fur, from water-softening plants, 192
furnaces, corrosion of, 186–91
fusite, 62

gabbro, 46, 51, 55, 67, 113
  alkali, 46
gabbroic magmas, 48, 55
gadolinite, $Y_2FeBe_2(O/SiO_4)_2$, 95
gaize, 146
galena, *see* 'lead-glance'
gallite, 87
gallium, 87
gallstones, 206
gangue minerals, 74, 171
ganister, 116, 127
garnet, 24, 65, 66, 82, 106, 109, 186
  biotite gneiss, 67
garnierite (nickel chrysotile is hydrated
  nickel silicate), 78, 92
gaseous inclusions in glass, 137
gases, 5
gehlenite, *see* 'melilite'
gem- and precious stones,
  synthetic, 199
gemstone pegmatites, 72
geochemical balance, 40–1
geochemistry, 31–42
geological eras, 44
geotechnics, 158
geothermal gradient, 161–2
germanite, $Cu_3(FeGe)S_4$, 87
germanium, 87
geysers, 61
gibbsite, 57
glacial deposits, 57
glass, 134–8
glass faults, 137–8
glass-formers, 134
glass manufacture (raw materials),
  137
glass-pot clay, 120
glass structure, 134–5
glassy meteorites, 184
glassy state, 134–7
glauberite, $CaNa_2(SO_4)_2$, 116–17
glauber salt (mirabilite), $Na_2[SO_4]$
  $.10H_2O$, 78, 117
glauconite, 59
glazes, 139–40
glazing clay, 120
glide-planes, 27
gliding, 27
gneisses, 67, 68–9

goethite (needle iron ore), α-FeOOH,
  57, 78, 88, 200
gold, 18, 24, 25, 82, 87–8
  deposits, 73, 74
  pegmatites, 72
  placers, 77
Goldschmidt, V. M., 4, 37
goschenite, 108
gossan, 76
gouty deposits, 207
grain size, estimation of, by X-rays, 210
grammatite, *see* 'tremolite'
granite, 46, 47, 51, 52, 67, 112
  porphyry, 51, 53, 112
granitic magmas, 49
granoblastic texture, 65
granodiorite, 46, 47, 51, 54
granulite, 67, 69
graphite, 23, 61, 111, 141, 142, 182, 186
  -bearing products, 130
  thermal conductivity of, 29
gravel, 57–8, 59
gravity concentration (ore-dressing), 174
green beryl, *see* 'emerald'
green corundum, *see* 'sapphire'
greenockite, CdS, 18, 85
greenschists, 67
greywacke, 58, 59
grossular (lime alumina garnet, hessonite, grossularite), 109
Groth, P. von, 4
guano, 180
gummite, 97, 146
gypsum (selenite), $CaSO_4.2H_2O$, 12, 25,
  33, 60, 63, 111–12, 114, 143
  blowing, 149
  hemihydrate, $CaSO_4.\frac{1}{2}H_2O$, 143–4

habit, *see* 'crystal habit'
hafnium, 18, 88, 142
halite, *see* 'rock salt'
halloysite (endellite), Al_4 $[(OH)_8Si_4O_{10}]$
  $(H_2O)_4$, 57, 103, 123
hardness, 25–6
  of rocks, 159–60, 166–7
  testing, 25
hard porcelain, 131
hausmannite, $MnMn_2O_4$, 81, 91
Hauy, René Just, 4
haune, $(Ca,Na)_{8-4}[(SO_4)_{2-1}(AlSiO_4)_6]$, 44
hawk's Eye, 110
hedenbergite, $CaFe[Si_2O_6]$, 154
heliodor (golden beryl), 108
heliotrope, 110

hematite, 57, 65, 75, 88, 111, 181, 200
  mica schists, 81
hemimorphite, $Zn_4[(OH)_2Si_2O_7]H_2O$, 98
hermesite, 91
hessonite, *see* 'grossular'
heterogenite, approx. $Co(OH)_2$, 86
hiddenite, 111
high-alumina,
  bricks, 128
  cement, 149
hilgenstockite, $Ca_4[O/(PO_4)_2]$, 155
holocene, 44
holocrystalline (encrystalline) (rocks), 50
honeystone (mellite), $Al_2(C_{12}O_{12}).18H_2O$, 24
hornblendes, *see* 'amphiboles'
hornblende, 24, 26, 47, 48, 49, 51, 65, 66
  gneiss, 67, 69
hornfels, 67, 68
hornstone, 60
Hume–Rothery phases, 23
humus content, 179
hyaline rocks, 51
hybrid magmas, 49
hydrargillite (gibbsite, in part),
  γ-$Al(OH)_3$, 84
hydrosphere, 41
hydrothermal mineral deposits, 48, 74–5
hydrothermal stage, 48
hydrothermal synthesis, 193
hypabyssal rocks, 50–1, 53
hypersthene, $(Fe,Mg)_2[Si_2O_6]$, 154
hypoxanthite, *see* 'Terra di Sienna'

ideal crystals, 14
idioblastic series, 65
idiomorphic (crystals), 50, 52
idocrase, 111
igneous rocks (magmatic rocks), 44 ff., 112–13
  chemical composition, 45–9
  descriptions, 52–5
  mineral composition, 49
  review of, 44, 50
  structures, 50–2
illite, $K_{0.5}(Al_2,Fe_2,Mg_3)$
  $[(OH)_2/Al_{0.5}Si_{3.5}O_{10}]$, 104–5, 124, 125, 155
  action of heat on, 126
ilmenite (menaccanite), $FeTiO_3$, 53, 65, 71, 77, 89, 96
impregnations, pneumatolitic, 73
indium, 88
inertinite, 62

insulating bricks, 130
intergrowths, oriented and regular, 11–13
interlamellar water, 122
intermediate rocks, 46
intermetallic compounds, 23
iodine, 114
ionic conduction, 29
ionic-exchange, 123–4, 125
ionic radius, 17, 19
ionic spacing, 15
iridium, 18, 24, 93
iron, 18, 31, 56, 88–90
  disintegration (iron spot), of slags and bricks, 153
  jaspilite (iron-bearing flinty rock), 81
  meteorites, 183
  oxides, 200–1
  phosphate coatings on, 203–4
  pyrites, FeS_2, 79
  smelting slags, 150, 151–3
  spathose-, *see* 'siderite'
isochemical recrystallization, 64
isomorphism, 14, 18
isophase recrystallization, 64
isotrophy, isotropic, 5
itabirite, see 'hematite mica schists'

jadeite, $NaAl(Si_2O_6)$, 109
jamesonite, $4PbS.FeS.3Sb_2S_3$, 84
jasper, 110
joints, 52
Jurassic system, 44

kaillite, *see* 'turquoise'
kainite, $KCl.MgSO_4.3H_2O$, 63, 117
kaolin, 77, 103
kaolinite (porcelain earths),
  $Al[(OH)_8Si_4O_{10}]$, 57, 64, 103–4, 123, 124, 125, 156
  action of heat on, 126
katazone, 66
Kepler, Johannes, 4
kernite (rasorite), $Na_2B_4O_7.4H_2O$, 100, 141
kieselguhr, 60, 116, 120
kieserite, $MgSO_4.H_2O$, 63, 117
kimberlite (mica peridotite), 72
kinetic metamorphism, 63
kliachite, *see* 'alumogel'
knot (fault in glass), 138
knotenschiefer, 67
krennerite, $(Au,Ag)Te_2$, 88

kunzite, 111
kyanite (disthene), $AlAl(OSiO_4)$, 26, 65, 66, 73, 117, 119

labradorite (lime-soda felspar), 55, 107, 109
lacustrine Cretaceous rocks, 168
lake ores, 79
landslides, 169–70
lapis-lazuli, see 'lazurite'
larnite, β-$Ca_2(SiO_4)$, 152
larvikite, 54
lasers, crystals for, 199
laterite deposits, 77
lattice(s), 6–7, 17–24
 energy,
  and specific heat, 25
  and hardness, 26
 imperfections, 13
 planes, 6
 points, 6
 spacing, 6
 structures
  list of, for many compounds, 18–24
  and piezoelectricity, 30
  and whiskers, 199
Laue, M. von, 4
Laue diagrams, 34
laurite, RuS_2, 93
lautarite, $Ca(IO_3)_2$, 114
Laves phases, 23
lazurite (lapis lazuli), $(Na,Ca)_8$ $[(SO_4,S,Cl)_2(AlSiO_4)_6]$, 109
lead, 18, 90
 -glance (galena), PbS, 23, 74, 79, 81, 82, 90, 154
 slag, 150, 154
lenses, 195
lepidocrocite, γ-FeOOH, 57, 88, 200
lepidolite (lithium mica zinnwaldite), $LKi_{1\cdot5}Al_{1\cdot5}[(F,OH,\frac{1}{2}O)_2AlSi_3O_{10}]$, 85, 90, 112
leptite iron ores, 82
leucite, α-$K(AlSi_2O_6)$, 22, 24, 56, 66, 107, 108, 153
 basalt, 55
leucocratic rocks, 44
leukosaphir, 108
light metal pegmatites, 72
light-weight firebricks, 128
light-weight refractories, 128
light-weight zirconia bricks, 128
lignite, 60, 61, 80, 187, 189
 clays, 77

lignite, flue dust, 190
lime (including $CaCO_3$ = limestone and CaO), 33, 42, 58, 59, 60, 62, 67, 113, 119, 157
 -alumina garnet, see 'grossular'
 -iron garnet, see 'demantoid'
 mortar, 144–5
 -olivine, 152
 -soda felspar, see 'plagioclase'
 -uranite, see 'autunite'
limonite (mixture of iron hydroxides, 76, 78, 181
linnaeite, 86
liparite, see 'rhyolite'
liquid metals, oxide layerson, 203
lithiophilite, $Li(Mn\cdot,Fe\cdot\cdot(PO_4)$, 91
lithium, 18, 90
 mica, (see 'lepidolite')
lithophile elements, 38
lithopone, 182
load metamorphism, 63
loam, 59, 121, 143
 fat, 143
 lean, 143
loess, 58, 59
löllingite, $FeAs_2$, 85
Lomonossov, M. W., 4
lubricating and polishing materials, 186
luminescence, 33–4
lump slag, 152–3
lutelium, 36
lydites, 61

M-lattice, 18, 23
macerals, 62
maghemite, Fe_2O_3, 88
magma, 45 ff.
 crystallization of, 45–8, 50
 diorite, 49
 flow in, 51
 gabbroic, 48
 granitic, 49
 hybrid, 49
 peridotitic, 48
 syenitic, 49
magmatic, ore deposits, 71–2
magnesia-alumina garnet, see 'pyrope'
magnesia blowing, 149
magnesite, $MgCO_3$, 33, 100, 102, 119, 140
 bricks, 129
 deposits, 75
magnesium, 18, 91, 142
 oxide layer on, 203
 salts, 80

magnetic separation, 173
magnetism, 31, 160
magnetite (magnetic iron ore), Fe_3O_4, 31, 52, 53, 57, 65, 77, 81, 82, 88, 131, 154, 181, 200
  deposits, 74
  coatings in high-pressure steam generators, 191
magneto-hydrodynamic process (MHD), materials for, 132
malachite, $Cu_2[(OH)_2/CO_3]$, 76, 87
manganese, 75, 76, 78, 79, 81, 82, 91
  phosphate coatings, 204
manganite, MnOOH, 91
manganoferrite, 131
manganosite, MnO, 155
marble, 67, 68, 114
marcasite, FeS_2, 23, 61, 111, 118
marine salt deposits, 80
marl, 59, 60, 61, 67, 144, 145
marl clay, 61, 67
marl-limestone, 61
marly clay, 61, 67
marly limestone, 61, 67
martite, 88
masers, crystals for, 199
materials-testing, 212–14
meadow ore, 79
mechanical,
  deformation of rocks, 65–6
  metamorphism, 63
  twinning, 27
  weathering, 55, 56
mechanically-formed sediments, 57–9
Mediterranean-type rocks, 49
meerschaum, see 'sepiolite'
melanocratic rocks, 44, 46
melaphyre, 51, 55
melaphyric tuffs, 59
melilite (mixed crystals of gehlenite, $Ca_2Al[(Si,Al)_2O_7$ and åkermanite, $Ca_2Mg[Si_2O_7])$, 152
mellite, see 'honeystone'
melting points, 15
menaccanite, see 'ilmenite'
mercury, 24, 74, 91
merwinite, $Ca_3Mg[SiO_4]_2$, 153
mesomeric bonding, 18
mesosiderites, 184
Mesozoic, 44
mesozone, 66
metacinnabarite, 91
metahalloysite, $Al_4[(OH)_8/Si_4O_{10}]$, 104
metamict minerals, 36

metamorphic mineral deposits, 81–2
metamorphic rocks (altered rocks), 44, 63–9, 114
metamorphism, 63–6
metasomatism, 63, 64
meteorites, 42, 183–4
  definitions, 183–4
methane, 62
mica, 11, 22, 49, 55, 65, 66, 112
  gneiss, 69
  peridotite (kimberlite), 72
  schists, 65, 67, 68
microcline (triclinic potash felspar), $KAlSi_3O_8$, 65, 107, 109
microlithotypes, 62
micro-organisms, stone damage by, 176
microscopic examination, 212–14
Miller indices, 11
mineral deposits, 70–82
  exploration for, 70, 170–1
  investigation of, 171–2
  magmatic, 70, 71–75
  metamorphic, 70, 81–2
  origin of, 70–1
  sedimentary, 70, 75, 76–81
mineral fertilizers, 180
mineral formation, 70–82
mineral pigments, 181–2
mineralogy,
  branches of, 2–3
  history, 3–4
  systematic, 83–118
minerals,
  separation of, 173–5
mining, 158
mirabilite, see 'glauber salt'
mixed crystals, 15
moderating substances for nuclear reactors, 141
mohavite, see 'tincalonite'
Mohs, F., 25
Mohs' Scale of Hardness, 25, 184–5
molecular lattice, 23
molecular sieves, 177–8
molybdenite, MoS_2, 23, 92, 182, 186
  deposits, 73, 74
molybdenum, 18, 92, 142
  deposits, 48
  pegmatites, 72
molybdite (molybdic ochre), $Fe_2(MoO_4)_3$, 91
monazite, $Ce(PO_4)$, 95, 140, 141
  placers, 77
monticellite, $CaMg(SiO_4)$, 153, 154, 155

montmorillonite, $(Al_{1.67}Mg_{0.33})$ $[(OH)_2Si_4O_{10}Na_{0.33}(H_2O)_4]$, 57, 59 104, 124, 125, 126
  action of heat on, 126
moonstone, 109
morganite, *see* 'rose beryl'
morphotropy, 14
mottramite, $Pb(Cu,Zn)[OH/VO_4]$, 97
moulding sands, 155-7
mudstones, 58
mullite, $3Al_2O_3.2SiO_2$, 125, 126, 128
  bricks, 128
muscovite, $KAl_2[(OH,F)_2AlSi_3O_{10}]$, 24, 44, 56, 57, 112
  biotite gneiss, 67, 69
  gneiss, 69
mylonites, 66

NaCl, 15, 28
nacrite, $Al_4[(OH)_8/Si_4O_{10}]$, 103
nagyagite, $AuTe_2.6Pb(S,Te)$, 88
NaOH, 33
naphthalene, 62
natural gas, 62, 80
Naumann, C. F., 4
nepheline (eleolite), $KNa_3[AlSiO_4]_4$, 22, 24, 44, 51, 66, 107, 108
  basalt, 51, 55
  syenite, 51, 54
nephrite (dense actinolite or anthophyllite), 109
network-formers (glass), 134, 137
network-modifiers (glass), 134, 137
neutron diffraction, 35
niccolite (kupfer nickel), NiAs, 92
nickel, 18, 31, 92
  ferrite, $NiFe_2O_4$, 131
  -iron core (of the earth), 37
  pyrrhotite-copper pyrites deposits, 71
  silicate deposits, 78
Niggli, P., 4
niobates, 131
niobite, $[(Fe,Mn)(Nb,Ta)_2O_6]$, 92
niobium, 18, 92
nitratine, *see* 'soda-nitre'
nitre (nitrate of potash), KNO_3, 114
nitrides, 133
nitrogen, 62, 114
'non-fluid' water (in clays), 121-2, 124-5, 156-7
nontronite, $Fe_2[(OH)_2Al_{0.33}Si_{3.67}O_{10}]_{0.33}$, 104
norite, 51, 55, 113

nuclear fuels, 140, 141-2
nuclear reactors,
  constructional materials, 149
  raw materials, 140-1, 142

obsidian, 51, 53, 113
ochre, 182
octahedron, 10
oil, 188
  clinker, 189, 190
  in moulding sands, 157
  shales, 60, 62
  well drilling, 171
oldhamite, CaS, 155
olefines, 62
oligoclase (soda-lime plagioclase), 107
olivine (peridot), $(Mg,Fe)_2(SiO_4)$, 20, 24, 45, 47, 48, 51, 52, 56, 110, 156
  basalt, 47, 51
  gabbro, 55
  gneiss, 67
onyx, 110
oolitic iron ores, 79
oolitic limestone, 60
opal (amorphous, hydrated SiO_2), 57, 110, 115
optical elements, 195
Ordovician System, 44
ore(s),
  deposits, 170-1
  summary of, 83-118
organic minerals, 42
oriented overgrowths or intergrowths, 11-13
orpiment, As_2S_3, 74, 85
orthite (allanite), $(Ca,Ce,La,Na)_2(Al,Fe,Be,Mg,Mn)_3$ $[O/OH/SiO_4/Si_2O_7]$, 95
orthoclase (potash felspar), $KAlSi_3O_8$, 24, 33, 47, 51, 52, 65, 107
  porphyry, 54
ortho gneisses, 66, 69
Oschatz, 4
osmiridium, 93
osmium, 18, 93
oxide(s), 133
  ceramics, 132
  coatings, 200-3
  on alloys, 203
  ores, 48
oxide-metal ceramics, *see* 'cermets'

Pacific-type rocks, 49
padmaragaya, 108

Palaeozoic Era, 44
palingenesis, 63
palladium 18, 72, 93
pallasite, 184
palygorskite, *see* 'attapulgite'
pandermite (priceite),
     $Ca_2B_5O_9OH.3H_2O$, 100, 141
paraffins, 62
paragneiss, 66, 69
parallel growths, 11
paramagnetism, 31
patronite, VS_4, 97
peat, 60, 61, 80
pegmatites, 48, 51, 53, 72–3
     aluminium silicate, 73
     felspar, 48, 73
     garnet, 73
     gemstone, 72
     gold, 72
     graphite, 73
     light-metal, 72
     mica-, 73
     phosphate, 73
     thorium, 72
     tin, 72
     tungsten, 72
pegmatitic stage, 48
pelites, 57, 58, 59
penninite, 105
pentlandite $(Fe,Ni)_9S_8$, 71, 92
periclase, MgO, 33, 148, 154, 155
peridot, see 'olivine'
peridotite, 47, 51, 55
     magmas, 48
perlite, 51, 53, 120
permeability,
     of rocks, 162–3
     of soils, 165
Permian System, 44
petalite, $Li[AlSi_4O_{10}]$, 90
petroleum, 60, 62, 80
petrology, 43–69
pH, and solubility, 56
phase rule, 49–50
phenocrysts, 51, 52
phlogopite, $KMg_3[(F,OH)_2/AlSi_3O_{10}]$,
     112
phonolite, 44, 51, 55, 113
phosphate(s), 45
     coatings on sheet-iron, 203–4
phosphorite, 98, 180
phyllites, 67, 68
picrite, 55
     basalt, 51

piezoelectricity, 30
piezoelectric crystals, 30, 196–8
pigeon droppings, 176
pig iron, 150–1
pigments, 181–2
pimelite (hydrated nickel
     alumino-silicate), 78, 92,
pinacoids, 10
pitchblende (uraninite), $(U,Th)O_2$, 74,
     96, 97, 140
pitchstone, 51, 53, 113
placer and detrital deposits, 76–7
plagioclase (lime-soda felspar), 24, 47,
     51, 52, 65, 108
     gneiss, 67
plasters, 143–4
plasticity,
     of clays, 124–5, 164
     number, 164
platinum, 18, 24, 72, 93
     metals, 71, 93
     placers, 77
pleistocene, 44
pleochroism, 32
Pliny, 4
plutonic rocks, 50–3, 53–4, 55
plutonium, 142
pneumatolytic,
     stage, 48
     veins, 73
podsol, 178–9
point groups (space groups), 8
polarization, 15–16
     -microscopy (applications of), 212–
     214
polarized light, 32
polarizers, 195
polar–nonpolar resonance lattices, 15–16
polishing earth (tripoli), 61
pollucite, $(Cs,Na)[AlSi_2O_6].H_2O$, 85, 86
pollution of the atmosphere, 190–1
polybasite, $8(Ag,Cu)_2S.Sb_2S_3$, 94
polycrystalline materials, investigation
     of, 210–11
polyhalite, $2CaSO_4.MgSO_4.K_2SO_4.H_2O$,
     63, 117
polymorphism, 15
porcelain, 131
     -earths, *see* 'kaolinite'
pore water (clays), 121
porfido rosso antico, 55
porosity,
     of rocks, 162–3
     of soils, 165

porphyrite, 51, 54
porphyroblasts, 65
porphyry, 51
portland cement, 149
potash, felspar, *see* ' orthoclase'
potassium, 18, 35, 36, 93
  chloride, *see* 'sylvine'
  salts, 80
power generation, 186–92
pozzolana, 146
precipitated deposits from inland lakes and seas, 79–80
priceite, *see* 'pandermite'
prisms, 195
prism faces, 10
prochlorite, 105
promethium, 36
protective coatings on metal surfaces, 200–4
proustite, Ag_3AsS_3, 94
psammites, 57, 58, 59
psephites, 57, 58, 59
psilomelane, $(Ba,H_2O)_2MN_5O_{10}$, 75
pumice, 51, 53, 113
purification of drinking water, 177
pyramid faces, 10
pyrargyrite, Ag_3SbS_3, 94
pyrites, 61, 74, 78, 81, 90, 111, 118
pyroclastics, 58
pyrochlore, $(Na,Ca)_2(Nb,Ta,Ti)_2O_6(OH,F,O)$, 92
pyroelectricity, 30–1
pyrolusite (polianite), β-MnO_2, 91
pyromorphite, $Pb_5[Cl/(PO_4)_3]$, 78
pyrope (magnesia-alumina garnet), $Mg_3Al_2(SiO_4)_3$, 109
pyrophyllite (agalmatolite, bildstein), $Al_2[(OH)Si_4O_{10}]$, 22, 118, 120, 186
pyroxenes (augites), 21, 47, 154
pyrrhotite (pyrrhotine, magnetic pyrites), FeS, 71, 81, 82, 90, 154

quartz, SiO_2, 22, 24, 25, 28, 29, 44, 47, 51, 52, 55, 57, 59, 61, 65, 74, 110, 114–16, 119, 155, 157
  diorite, 46, 51, 54
  mica-schist, 68
  piezoelectricity in, 30
  refractive index, 33
  sands, 114–16, 156, 186
  in silica bricks, 127
  veins, 67
quartzite, 65, 67, 68, 116, 119

quartz porphyry 51, 52, 53, 113
  tuffs, 59
Quaternary Era, 44

radiation-protective materials, 141
radioactivity, 35–6
radiolarian mud, 60
radiolarite, 60
radium, 96–7
railway construction, 168
rankinite, $Ca_3(Si_2O_7)$, 153
rapakiwi, 53
rare earth, 95
  elements, 95
  pegmatites, 72
rasorite, *see* 'kernite'
raw sugar, 30
reactor metals, 140–2
  crystallographic data for, 141–2
realgar, AsS_4, 74, 84
recrystallization, 64
red clay, *see* 'glazing clay'
red ochre, 181
reef limestone, 60
refractive indices, 32–3
refractories, 127–33
  non-silicate, 129–30
  silicate, 127–8
refractory clay, 120
regional metamorphism, 63, 67
renal calculi, 206
renserite, 87
rhenium, 36
rhodium 18, 93
rhodochrosite, $MnCO_3$, 74, 91
rhodonite, $(Mn,Fe,Ca)[SiO_3]$, 91, 111
rhombdodecahedron, 10
rhombohedral face, 10–11
rhyolite (liparite), 53
Riecke's Principle, 64
road-, railway- and runway construction, 168
rock crystal, 110
rock salt, 31, 33, 63, 80, 116
rocks,
  age-division of, 43
  behaviour as foundation ground, 167–70
  classification, 159
  consolidated, 159
  density, 159
  drillability of, 172
  elastic properties of, 160–1
  electrical properties of, 161

rocks, magnetic susceptibility, 160
  magnetism, 160
  permeability of, 162–3
  physical properties of, 158
  porosity of, 162–3
  stability of (in mining and tunnel construction), 172–3
  strength of, 159–60
  thermal properties of, 161, 172–3
  unconsolidated, 159
  workability of, 170
roe-stone, 60
roméite, see 'antimony ochre'
roscoelite, $KV_2[(OH)_2/AlSi_3O_{10}]_6$, 97, 112
rose beryl (morganite), 108
rose quartz, 72, 110
Rosenbusch, H., 4
rubidium, 36
ruby (red corundum), Al_2O_3, 108, 199
rudites, 57
running ground, 173
runway construction, 168
ruthenium, 93
rutile, TiO_2, 12, 24, 33, 65, 77, 96

Saeber, L. A., 4
safflorite, 86
saggar clays, 120
salt(s)
  action, 56
  minerals, 116–17
  -petre, see 'Chile saltpetre'
  terrestrial, 78–9
samarium, 36
samarskite, $(Y,Er)_4[(Nb,Ta)_2O_7]_3$, 95
sammelkristallization, 203
sands, 57, 58, 59, 155–7
  filtering, 177
sandstones, 58, 59, 67, 113
sanidine (high-temperature modification of orthoclase), $KAlSi_3O_8$, 54, 107
saponite, $Mg_3/(OH)_2[Al_{0.33}Si_{3.67}O_{10}]_{0.33}Na_{0.33}(H_2O)_4$, 104
sapphire (green corundum), Al_2O_3, 108, 199
sapropel 60, 62
sapropelites, 62, 79
sardonyx, 110
sassoline, $B(OH)_3$ 100
scalar properties of crystals, 24–5
scapolite (mixed crystals of marialite, $Na_8[(Cl_2,SO_4,CO_3),(AlSi_3O_8)_6]$ and meionite, $Ca_8[(Cl_2,SO_4,CO_3)_2(Al_2Si_2O_8)_6]$), 66

scheelite, $CaWO_4$, 22, 34, 96
  deposits, 74
schillerization, 54
schistosity, 66
schists, 67, 81
schlieren, 72
Schneiderhöhn, H., 4
Schönbein, C. F., 4
Schönfliess, A., 4
schuchardtite (nickel serpentine), 78, 92
schwazite, 91
scintillation counters, 195–6
scolecite, $Ca[Al_2Si_3O_{10}].3H_2O$, 30
sedimentary rocks, 44, 55–63, 113–14
  classification, 57–63
  composition, 55
  formation of, 55–7
sedimentary, mineral deposits, 76–81
sediments, 58–63
  aeolian, 57
  biogenic, 57, 59–63
  chemical, 57, 59–63
  clastic, 57–9
  fluviatile, 57
  glacial, 57
selenite, see 'gypsum'
selenium, 23, 75, 94
semi-conducting crystals, 198–9
sepiolite (meerschaum), $Mg_4[H_2O)_3(OH)_2(Si_6O_{15}].3H_2O$, 105
sericite (fine-grained muscovite) gneiss, 67, 69
serpentine (antigorite), $Mg_6[(OH)_8Si_4O_{10}]$, 67, 99, 114
  asbestos, 181
shales, 42, 58, 59, 120, 128
shearing strength, 160, 165
shearing stress, and gliding, 27
sheet silicates, see 'phyllosilicates'
shells, 207
sial, 37
siderite (spastose-iron), $FeCO_3$, 31, 57, 75, 81, 89
siderophile elements, 38
Siemens–Martin steel, 151
silica, 56
  bricks, 127
silicate(s), 20, 44
  ceramics, 130
  melts, 45 ff.
  refractories, 127–8
  shell, 37
  weathering of, 56

siliceous,
  limestones, 60, 145
  rocks, 61
  shales, 60, 61
  sinter, 60, 61
silicides, 133
silicocarnotite, 155
silicon,
  carbide, 18, 20, 186
  carbide bricks, 129
silicones, 207–9
silicosis, 204–6
sillimanite, AlAl[O/SiO$_4$], 66, 73, 117, 119
  bricks, 128
siloxane bonding, 208–9
silty sands, 58
Silurian System, 44
Silver, 18, 24, 29, 74, 94
  deposits, 78
  -glance, see 'argentite'
sima, 37
Skarns, 81
sklodowskite, 140
slag, 150–5, 187–9
  foamed, 151–2
  inclusions in steel, 157–8
  wool, 152
slates, 67, 68, 114
slip clay, 120
Slopes, angle of rest of, 169
smaltite, CoAs$_{3-2}$, 86
smelting,
  industry, 150–8
  sand, 151
  slags, 155
smithsonite (zinc spar), ZnCO$_3$, 98, 141
smoky quartz, 110
soda felspar, see 'albite'
sodalite, Na$_8$[Cl$_2$(Al,SiO$_4$)$_6$], 22, 44, 66
soda-nitre (nitratine), NaNO$_3$, 114
sodium, 18, 94
  chlorate, 30
  chloride, 15
softening of hard water, 177
soft porcelain, 131
soil(s),
  classification, 163–6, 178–9
  compaction and stabilization of, 168–9
  fat, 164
  fertility, 180
  formation, 178
  lean, 164

solifluction, 170
solubility of rocks, 56–7
Sorby, 4
sorel cement, 150
space groups, 8
Space lattices, 6–7
space vehicles, materials for, 132
specific heat, of crystals, 24–5
specular iron, 75
sperrylite, PtAs$_2$, 93
spessartine, 3MnO.A$_2$O$_3$.3SiO$_2$, 186
sphene (titanite), CaTi(OSiO$_4$), 54, 65, 96
spinel, 11, 12, 110, 126
spinel Law, 11
spinel twinning, 11, 12
spodumene, LiAl(Si$_2$O$_6$), 72, 90, 111
spotted hornfels, 67, 68
stabilization of foundation soils, 168
stannine (tin pyrites), Cu$_2$FeSnS$_4$, 96
stannite, 23, 74
star ruby, 108
star sapphire, 108
staurolite, Al$_4$Fe(OOHSiO$_4$)$_2$, 65, 66, 106
steatite, see 'talc'
  bodies, 130
  bricks, 130
steel slags, 151, 154–5
  inclusions, 157–8
Steno, Nicolaus, 4
stephanite, 5Ag$_2$S.Sb$_2$S$_3$, 94
stibnite, see 'antimonite'
stones (faults in glass), 138
stone structures, weathering of, 175–6
stoneware, clay, 120
stony meteorites, 184
stottite, FeH$_2$[GeO$_4$].2H$_2$O, 87
strength, 26–7, 159–60
stress minerals, 65
striae (faults in glass), 138
strontianite, SrCO$_3$ 81, 118
structural ceramics, 127
structure of rocks, 50–2
struvite, 206, 207
sub-bituminous coal, 61
submarine-exhalative sedimentary ore-deposits, 75
sugar, 30
sulphates, 45, 60, 80
sulphide(s), 45, 153
  ores, 48, 75, 82
  -oxide shell, 37
  shell, 38
sulphite waste liquor, 119
sulphur, 23, 25, 63, 75, 80, 118

sun, composition of, 41
sunstone (aventurine), 109
super-lattices, metals, 18
surface tension, of glass, 136–7
susceptibility, magnetic, 160
syenite, 47, 51, 53–4, 67, 113
    porphyry, 51
syenetic magmas, 49, 53–4
sylvanite, $AuAgTe_4$, 88
sylvine, KCl, 33, 63, 117
symmetry, 68–9
    axis, 8
    plane, 8
synthetic gemstones, 199

talc (steatite), $Mg_3[(OH)_2Si_4O_{10}]$, 22, 25, 66, 186
    schists, 67, 118
tantalite, $(Fe,Mn)(Ta,Nb)_2O_6$, 92
tantalum, 18, 94
tartaric acid, 30
teallite, $PbSnS_2$, 96
teary ground, 173
technetium, 36
teeth, 206
tektites, 184
tellurium, 18, 94
tensile strength, 27, 160
Terra di Sienna (hypoxanthite), 182
terrestrial salt deposits, 78–9
Tertiary Era, 44
testing of materials, 212–14
tetrahedrite, Cu_3SbS_{3-4}, 74, 82, 84
texture, 50
thenardite, $Na_2[SO_4]$, 117
Theophrastus, 4
thermal,
    conduction, 29
    conductivity of rocks, 161
    expansion, 28–9
    and crystal system, 29
thermoluminescence, 33
thioantimonides, 48
thioarsenides, 48
thixotropy, 122
Thomas steel, 51
thorianite, $(Th,U)O_2$, 95, 140
thorite, $Th(SiO_4)$, 95, 140
thorium 18, 35, 36, 72, 95, 140, 142
    in lead, 36
thuringite, $(F3,''Fe''', Al)_3[(OH)_2/Al_{1\cdot2-2}Si_{2\cdot8-2}O_{10}]$
    $(Mg,Fe,Fe''')_3(O.OH)_6$, 90
tiger eye, 110

tin, 95–6
    deposits, 48, 73
    oxide layer, 203
    pegmatites, 72
    pyrites, see 'stannine'
tincal, see 'borax'
tincalonite (mohavite), $Na_2B_4O_7.5H_2O$, 100
tinstone, see 'cassiterite'
titaria materials, 131
titanite, see 'sphene'
titanium, 18, 71, 96, 142
titanomagnetite (titaniferous magnetite), 96
    deposits, 71
tonalite, 47, 51, 54
topaz, $Al_2(F_2SiO_4)$, 25, 44, 48, 72, 111, 120
torbernite (uran-mica), $Cu(UO_2/PO_4]_2).8H_2O$, 97, 140
tourmaline, 24, 30, 48, 65, 72, 73, 111
trachyte, 51, 54, 113
trachytic,
    obsidian, 54
    pumice, 54
    tuffs, 59
transformation range (glass), 138
translation unit, 6
transverse strength, 160
travertine, 60
tremolite (grammatite), $Ca_2(MgFe)_5[(OH)/Si_4O_{11}]_2$, 56, 99, 181
Triassic System, 44
triboluminescence, 33
tridymite (high-temperature form of SiO_2), 115, 127
triphane, see 'spodumene'
triphylite, 90
tripoli (polishing earth), 60, 61
trona, $Na_3H[CO_3]_2$, 79
tuffs, 58, 59, 113–14
tujamunite (tyuyamunite), $Ca[UO_2/VO_4]_2.3-8H_2O$, 97, 140
tungsten, 96
    carbide, 186
    deposits, 48
    pegmatites, 72
tungstite (wolfram-ochre), 186
turbine blades, deposition, 192
Turkish umber, see 'Cyprian'
turquoise (kaillite), $CuAl_6[(OH)_2/PO_4]_4.4H_2O$, 111

twinning, 11–12, 28
Tyrolean green, 182
tysonite, $(Ce,La)F_3$, 95

ulexite, $NaCuB_5O_9.8H_2O$, 100, 141
ultra-basic rocks, 46
unconsolidated rocks, 159, 163–6
    foundations of, 167–8
    landslides of, 169–70
unit cell, 6
uranblüte, see 'zippeite'
uraninite, see 'pitchblende'
uranium, 35, 36, 80, 96–7, 141–2
    in lead, 36
    ores, 140
    pegmatites, 72
uranophane (uranotile),
    $Ca(H_3O)_2[UO_2/SiO_4]_2.3H_2O$, 97,
    140
uric acid, 206

valentinite (antimony bloom), Sb_2O_3 84
vanadinite $Pb_5[Cl/CVO_4)_3]$,97
vanadium, 18, 81, 97, 142
Van Dyke brown, 182
variegated copper ore (collective term
    for bornites of varying com-
    position), see 'bornite'
vectorial properties of crystals, 25–36
vermiculite, $Mg_{2\cdot36}Fe_{0\cdot48}Al_{0\cdot16}[(OH)_2/$
    $Al_{1\cdot28}Si_{2\cdot72}O_{10}]_{0\cdot64}Mg_{0\cdot32}(H_2O)_4$,
    105–6, 120, 124
verneuil process, 199
vitreous rocks, 51
vitrinertite, 62
vitrinite, 62
vitrite, 62
vitrophyric rocks, 51
volcanic,
    agglomerate, 58
    rocks, see 'extrusive rocks'

water,
    absorption, 163–4
    in clay minerals, 121–5
    softening, 177
    treatment, 177–8
weak ground, 173
weathering 55–7, 76, 175–6
    chemical, 56–7, 176
    continental deposits formed by, 77–9

mechanical, 56
physical, 176
wedellite, $Ca(C_2O_4).2H_2O$, 206
Weiss, C. Samuel, 4
Werner, Gottlob Abraham, 4
wheel-ore, see 'bournonite'
whewellite, $Ca(C_2O_4)H_2O$, 206
whiskers, 194–5, 199
white ware clay, 120
whitlockite, β-$Ca_3(PO_4)_2$, 206
Widmanstätten structures, 183, 98, 154
willemite, $ZnSiO_4$, 30, 33, 82 98, 154
windows, 195
witherite, $BaCO_3$, 99
wolframite $(Mn,Fe)WO_4$, 96
    deposits, 73
wollastonite, α-$CaSiO_3$, 64, 66, 153
wood, 61
workability of rocks, 170
wulfenite, $Pn[MoO_4]$, 92
wurtzite, ZnS, 98, 141, 154
wüstite, FeO, 155, 200, 201

xenomorphic crystals, 50, 52
xenotime, $Y[PO_4]$, 95
X-ray-amorphous materials, 35, 36
X-ray diffraction, 34
    monochromators, 195
    structural investigation, 209–12

zeolites, 177–8
zinc, 18, 27, 28, 97–8
    blende, ZnS, 21, 30, 33, 74, 78, 81,
        82, 97, 141, 154
    ferrite, $ZnFe_2O_4$, 131
    oxide, 201–2
    phosphate coatings, 204
    spar, see 'smithsonite'
zinnwaldite (lepidolite)
    $KLiFeAl(Fe,OH)_2/AlSi_3O_{10}]$, 90,
    112
Zintl phases, 23
zippeite (uranblüte),
    $[8UO_2/3(OH)_2/3SO_4].12H_2O$, 140
zircite, 98
zircon, $ZrSiO_4$, 24, 29, 53, 77, 98, 111,
    119, 141
zirconia bricks, 128
zirconium, 18, 98, 142
ZnS, 79
zoisite, $Ca_2Al_3[O/OH/SiO_4/Si_2O_7]$, 66